ωb

Museums and the Environment:
a handbook for education

Museums and the Environment:

a handbook for education

The Environmental Committee
American Association of Museums

A Publication of the American Association of Museums

Arkville Press

The American Association of Museums presents this book and the suggestions in it for the benefit of museums and the public they serve. The Association can accept neither credit nor responsibility for specific techniques, publications, films and other products described or referred to herein. We hope you will find this handbook of interest and value, both technically and philosophically.

Kyran M. McGrath, Director
American Association of Museums

Edited by Ruth Norton Oliver

Designed by Lurelle and Hollis Cheverie.

This is the way the world ends

This is the way the world ends

This is the way the world ends

Not with a bang but a whimper

T. S. Eliot

The end of our world could be neither a bang nor a whimper.
We could simply smother in the wastes of our own affluence

Laurance S. Rockefeller

We have learned in all the biological and anthropological sciences
that all the species that become extinct do so by virtue of
over-specialization and losing general adaptability. We have to
think about our spaceship earth as a machine to regenerate life,
but the pollution point of no return is probably within only ten
years and we are not going to be able to move fast enough unless
we start to talk comprehensively now.

R. Buckminster Fuller

Preface

Museums are admirably equipped, through their diverse collections, their expertise in display, their long experience in conservation, and their vast clientele, to play an important role in making the public aware of environmental problems as well as of the means for their solution.

Museums can bring vividly and unforgettably to the American public, especially to its youth, the basic facts of the human environment—how it deteriorates and how it can be improved. People visit museums because they enjoy doing so, a circumstance that makes learning a pleasant experience with a "do-it-yourself" quality, instead of drudgery. Examining three-dimensional objects in exhibits and demonstrations, rather than just reading about them, makes the learning process much easier. The enormous, and increasing, number of museum visits—nearly six hundred million each year—guarantees a very real impact on the public by museum programs devoted to environmental pollution and its control.

The American Association of Museums made an analysis of the degree of activity and potential interest of museums in the area of human ecology and environment. The results are highly encouraging. Although 157 museums (76 museums of art and 81 of history) quite predictably expressed little or no interest in programs or exhibits concerned with environmental deterioration, 525 institutions (73 percent of those responding) were interested in initiating or expanding such efforts. Virtually all the 525 interested institutions expressed a need for help in the form of financial support, technical assistance, additional space, or exhibit materials in order to conduct such programs. A much fuller account of the results obtained from the analysis is presented in tables I and II of Appendix F. I introduce the topic here only to emphasize that we discovered an active, healthy interest on the part of the museum community in participating in programs devoted to human ecology.

In the middle of 1969, the AAM was pleased to be awarded a contract from the Consumer Protection and Environmental Health Service, Public Health Service, U.S. Department of Health, Education, and Welfare, to undertake the study of and to prepare a report on "Development of Museum Education Techniques for Human Ecology." The growing stature and role of museums as educational institutions amply merits such recognition, and the AAM had already acquired considerable experience in undertaking and successfully completing major enterprises of this sort.

For example, in 1967, President Lyndon B. Johnson requested from the Federal Council on the Arts and Humanities a status report on the needs and resources of America's museums, a request that the Federal Council then forwarded to the AAM as the most appropriate organization to carry out the actual study and prepare a report. An outstanding special committee, established by the AAM, met regularly at Belmont House, a country estate in Maryland, and in one year produced a highly effective and influential document, *America's Museums: The Belmont Report*, published by the AAM in October, 1968. This report has already been reprinted.

More recently, another special committee of the AAM concluded its work on the development of a program of accreditation for America's museums. The committee's definition of a museum has an important bearing on the present report; it follows:

For the purpose of the accreditation program of the AAM, a museum is defined as an organized and permanent non-profit institution, essentially educational and aesthetic in purpose, with professional staff, which owns and utilizes tangible objects, cares for them, and exhibits them to the public on some regular basis.

This definition is intentionally broad enough to comprehend several categories of cultural and educational institutions that, at first thought, might not be considered museums: historic houses, planetariums, botanical gardens, zoological parks, and aquariums, for example. The scope of their activities gives that much more opportunity for development of education techniques for human ecology.

In the actual implementation of the contract between the Consumer Protection and Environmental Health Service and the AAM for preparing the report on the role of museums in teaching human ecology, the most important first step was to appoint an effective committee and, even more important, to find the right chairman. We consider ourselves fortunate indeed that Dr. James A. Oliver, Director of The New York Aquarium, who has long been active in developing environmental programs, agreed to serve as chairman. Dr. Oliver, Kyran McGrath, Director of the AAM, and I held preliminary discussions on the report, and the committee began to take shape. As finally constituted, it represented an extraordinarily broad spectrum of background, discipline, interest, and experience, and consisted of the following members: James A. Oliver, Chairman, Norman C. Bilderback, Richard F. Brown, Frederick Dockstader, G. Carroll Lindsay, George E. Lindsay, Kyran M. McGrath, Charles E. Mohr, M. Graham Netting, Charles P. Parkhurst, Jr., George O. Pratt, Charles Roth, William C. Steere, Malcolm Wells, and William Woodin. Biographical data concerning each committee member appears in Appendix G.

In my opinion, Dr. Oliver's committee has responded nobly to its charge. I also want to compliment the Consumer Protection and Environmental Health Service, Public Health Service, U.S. Department of Health, Education, and Welfare, and the Environmental Health Service of HEW for its perspicacity in recognizing the vast educational potential of the museum community in a direction that has obviously been inadequately developed. The AAM hopes that the original report and this more inclusive volume will stimulate museums to increase their programs in human ecology, to assume leadership in this vital endeavor, and through their work to open new vistas to the American public.

William Campbell Steere, Past President
American Association of Museums

Table of Contents

Preface by William C. Steere VII
Introduction by James A. Oliver .XI
Letter from Russell E. Train to James M. Brown,III XVII

Chapter 1 **Man and the Environment** 1
Background 3
Energy and the Chain of Life • Land and Water Resources • Interrelationships of Species • Summary
Exhibits and Projects 15
Man—Unique Threat to Environment • Anthropomorphism • Lurrain vs. Terrain • The Relevance of Man and the Environment • TheLandscape in Art • A Sense of Space • Art Creates Environments • The Artist or Photographer as Recorder of Nature • The Artist or Photographer as Recorder of Man-made Disasters • Farmers of the New Stone Age • The American Indian: Cultures in Harmony with the Environment · Ice People • The History of Conservation • What Good is Wilderness? • Our Forests Primeval • Uses of the Forest • Needs for Energy • Search for Energy • The Balance of Nature • Food Webs • Chlorophyll and You ("Food Chain") • Our Versatile Grasslands • The Sea Around Us • Minerals: Treasures Lost Forever • The Endangered Species • How to Score the Environmental Picture •The Wave Hill Center for Environmental Studies

Chapter 2 **Population** 45
Background 47
Hunger in the Present and in the Future • Loss of Elbowroom: Increased Urbanization • The Responsibility of Individuals • Summary
Exhibits and Projects 61
Overpopulation • Population—Human • The Security of Change • Reproduction and the Continuity of Life • Posters and Other Graphics • Population Trends in the United States • Problems of the City: A Study on Population and Pollution • Creating a Film-Strip on Overpopulation • Creating a Motion Picture on Overpopulation • Concrete Deserts: The Growth of Urbanization • Street Museums • Disaster and Urban Renewal • Historic Landmarks in our City • Adler Planetarium • The Contemporary Art Center of Cincinnati • Cityscapes • The Drug Scene in New York City • The Architectural Vision of Paolo Soleri

Chapter 3 **Environmental Pollution** 87
Background 89
The Cost of Pollution • Classification and Occurrence of Pollutants • The Atmosphere • Water • Land • Radiation • Thermal Pollution • and Noise • Summary
Exhibits and Projects 103
Changing Values • "This? Or That?"• A Good Life or a Life of Goods? • The Automobile • A Group of Exhibits and Project—Easy to Execute • One-Step Air Pollution Exhibits • A Closeup View of Stream Pollution • Save the Bay for Life • How to Kill`or Cure a Lake • The History of a River • "Clearwater"—A Hudson River Sloop Restoration • The Depletion of Minerals • Pollution in Food • An Exhibit in OMSI • The Noise Factor • No Place to Play • An Air Quality Monitoring Station • Smog in a Big Way • A Breath of Air • Posters Carry the Message • The Power of Museum Publications • Destruction of Art at Home • Plants and Human Ecology • "There's Cash in That Trash"—(A Symposium) • Perhaps not, if...

Chapter 4   **Creating and Building Environmental Exhibits** **125**
Principles of Environmental Exhibition by G. Carroll Lindsay ● Conceptual Exhibits on the Problems of the Human Environment by Charles E. Roth ● Practical Exhibit Materials and How to Use Them by the Exhibit Department of the California Academy of Sciences

Chapter 5   **Added Dimensions Through the Use of Films** **151**
Films ● Multimedia Presentations ● A Multimedia Show

Chapter 6   **The Emerging Role of Museums in Environmental Education.** . **159**
Art Museums and Environmental Education by Charles Parkhurst; ● Botanical Gardens and Environmental Education by William C. Steere; ● Urban Ecology and the Inner City Museum by Zora B. Martin; ● The Role of Zoos and Aquaria in Environmental Education by William G. Conway; ● Museums and the Ecological Imperative by Malcolm B. Wells

Chapter 7   **Programs of Action** **183**
Public Awareness: The Necessary Basis for Public Action by James A. Lee; ● Consequences of Activism by George O. Pratt, Jr.; ● Expanding the Museum Outward ● How to Involve the Community in Museum Programs ● The Power of the Group ● The Role of Volunteers ● The Role of Local Experts ● Working with Students ● Developing an Apprenticeship Program ● Cooperating with Other Museums ● Setting up General Program ● A Specific Action Program ● Proposed Group Projects ● Charts Showing Programs for Immediate Action by Citizens

Appendix A **210**
Excerpts from President Nixon's message transmitting the First Annual Report of the Council on Environmental Quality

Appendix B **215**
Letter from William C. Steere to Jack Hardesty

Appendix C **216**
Organizations conducting environmental programs

Appendix D **220**
Publications   Books   Periodicals   Handbooks   Journals   Catalogs

Appendix E **227**
Films on Environmental Education

Appendix F **244**
Analysis of Museum Activity in Human Ecology

Appendix G **246**
Biographies of Members of the Environmental Committee

Appendix H **254**
Notes

Glossary **255**

Introduction

Human ecology is the study of the relationship between man and his total environment—which includes both the natural world and the cultural and technological world he has created. To teach human ecology requires a holistic approach in which the causes and effects of the deterioration of the environment can be studied. Museums are equipped philosophically and practically for this task.

There are more than 6,700 museums in the United States, representing virtually every aspect of man in his environment: biological man, evolving among other forms of life; social and historical man, organizing his affairs, first building and then destroying his civilizations; philosophical and spiritual man, perceiving reality beyond the evidence of his five senses.

Some museums cover one of the broad-ranging categories of science, history, or art; others specialize in such single areas or subjects as transportation, currency or the commemoration of an individual. All such institutions—since they are involved to some degree in collecting, preserving, exhibiting and interpreting the natural or man-made objects of our environment—are in themselves classrooms and laboratories for teaching. Moreover, increasing numbers of museums are installing "satellite" exhibits and materials at such points in the community as shopping centers, banks, schools, hospitals and neighborhood centers—in this way actively reaching out to involve a broad spectrum of the community.

The Educational Force of Museums

The unique opportunity open to museums to function as educational institutions derives from their acceptance by the public as places where knowledge is presented in a palatable—even exciting—manner by means of real objects and personal experiences rather than illustrations or the written or spoken word. Museum exhibits and displays are designed to reach people of various ages with widely differing educational backgrounds. Since a good exhibit permits any visitor to relate to it at his own level of understanding, no barriers prevent his moving from one level to another as his knowledge increases. Thus, whether he is a child or adult, high-school drop-out or Ph.D., his involvement enhances his motivation to continue learning.

The teaching methods used in association with real objects in museums include, of course, the written and spoken word and a great variety of visual, auditory, and other sensory techniques. Increasingly, too, exhibits are designed to show causal relationships and to convey a concept and a mood. But the basic precept of museum teaching remains the same: there is no substitute for the real thing, whether it is a painting by Rembrandt, the thighbone of a mastodon, or Thomas Edison's first incandescent bulb. Further, because experience is part of the input, the message being conveyed is not static, but changes with time. To see the size of the beds in a restored colonial house helps us comprehend that the European men and women who came to this country several hundred years ago were not only considerably smaller in stature than the average American today, but that, as consumers, they were less taken with the modern social delusion "the bigger the better." To see the magnificent California condor or the graceful whooping crane is a vivid reminder that these and other wild creatures are in danger of extinction. Exhibits showing the development of the automobile from a horseless carriage tell us a great deal about social, technological and economic changes in our country. To have the opportunity to see the paintings, in all their diversity, of Alexander Calder or Georgia O'Keefe, Andrew Wyeth or Andy Warhol, is to confront not different realities but the same reality as seen through different eyes. Their statements can become ours; we can reject or accept their perceptions.

That the Future May Learn from the Past

As concern for our environment becomes a national priority, man's effect on all his surroundings will be increasingly subject to analysis, interpretation and legislation. Large-scale programs sponsored by government, industry and private organizations must deal for the most part with effects—pollution, destruction, overexploitation, crowding, ugliness.

But underlying these measures must be a basic attack on the causes within ourselves that have brought us to this crisis. If man is to learn the lessons of ecology and apply them to his own survival, the study must become an integral part of all his education, formal and informal. In man's effort to reorient himself to new values, develop new attitudes, reeducate, museums can make an invaluable and unique contribution.

The intellectual, scientific and artistic authority of museums commands great respect. Museums have seldom applied their influence to public issues; but the time has come when these institutions, which through the years have preserved man's treasures and nourished his spirit, must also apply themselves to the preservation of an environment fit for life.

The battle cry of the war on racism, "If you're not part of the solution, you're part of the problem," must in this broader context be taken a step further: "Since you are part of the problem, you will have to be part of the solution"—with perhaps the postscript "if there is to be a solution."

When our Committee began work on its report to the U.S. Public Health Service in the fall of 1969, only a few people understood the full meaning of the terms "ecology," biosphere" or even "environment." Today these terms are household words. Public awareness has developed suddenly and is, in turn, creating further awareness and action. For example, on January 1, 1970, President Richard M. Nixon appointed a Council on Environmental Quality, which has since issued a report on the state of our environment. In recent months the United States Congress, state legislatures and local governments have passed legislation aimed at halting further environmental damage and at improving the quality of the conditions under which we live.

The United Nations established a preparatory committee in April of 1969 to make plans for an international conference on the human environment, and Secretary General U Thant recently told a congress of World Federalists that "mankind must soon solve its problems of rising population, increasing pollution, and a multiplied capacity of destruction, or perish."

In April of 1970, widespread observances of "Earth Day," "Environment Day," "END Day" (for Environment Near Death) and other events with symbolic and sometimes grim acronyms called attention to the problems of the environment.

On October 13, 1970, Congress passed the Environmental Education Act, the purpose of which is to enable our nation to take a leading role in environmental education, both within our country and in other parts of the world. This Act has particular significance for museums because in it, for the first time in federal legislation, museums are designated educational institutions.

The Continuing Process of Communication

With our expanding awareness of environmental problems must come investigation of as many aspects of the environment as our scientific knowledge and technology permit. This activity, in turn, will be followed by an almost-daily output of new information. Communication of information about specific environmental problems, and the assimilation and implementation of such information, is a continuous process—as is well illustrated by the story of mercury pollution in our waters.

Until the spring of 1970, we in the United States paid very little attention to the threat of mercury as a pollutant, despite reports from Japan and Sweden of incidents of mercury poisoning in those countries. Then the Canadian Department of Fisheries and Forestry revealed the discovery of dangerously-high mercury levels in fish caught in some of its Great Lakes waters. Canada banned commercial fishing in two of the lakes and began a crash survey of fish from other waters. Various state and federal government agencies in the United States followed suit. The result of focusing on this problem has been the discovery that mercury pollution is now continent-wide and extends even to the oceans off our shores. Our perception of this problem is changing continually. In mid-July of 1970 the United States departments of Agriculture and the Interior formally designated mercury pollution a hazard in 14 states. By September, 1970, 33 states were involved —more than double the number reported in mid-July. Happily, this is one type of pollution in which quick and simple steps can be taken to reduce the continuing entry of the harmful element into the environment—in this case, by drastically cutting down the amount of mercury wastes dumped, although it will require much time and effort to remove mercury pollution from the environment.

We hope that, through the rapid communication of information about newly-recognized environmental hazards, remedial action and enforcement of new regulations can come in time to prevent more of the kind of damage —much of it irreversible—that our environment has already suffered. We are beginning to realize, however, that what we need if we are to survive is a change in the minds of men and in their attitudes.

This handbook has evolved in response to the needs expressed by museums for resources with which to interpret environmental problems and to initiate or to expand environmental exhibit and education programs. In addition to background information on various aspects of the environmental situation, the book provides outlines, themes, techniques and illustrations that museums can adapt to their individual needs. The suggestions were contributed by members of the Committee and by other museum people in many parts of the country. The Committee concluded that this approach would be the most practical because the dynamics of the environmental problem and the individual differences among museums and their communities vary so greatly.

Chapters 1, 2, and 3 each contain two parts—the first part, background; the second, techniques and tools for development of exhibits and projects. Chapter 4 offers fundamental principles for the design and development of ecological exhibits, and a section containing specific instructions on how to build display cases for small exhibits. Chapter 5 offers suggestions for some of the new ways in which film may be used to enhance environmental exhibits. Chapter 6 contains statements on the emerging roles of different types of museums in environmental education. Chapter 7 outlines programs of action and community participation. Appendices list some of the additional resources available to museums—in literature and films, through various government agencies, and through private organizations engaged in education and communication.

We take great pleasure in acknowledging the help of all members of the Environmental Committee, and in having the opportunity to thank them publicly for contributing their creative talent, experience, and knowledge to this project. Dr. William C. Steere, past President of the American Association of Museums, was a continuing and most generous source of wisdom and fruitful advice. His encouragement and ready assistance were vital. Kyran McGrath, Executive Director of the AAM, was an able counselor to the Committee. We are indebted to him for his enthusiastic cooperation, as well as for his expert advice on practical and legal matters.

The professional skill, experience and constant contribution of Ruth Norton Oliver, the editor, eased the report through many trials and frustrations. We wish to thank her and her associates—Ann Breen, Suzanne Dyer, Sally M. Gall, Harriet Hester, Tula Lilien, Casey Miller and Kate Swift—for their competent, skilled, and devoted help to the Committee in the many and varied tasks of preparing the report and this book. The designers of the book, Lurelle and Hollis Cheverie, deserve special appreciation. Their exceptional creativity and talent were matched only by their dedication to the effective completion of the project. Stanley Salmen, Jacqueline Allen and

Rosemary Tyndall of Arkville Press were of enormous help in seeing the book through publication.

To the museum people throughout the country who supplied information about present or projected programs, sent films and publications for review, and offered advice and suggestions for future programs, the Committee is deeply indebted.

Many friends and colleagues not on the Committee have contributed assistance in numerous ways. Some are acknowledged in the body of the report, in connection with articles or specific exhibits; to those others who exerted equal effort but whose contributions are less tangible, we would like now to take this opportunity to express our gratitude and appreciation.

James A. Oliver, Chairman
Environmental Committee
American Association of Museums

EXECUTIVE OFFICE OF THE PRESIDENT
COUNCIL ON ENVIRONMENTAL QUALITY
722 JACKSON PLACE, N. W.
WASHINGTON, D. C. 20006

January 14, 1971

Dear Mr. Brown:

On behalf of President Nixon, I would like to congratulate the American Association of Museums for preparing this report. Our nation's museums can play an active part in our efforts to obtain a high-quality environment, and there is no end more worth the effort.

Just as museums are turning up their lights and generally adding life to their exhibits, so have we taken "ecology" from the textbooks and made it a way of life. All individuals, organizations and institutions in our country must concern themselves with the preservation of our natural resources if we are to succeed.

The Environmental Quality Education Act of 1970 recognizes that America's 6,700 museums have a unique opportunity to serve the educational demands aroused by our interest in ecology. Through the use of the national treasures they house, museums are in a position to exhibit not just a collection of superficially related specimens, but to demonstrate the complex and changing interrelationships among the plants, animals, and inorganic materials that compose our environment.

A proliferation of educational resources, coupled with the fact of skyrocketing museum attendance, points up the necessity of museums becoming involved in telling the message of the ecological crisis. This report should serve as a guide to museums of art, history, and science that want to develop techniques, exhibitions and special programs concerned with ecology.

Not only museums, however, but schools, libraries and all other educational institutions will be able to benefit from utilizing the information in this report.

It is my hope that we are entering an era where museums will not only preserve the past--but where they will help to preserve the future as well.

Sincerely,

Russell E. Train
Chairman

Mr. James M. Brown, III
President
American Association of Museums
2233 Wisconsin Avenue, N. W.
Washington, D. C.   20007

chapter 1 / man and the environment

Man and the Environment

The first section of this chapter contains an introduction to the nature of our environment. It includes the basic definitions and descriptions of natural resources that are needed to understand the problems of environmental deterioration and conservation.

The second part, starting on page 15, offers suggestions for exhibits and various activities that can help increase public awareness of the nature of the environment. This material can also be interwoven with material from the other chapters in the handbook, and the bibliography starting on page 220 should be consulted for appropriate references.

Since the staff of each institution will probably want to develop exhibits and programs concerning environment that are unique and relevant to a specific geographic area, we are including suggestions that we hope will prove stimulating, as well as more fully worked out exhibition scripts. We are also including projects that might be suitable for preparation by volunteers or trainees.

"The world is a mirror of infinite beauty, yet no man sees it. It is a region of Light and Peace, did not man disquiet it."

Thomas Traherne

"Everybody needs beauty as well as bread, places to play in and pray in, where nature may heal and cheer, and give strength to body and soul alike."

John Muir

"To create a new land ethic, we need to return to the sense of awe and kinship for the natural world that characterized both primitive man and our intellectual ancestors, the Greeks. Our aim should be not to control nature, but to live in harmony with it."

Roger Revelle

Background

Man is a historical, social, philosophical, aesthetic, and spiritual being. He is also an animal who shares the earth with an immense variety of other organisms. He has evolved, as have all species, through interaction with the environment; and despite his remarkable capabilities, he is still completely dependent upon the biological and physical components of the environment for life itself. His food, for example, ultimately derives from the unique ability of green plants (on land or in water) to convert light energy from the sun into chemical energy through the process of photosynthesis, and the oxygen in the air he breathes also is produced by these green plants. Despite his role as the dominant species on earth, man is still inextricably interrelated to other living organisms and interdependent with them on the physical environment.

Plants and animals live in distinctly structured groups known as *biotic communities*, in which the various species are linked together by food chains and complex food webs. These plants and animals, the biological components of the environment, form the living portion of an ecological system, or *ecosystem*, which also includes a nonliving portion—the physical components of the environment. These include soil, air, water, light and heat energy from the sun, and the physical characteristics of the earth and atmosphere. *Ecology* is the study of ecosystems, of the networks of living creatures, from microorganisms to man, living in precarious balance with their physical environment.

All living things depend absolutely on the earth's natural resources. Any threat to these elements of the environment is a threat to life itself. Some of the earth's resources, like water, are renewable. Some, like minerals, are not. Some, like fossil fuels, are not renewable but can be replaced with other forms, such as atomic energy.

Rene Magritte. "The False Mirror" (1928). Oil on canvas, 21-1/4" x 31-7/8". Collection, The Museum of Modern Art, New York, Purchase.

Man, through his creative activities, has used and modified his environment more extensively than any other living organism. It is primarily his use—and abuse—of environmental resources that has brought about the ecological imbalance we need to correct.

Environment has become a popular word. It is used today, not always accurately, to cover a wide variety of situations. But in the natural sciences, environment has long been a valid biological term meaning the biophysical surroundings in which organisms live; the land and rocks we walk and drive upon and feed from, called the *lithosphere*; the waters we drink, and swim in, and use for transportation, called the *hydrosphere*; the air we breathe, and fly in, called the *atmosphere*; and the plants and animals that share this planet with us and upon which we depend for many life-supporting relationships, called collectively the *biosphere*. These are the major biophysical components of the natural environment.

Man, however, has added to and modified the environment to such a degree that he has created other

Joseph Stella. "Factories" (1918). Oil on burlap, 56" x 46". Collection, The Museum of Modern Art, New York, Acquired through the Lillie P. Bliss Bequest.

major components—which we will call the *technosphere* and the *aesthetosphere*.

The technosphere includes the vast urban areas of paved land, houses with controlled environments, office buildings with their own regulated temperature and humidity, industrial developments, man-made objects of every description, all contributing to the unnatural, but generally secure and comfortable character of man's habitat. The aesthetosphere refers to an organization of the environment in terms of visual and sensory perception and apprehension.

One of the key relationships that involves all elements of the biosphere as well as other parts of the total environment is the generation and transfer of energy.

Energy and the Chain of Life

Energy is the mainspring of everything that *happens*, from the movement of ocean waves to the metabolism of cells, from the activity of animals to the acceleration of a jet plane. All these activities result from an expenditure of energy. In the biosphere the generation and transfer of energy is based on what biologists call the "chain of life." The chain of life in any ecosystem has four major components: nonliving matter, which consists of the physical components of the environment; producers, which are the plants; consumers, which are the higher organisms that feed directly or indirectly on the producers; and decomposers, such as carnivores, bacteria, and fungi, which break down dead plants and animals and return their chemical components to the soil for reuse by plants, thus completing the cycle.

The principal source of the energy that makes life possible in a biotic community is sunlight. For example, green land plants utilize light, carbon dioxide (from the atmosphere), water (from the soil), and chlorophyll (present in green leaves) to synthesize glucose, a simple carbohydrate which is the primary food of all organisms. From glucose they can make more complex carbohydrates, proteins, fats, and vitamins by utilizing additional chemical compounds

from the soil. All these nutrients, so vital to animals, are thus derived from plants. In natural systems simple food chains, such as the *grass—rabbit—owl* chain, are interwoven into complex food webs. Animals other than rabbits eat grass, and a variety of mammals, reptiles, and birds prey upon rabbits; the predators also have other animals for their prey. Such alternative pathways in a food web help maintain the stability of the ecosystem. If rabbits become scarce, more grass will grow, providing better shelter and more food for mice. The population of mice will increase; the owls will hunt mice more frequently, thus giving the rabbits a chance to multiply; and the ecosystem will return to equilibrium. Even if as much as one-half of a certain species in a natural ecosystem is destroyed by disease or some other cause, the population is frequently able to recover within a few years—that is, if man has not intervened to upset the balance further.

Every shift of balance in the ecosystem involves a transfer of energy, and it was the conscious management of energy—fully as much as the development of the opposable thumb—that lifted early man into his unique position among animals. Beyond the use of animals as a prime source of food energy, our forebears learned to conserve that energy by developing garments. When they discovered how to make fire they were able to produce energy outside their own bodies; and they developed still further energy when they harnessed beasts to pull their plows. In the 1800s man hit the mass-energy jackpot by applying the energy from fossil fuels to power the steam

5

engine and its mobile form, the locomotive, and to produce electricity. In the 1900s he has shaken the world by splitting the atom and thereby developing nuclear power.

Of all resources, the most readily available, in unharnessed form, is energy. But like the others it is a limited resource. It is an irony of the twentieth century that at the very time we have come to recognize the limitation of the sources of energy, we are, paradoxically, confronted by the specter of destructive energy loosed upon the environment by nuclear reactions.

cades that it takes the reservoirs to fill with silt. Tidal and geothermal power are available in limited locations and are severely restricted in the amount of power they can supply. It is not economically feasible at present to utilize solar energy as a major source of industrial power, for although it is daily renewable and exists in huge quantities, the complexity of the process of collecting, transmitting, storing, and ultimately transforming the sun's energy into conventional electropower makes such undertakings impractical.

Mineral fuels, in which category

Frederick Edwin Church. "Niagara Falls." Collection, The Corcoran Gallery of Art, Washington, D.C.

Known or potential sources of energy include water power, both conventional and tidal, geothermal power, solar energy, and mineral (including fossil) fuels. Conventional sources of water power, although not yet fully developed, are finite, erratically distributed, and when dependent on large dams and reservoirs, available only during the de-

nuclear energy is included, offer the most readily available sources of power, but of course they are also limited. We estimate that in 50 years or so most of the recoverable petroleum liquids and natural gases will be exhausted. Liquid fuels from tar sands and oil shales might be recovered in sufficient quantity to make the petroleum family of fuels available for as long as a hundred years. Coal, if used at the increasing rate that we expect, may be available for two or three centuries.

Nuclear fission can provide immense quantities of energy, but the fissionable elements uranium and thorium may be exhausted within a few decades unless nuclear reactors are made more efficient. Also, as we will point out later, if there is to be increased use of nuclear power, the disposal of nuclear fission wastes must be made safer, and methods must be developed for controlling any thermal pollution caused by the reactors.

Nuclear fusion provides a potential source of energy even more powerful than that of nuclear fission; but controlled fusion has not yet been achieved. If and when the necessary control is assured, it will result in the most fantastic achievement of man's technology. The energy obtainable from the deuterium contained in 8 cubic miles of sea water would be about equal to that of the earth's initial supply of fossil fuels!

As for the chemical energy upon which all animals depend, that, too, is in jeopardy as long as the green plants on earth are threatened by massive pollution. And, when we recall that the sun is the source of all this life energy, it becomes even more urgent to know what effect the billions of tons of pollutants poured annually into the sky may have on the ability of solar rays to penetrate the atmosphere. We know that the atmosphere encasing the earth is just thick enough to prevent living things from being irradiated to death by the sun's emissions. But we do not know what effect a further thickening of the atmosphere by particulate pollution will have on the life-essential process of photosynthesis.

Land and Water Resources

Our life-giving, life-supporting resources must be husbanded. Once thought inexhaustible, they are in fact all too limited.

The dry-land areas of the earth comprise less than 30 percent of the total surface area. This lithosphere of rock, soil, and minerals provides living space, shelter, building materials, food materials, fuel, and foundations for the growth of all plants and animals, including man. Over the eons the earth's surface has changed through slow ecological modifications of the environment and through sudden cataclysmic events that occurred in localized regions. Such changes continue. For example, hills and mountains have been worn down slowly by erosion, which may be caused by any of a number of natural forces including wind, snow, rain, and the force of gravity; or these land features may be modified suddenly by flood, avalanche, earthquake, oceanic storm, or volcanic eruptions. Volcanic dust can smother acres of verdant vegetation and wipe out all life dependent upon it.

Man, too, has changed the lithosphere. The evidence is growing that even primitive man's agricultural practices had deleterious effects previously unrecognized. For example, many old centers of civilization are surrounded by deserts, and we now believe that, irrespective of climatic changes, some of the modifications must have been caused by acts of man. However, man is able to learn from his mistakes, and some improvements in the care of the land were made in ancient times: the Phoenicians used terracing techniques for hillside farming; the Greeks learned the advantages of manuring the land and rotating crops; and the Romans developed greatly improved techniques of irrigation.

The primeval forest found by Petersham Settlers in 1733 could support life only on the basis of hunting. Land Use Dioramas. Courtesy, Harvard Forest.

Land destruction in North America has been extensive. Settlers in the southern states cleared and burned the forest to plant corn, tobacco, and cotton, crops that make heavy demands on the soil and yet provide poor protection to it. Erosion and loss of fertility resulted, since little effort was made by the westward-moving settlers to care for the land properly. In some parts of the North, where corn was the predominant crop, the same damages occurred. And, in both the North and South, logging and man-made forest fires further destroyed the hardwood and pine forests. In the West, man's agricultural tilling of the southern Great Plains, especially during the 1900s,

exposed the soil to the effects of wind erosion, giving rise to the name "Dust Bowl" and turning vast areas of formerly tilled fields into unproductive land.

In the United States about 20 percent of our land area is devoted to agriculture and 28 percent to grazing. The U.S. Soil Conservation Service estimates that 180 million acres of crop land are affected annually by erosion at a financial loss estimated at $1 billion.

Although in this country only about three percent of the land is devoted to urban and transportation uses, the figure is deceptive, for the influence of this use on all the rest of the land is immense. A report of the Council on Environmental Quality pointed out that "Land is not just acreage. Land embraces the complex biological systems of the soil and the plants and animals which are all part of a continuing life cycle. Man's understanding of these biological processes, particularly of the permanent damage that begins subtly with piecemeal alterations of the land, is still limited. Yet his dependence upon its stability is enormous," the report stated.

For a large part of this century people poured off the farm land and into the cities. Today they, or their children, are leaving the cities for the suburbs and both types of community are experiencing severe difficulties. The downtown and central areas of cities have become shabby and in many cases only the very poor are living there. The upwardly mobile and the solidly successful move to the suburbs, wave upon wave, where not shabbiness but look-alike houses, garish shopping areas, difficult transportation and other problems await them.

The rising population and increased technology results in a competition over the use to which given sections of the land will be put. The inevitable result is that less and less land is left in its original state. The urbanization, followed by the sub-urbanization of America have turned huge areas of open land into sites for housing, factories, airports, parking lots—all with virtually no open space being left to support green life. This has in turn put more pressure on the beaches and parkland, to which people flock on vacations seeking relief from city and suburban conditions. This desire for "getting back to nature" has resulted not only in increased visits to parks but also in greatly increased construction of vacation homes, many of them in places where previously open space contributed to beauty and to a balanced environment. Such changes are particularly noted along the coasts, where the human population in a thirty-year period increased by 78 percent. Competition for coastal space comes from vacationers, mining and oil drilling, shipping, industry, airports, highways and commercial fishing. The dredging and filling has a profound effect on the biology of an area; when estuaries are involved the effect is on both freshwater and ocean life.

The minerals of the soil, so vital to vigorous plant growth, are removed by the very process of that growth as well as by erosion. They must be replaced through regular applications of suitable fertilizers to insure continued production of a successful crop.

The mineral resources of the world are being used at a rapidly accelerating rate to support the needs of our expanding technology. Naturally occurring mineral resources are irreplaceable and accumulate so slowly as to be considered, in a pragmatic sense, non-renewable. However, newly discovered marine deposits may do much to relieve threatened shortages of some minerals and new methods are being developed for large-scale recycling of such minerals as aluminum and tin alloys. It is also becoming economically feasible to "mine" or reclaim minerals from the sanitary landfills now rapidly developing over our land and seascapes.

One technique for the large-scale removal of minerals from the earth —the practice of surface mining—has marred wide areas. The U.S. Department of the Interior estimates that 2 million acres of land have been scarred in this manner. Furthermore, two-thirds of this disturbed land is at present unreclaimed.

Over the years the forests of the world have been declining in total area. A few large-scale efforts at reforestation have been made, notably in the United States[1] and the U.S.S.R., but these efforts have brought about only a slight reversal in the worldwide trend. Our forests represent a complex, well-integrated ecological unit that has a far wider effect on surrounding environments than is usually recognized. Not only do forests provide numerous products to man and shelter and food to a variety of wildlife, but they also protect soils from erosion, hold water in the soil and in the foliage, provide windbreaks for adjacent agricultural land, and serve as modifiers of weather.

The importance of forests in regulating the flow of water has been one of the primary purposes of reforestation. In many places, projects have been undertaken to help the earth hold more water. In other areas, however, when quick and nearly complete runoff of rain is required for hydroelectric power or for agriculture, the forests have been cleared.

Water is one of the most important of all natural resources—and one about which there have been, and probably will continue to be, con-

The need for fresh, potable water for drinking and agriculture increases as rapidly as the population expands, and industrial requirements multiply even faster. According to The 1970 National Environmental Quality Index published by The National Wildlife Federation, every American uses an average of 1,600 gallons of water per day as compared with an average of 60 gallons per day used by a resident of Western Europe. These per capita figures include the amount of water required daily to produce our food and the quantities needed for our industrial operations. When the total

Marlin Johnson Heade. "Approaching Storm: Beach near Newport." Courtesy: Museum of Fine Arts, Boston, Fund: M. and M. Karolik Collection.

flicts, local and international. The first issue is how to insure an adequate supply of potable water. The second concerns the abatement of pollution of fresh and salt water. The third relates to flood control. All present real and growing problems, but they can be solved, given analysis, planning, appropriate legislation, and money.

consumption is considered, it becomes possible to believe the predictions that a future water shortage may be an even more serious threat than an inadequate supply of food.

Our uses of water, therefore, must be planned with the utmost care, and we must change from what has been called a "once-through nation" to a "re-use nation."

Interrelationships of Species

From ancient times the resources on which man has depended most immediately have been the living organisms with which he shares the earth. Although most of his food comes from only some one hundred species of animals and plants, there are many thousands more species in the food chains of the ecosystem of which man is a part. Disruptions anywhere in this system may effect changes elsewhere with totally unforeseen results, including the extinction of a species.

In the early 1900s, it must have been difficult for people in the United States to believe that the passenger pigeon might ever become extinct; in the 1930s for New Yorkers to see a threat to the peregrine falcon; in the 1950s for Californians to be concerned for the brown pelican. Yet the extinct and threatened species provide prescient models, and man may, as Nathan Hale said in his warning to George III, "profit from their example."

Our concern and our feelings about endangered species are perhaps deeper and go back further in time than does our concern about some of our other environmental ills. Creatures were evolving, propagating, and becoming extinct many millions of years before the appearance of human beings. Climate, food supplies, predators, and natural disasters all contributed to the extinction of early species. But in the United States in the past 150 years nearly 40 mammals and birds have become extinct as the result, directly or indirectly, of man's action. Thus, human concern and human responsibility both are involved.

One viewpoint is well expressed by Faith McNulty in her book *The Whooping Crane:*[2]

> The extinction of a species, no matter how alien to us the creature may be, is an awesome thing. In its presence, we experience a sort of shiver, perhaps an instinctive (should I say premonitory?) awareness that this is a death quite different from the death of an individual; that it has a different finality. This extinction of something that will never, in all eternity, be duplicated, is an occurrence that seems to break the strand of life itself.

Whooping Crane group in the American Museum of Natural History. Photo courtesy of the Museum.

The ethical and psychological factors in the preservation of threatened animals and plants notwithstanding, there are strong practical reasons for recognizing that every species must be preserved. Every animal and plant is part of the ecosystem; we have no notion of the complexity of roles any given species may play. The ivory-billed wood-pecker is extinct in the United States. Did this beautiful bird feed on some wood-boring insect pest which, when its predator was destroyed, multiplied in such numbers as now to require massive treatments of an insecticide? Or, in a more positive vein, does one of the currently threatened Southeast Asian mammals harbor an antibody that might be crucial in treating some present or future human disease?

Every species living today has a unique genetic composition containing the potential for characteristics vital to the survival of mankind. The loss of any species, no matter how obscure or seemingly unimportant, is an irretrievable loss from the storehouse of scientific materials for man's expanding skills—and for his very existence.

Man's concern—if it is followed by positive action—can still save many species that are now endangered. The Survival Service Commission of the International Union for Conservation of Nature and Natural Resources keeps track of threatened wildlife on a worldwide basis. The IUCN publishes the *Red Data Book*, the basic reference work on species of animals and plants that are in danger of extinction. Subscribers receive periodic additions to and revisions of the *Red Data Book* as the status of organisms changes. In 1969 the IUCN published *Wildlife in Danger*, a popular, illustrated version of the *Red Data Book*. It was the first complete and authoritative account of all the threatened species of vertebrates—mammals, birds, reptiles, amphibians, fishes—as well as selected invertebrates and plants of the world.

In the United States, 89 forms of fish and wildlife (including 14 mammals, 46 birds, 8 reptiles and amphibians, and 21 fish) are listed as "endangered" by the Bureau of Sport Fisheries and Wildlife of the U.S. Department of the Interior. Several hundred more species are listed in the successive classes of "rare," "peripheral," and "status undetermined."

In recent years an increasingly heavy demand has been made on fish and wildlife, especially by the people of the United States, who are by far the largest consumers in the world. William G. Conway, General Director of the New York Zoological Society, discussed this problem in the June 1968 issue of the Society's magazine, *Animal Kingdom*. In an editorial entitled "Consumption of Wildlife by Man" Mr. Conway provides many figures that indicate the extent of the use of the world's wildlife resources. In the year 1967, for example, the United States alone imported more than 28 million live wild animals and more than 22 million pounds of wild-animal skins. In the same year hunters in this country killed more than 60 million birds and mammals. These figures do not include any domestic animals or their hides, nor do they include any of the vast tonnage of fish and other sea foods consumed annually. Moreover, the number of animals shot by hunters in the United States in 1967 includes an almost incredible figure: 41.9 million mourning doves killed!

The story of whales and whaling illustrates the eagerness of technological man to add to his harvest regardless of the supply and is a clear example of what happens to our environment when protective mea-

12

sures are not enforced. We think of whaling as an adventurous activity that disappeared with sailing ships and the discovery of kerosene, but, as Roger S. Payne of the New York Zoological Society has shown, whaling as a successful exploit is at its height today; and whalers generally show little interest in leaving resources for the future. In 1860, the

Killer Whales. Painting Courtesy of the New York Zoological Society.

best whaling voyages averaged only about one whale a month; in 1933, 28,907 whales produced 2,606,201 barrels of oil; in 1966, however, almost exactly twice that number of whales (57,891) produced only 1,546,904 barrels of oil. Modern ships can run down and process many more whales than earlier vessels, but the whales are being taken irrespective of their size—with foreseeable results.

On December 5, 1969, President Nixon signed the "Endangered Species Act." This law, which became effective June 3, 1970, is aimed at halting the importation of threatened foreign species, and, provided it is meticulously enforced, can contribute greatly to their protection. By stopping the importation of

threatened animals for the world's largest market, the law will place an effective deterrent on traffic in wildlife and animal products. (Zoos, museums, and other qualified scientific institutions may be granted import permits under carefully prescribed conditions.)

There is an analogy worth noting in the state of the endangered animals and the circumstances that led to their plight: although some were brought to their endangered state through hunting or commercial demand, most are being crowded off the earth by less direct but more pervasive human actions—overpopulation, technological innovation, urbanization, pollution of air and water, development of pesticides, and reckless destruction of wilderness areas. The endangered species serve as a reminder that we must modify our attitudes and behavior if the wild creatures—and man—are to survive in a fit environment.

Philip Wylie summed up the problem when he wrote in the *New York Times* of February 1, 1970:

If all the ecologists could pool all they know and add all the data from every science, they would be unable to say what life forms and life systems are essential for man's survival. We know too little about the intricate, living understructure supporting our species to risk losing any wild living form, weed or pest or predator, lest one break in the planetary, life-sustaining system be fatal.

There never was a guarantee by nature that man should survive for any particular time. But there are many points in the natural order of beings where a lost or broken system might result in an inexorable act of nature fatal to man.

There are x numbers of niches and wild lands that may have an indispensable function for man. The problem is, we don't know them; it is the major, formidable, overwhelming problem in the whole business. We don't know.

When there were fewer people on earth and technologies were simple, the environment was able to absorb considerable insult and abuse. But the rise of population and technology has brought extensive, sometimes irreversible, devastation.

Man now finds himself confronted with the need to reexamine his values and his desire for more and more material comfort and luxury. He is confronted with the need to change his concept of the relationship of his species to the planet that is his home. As this book attempts to delineate, museums have an unparalleled opportunity to help him in this process.

Summary

All living organisms including man are dependent on the biophysical environment. This dependence is expressed in the transfer of energy that biologists call the "chain of life." Early man's conscious management of energy in using the resources around him raised him to his unique position among the organisms. But because extensive and complex interrelationships exist among all components of the environment, living and nonliving, man's present over-exploitation of natural resources and the effects of his technology have modified the environment to such an extent as to threaten the wellbeing, even the survival, of many species including his own. Action to halt further destruction requires fundamental changes in human attitudes and values.

exhibits and projects / man and the environment

Man—Unique Threat to the Environment

This exhibit is planned in two dimensions, and is adaptable to the means and capabilities of any museum. It may be hung on walls, with legends adjacent to each unit; or it may be mounted on freestanding panels. In either approach, the exhibit title should be displayed in a manner that unifies the entire exhibit.

1. Photograph of seals on an ice pack

   Life flourishes in the grip of polar winter

2. Photograph of a desert in bloom

   Life persists in the hard dry furnace of the desert

3. Photograph of an equatorial region, showing animals and plants

   Life is abundant in the steaming heat of the jungle

4. Photograph of deep sea creatures and plants

   Life teems in the crushing pressures and bitter cold of the ocean depths

5. Photograph of a marsh

   Life thrives in the ideal environment of a marsh, bog or swamp

6. Photograph of a mountain environment

   Life adapts to the cold thin air and hard rock of the highest mountain peaks

7. Photograph of a flooded river, or tornado

   Natural catastrophe may disturb life —but it cannot destroy it

8. Photograph of a factory locale, with chimneys belching smoke

   But man may succeed in destroying life. His smoke, soot and smog disturb plant life, upon which he ultimately depends

9. Photograph of a liquid waste pipe, emptying into a stream

   Man fouls the water that is critical to his own life cycle and survival

10. Photograph of an open pit or strip mine

    Man robs the earth of minerals to make his life better. His very act makes life worse

11. Photograph of a Dust Bowl area with abandoned farm buildings

    Man ravages large areas, and with his help, nature destroys entire environments

12. Photograph of a massive oil slick or other extensive pollution

    Man pollutes the world that gives him life

13. Photograph of a human form against a bright sky

    Man—the agent of his own destruction
    Man—bright promise, unique threat

Anthropomorphism

Somewhere in the mists of time, Man set himself apart from other animals. In so doing, he decided that the Earth was created for his use, rather than as an environment to be shared with all other creatures. Therein, of course, lies the seed of much of our present difficulty.

Paradoxically, however, man has continued to give animals human attributes—both in his religions and in his legends.

An exhibit that portrays this paradox might begin by bringing focus on the religious beliefs of the Egyptians and Sumerians, and then continue through other cultures.

Its theme should center on the implications for human ethics, morals and beliefs. The exhibit should foster appreciation of the interrelationship of all forms of life, and man's obligation to justify his assumed superiority.

Lurrain vs. Terrain

The uniqueness and value of our good earth is immediately apparent when its surface (terrain) is contrasted with the surface of the moon (lurrain).

An exciting and impressive exhibit can be built around paintings such as those of Helmut Wimmer and Chesley Bonestell, and photographs from the National Aeronautics and Space Administration. The bleak NASA moon "shots" should be set against natural color photographs and paintings of earth vistas and forms.

View of the earth 1/4 million miles away. Photo: NASA.

The Relevance of Man and the Environment

Put up an exhibit of any day's newspaper. Tack the newspaper to a vertical surface. Run strings from stories in the paper to labels on a horizontal surface which show how each article is related to environmental issues. You will see that most articles have some bearing on man's utilization of resources.

Check all printed matter to gather material for general environmental-awareness exhibits. For example, make:

A montage of magazine covers and headlines, cartoons, graphs and other line drawings. It can be enlarged to dramatic size and is often very effective in reverse (white on black). Addition of color spots, arrows heightens the impact.

Enlargements of headlines and quotes from carefully-selected newspaper reports, hearings, enforcement rulings, etc. Whole newspaper pages can often be reduced to 8-1/2" x 11" size and still be legible (offset-printed or electronically stencilled). This is an inexpensive source of reprints and helps preserve ephemeral material.

The Landscape in Art

The landscape—natural or urban —is the reality of environment.

All art interprets feeling, and is therefore directly related to man and the effects of his environment upon him.

To show how artists have viewed nature through the ages, set up an exhibit of landscapes in painting, drawing or other media. Accompany each exhibit with an interpretation of the way in which the painter helped to shape our "normative concepts" of an ideal landscape.

Consider matching each exhibit with a comparable photograph of an "ideal landscape" such as appears in many magazines. For detailed suggestions, refer to *Man in the Landscape*, by Paul Shepard (Knopf, 1967); *Landscape into Art*, by Kenneth Clark (Penguin, 1956).

The thinking of the viewer should be directed toward the question of whether the scene pictured is the same today and whether changes have been for good or bad.

Asher B. Durand, whose "White Mountain Scenery, Franconia Notch" is pictured, belonged to the nineteenth-century Hudson River school that discovered the beauty of the American landscape and in turn shaped the thinking of Americans.

Vasily Kandinsky, "Rain", (1911). Oil on canvas, 27-7/8 x 31". Courtesy, The Solomon R. Guggenheim Museum.

As Shepard pointed out in his book, *Man in the Landscape* (see text, left), Vasily Kandinsky, who began as landscape artist, demonstrates that nature imitates art imitates nature. (Here: "Rain")

Asher B. Durand, "White Mountain Scenery, Franconia Notch." Courtesy, The New York Historical Society, New York City.

A Sense of Space

Concepts of space have engrossed artists as well as philosophers through the ages. Given the great new vistas of our modern era, an exhibit can be built to show how artists of various times and cultures have perceived space and presented it in their work.

Plan your exhibit to point up these two related questions:

1. Is an artist's perception of space influenced by rural versus urban upbringing?
2. Does population pressure affect the space perception of an entire culture?

Art Creates Environments

A number of contemporary artists concentrate on literal creation of "environments." An exhibit featuring the work of Louise Nevelson or Roy Lichtenstein would illustrate this. Some of these creations respond to the presence of activities of visitors. One by Robert Rauschenberg responds with flashing lights to sounds of persons passing. The lights illuminate a huge environment that is otherwise invisible. Point out that in this new form of art man creates his own world, excluding nature. Contrast this exhibit with a panel that illustrates the absolute interdependency of man and nature.

The Artist or Photographer as Recorder of Nature

What price have we paid for this "progress"? To let the viewer decide for himself, set up a pictorial exhibit around a geographic entity:

The Colorado River
The Great Lakes
The Hudson River
Baja California
The Great Divide

Include present-day pictures with pictures of "development" and virgin territory. The objective should be the same as in "The Landscape in Art."

The great habitat groups in many natural history museums stimulated ecological awareness long before the word "ecology" was popular. Here, in the Hall of North American Mammals at the American Museum of Natural History, is an example of a spectacular geographical entity. The landscape artist took photos of the Grand Canyon—fauna, flora and geological formations and then helped the exhibition team recreate a total environment.

Thomas Cole. "The Oxbow" "The Connecticut River near Northampton" (1836). Oil on canvas, 51-1/2" x 76". Courtesy: The Metropolitan Museum of Art, New York, Gift of Mrs. Russell Sage, 1908.

John Frederick Kensett. "River Scene" (1870). Oil on canvas, 24-1/8" x 36-3/8". Courtesy: The Metropolitan Museum of Art, Bequest of Collis P. Huntington, 1925.

The Artist or Photographer as Recorder of Man-made Disasters

Fire

Lightning is the most frequent natural cause of fire. Most fires are caused by man. Forest fires, prairie fires and hayfield fires, as well as city holocausts, are usually man-made. Currier & Ives, Frederic Remington and other artists have depicted such disasters in paintings and prints which can be used as the basis of an exhibit.

Floods

The floods of the 1930s cost many lives and robbed the nation of countless acres of valuable soil. Paintings by Grant Wood, John Steuart Curry, Thomas Hart Benton and other Americans might be coupled with photographs and newsfilms to form a meaningful exhibit.

The Dust Bowl

Over-exploitation of the land in combination with cyclic droughts, caused the first great environmental disaster in the continental United States, in the 1930s. Many artists and printmakers have used the Dust Bowl as subject material. Newsreels recorded the tragedy as it affected both land and people. An exhibit on this topic should point out the lessons learned from this experience.

Farmers of the New Stone Age

If your museum has resources showing early man, his tools, his utensils, here is a conceptual scheme that could be included in your educational program. (This unit is reprinted from *People and their Environment, Teachers' Curriculum Guide to Conservation Education*, with permission of the publisher, J.G. Ferguson Publishing Company, Chicago, Illinois. Copyright © 1968, 1969 by the Department of Education, State of South Carolina.)

Concept The characteristics of a community have taken different forms in different periods of history.

Purpose of Lesson To help students understand the effect of forces of nature in changing hunters of the Old Stone Age into farmers and herdsmen of the New Stone Age.

Introducing the Concept Study museum exhibits of early man, his tools, his utensils. Each student should be prepared to tell the class what he saw. Use a picture series, a film, or filmstrips.

Developing the Concept Discuss:
1. What aspects of the geographical environment accounted for the opportunities in agriculture?
2. What climatic factors made it necessary for man to produce his own food rather than to hunt?
3. How did raising his own food account for settling in communities?
4. What industries were developed that made use of resources?
5. Why were men free to trade, make pottery, or weave cloth?

Extending the Concept Ask:
1. How have the forces of nature continued to influence the evolution of plants and animals?
2. Why is man migrating into more compact urban areas today?

Fixing the Concept
1. How have the occupations of men been affected by the resources of the community?
2. How did government develop as individuals needed protection?

Have the students investigate and present the following information to the class: land formations, earth layers, fossil remains, and climatic conditions of areas of the world believed to be the home of earliest man; e.g., Nile Valley, Tigris and Euphrates valleys, southern France, etc. Using the above information, have a classroom discussion on the relationship between resources and the types of communities that have developed.

Instructional Materials

Books
Merrill, E.H. and J. Teal: *Atlas of World History*

21

The American Indian: Cultures in Harmony with the Environment

Although the cultures of North American Indians differed widely from tribe to tribe and there seems to have been little exchange among the tribes that were widely separated, respect for nature appears to have been basic to all of them.

Each tribe, whether nomadic or sedentary, adapted its mode of living to natural laws. The conception of the Earth as Mother was fundamental to the religion of many tribes with the widespread taboo: "Thou shalt not pollute the Earth, which is thy Mother." In all tribes, the Indians used nature to feed man and to heal man. Their artifacts—including everyday tools—were fashioned of natural products adapted to their needs, such as baskets made of grass and pots of earth.

An exhibit utilizing Indian artifacts, and focused on primitive adaptation to and protection of the environment, should attract wide interest. It could be centered on tribes who lived in your own area, or, if the resources of your museum permit, could demonstrate the varying life styles of tribes across the continent.

It would be well to accompany each artifact with some illustration of its use, in such forms as:

1. The work of Indian artists, showing Indian customs
2. Artwork created in cooperation with the schools as part of the regular social studies program
3. Dramatizations by schoolchildren, illustrating the uses of the artifacts. Such demonstrations could be photographed on 8 mm. or 16 mm. motion picture film and shown in continuous display
4. The use of commercially-produced filmstrips might also enliven your display. Almost every producer of filmstrips for schools has at least one American Indian program in his catalogue. Usually these films are silent, with a title superimposed on each frame

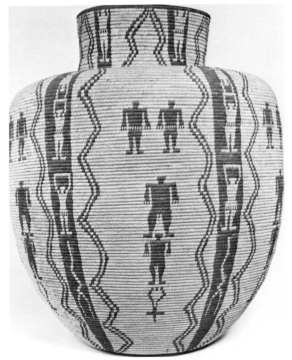

Apache Indian Basket. Photo: courtesy of Museum of the American Indian, Heye Foundation.

22

Ice People

The transition of Alaska's Eskimos into the twentieth century provides a timely and dramatic example of man's ability to adapt to change. A striking exhibit might compare the old and new, using pictures, films, artifacts and modern crafts.

Show the causes of change: the Gold Rush, 1898; the presence of American troops during World War II; the Alaskan Highway; the DEW Line; the growth of fisheries and canneries; the discovery of oil.

Show the changes: snowmobiles have replaced dogsleds; wooden houses have replaced sod houses; guns have replaced spears and arrows; diet has changed; electricity has brought "conveniences," including refrigerators and radios.

Show the good and the difficult in the adaptation.

An excellent documentary film on this subject was presented on NBC-TV in September of 1970. The title is *Ice People*; Hugh Downs serves as interviewer and narrator. It is available in a 23-minute, 16 mm. film version through NBC Educational Enterprises. (See Appendix for other films.)

The History of Conservation

The print resources of a history museum may provide material for exhibits related to your own locality. By showing progress made in the past, these displays could lead to questions pertinent to the present and future: what kinds of parks are desirable, and how should they be used.

Try to demonstrate the rise of park systems.
1. From Town Common to City Parks
2. From Reservoir to County Parks
3. From Abandoned Farmland to State and Federal Parks
4. From Grazing Land to National Parks
5. From Cemeteries as Parks to Cemeteries as Open Space

What Good is a Wilderness?

Prepare an exhibit showing the many uses of the wilderness; for example, watershed, animal habitats, recreation.

This exhibit can have as many variations as the wilderness itself!

Use a large mural map of the United States as background for an exhibit inspired by the Wilderness Act of 1964. Apply photographs of wilderness areas (5,000 or more acres) that are permanently preserved under the law, and of those being reviewed for admission. Label, and distinguish between them.

Set up a panel of portraits and thumbnail biographies of men whose work in conservation has led to appreciation of our wilderness areas. Among those included might be:

John James Audubon
William O. Douglas
Aldo Leopold
John Marshall
John Muir
Gifford Pinchot
Theodore Roosevelt
Howard Zahniser

Arrange a display to show what animals live in the wilderness.

Arrange a display showing uses of wilderness: for recreation, as a watershed. Make a scientific comparison of environments.

Include one or more films in the presentation or show them in a related program:

Man's work compared to the miracle of wilderness in fifteen ways . . .

Yesterday's Wilderness

	-100	-75	-50	-25	0	+25	+50	+75	+100	
destroys pure air						▓	▓	▓	▓	creates pure air [1]
destroys pure water						▓	▓	▓	▓	creates pure water [2]
wastes rain water						▓	▓	▓	▓	stores rain water [3]
produces no food						▓	▓	▓	▓	produces its own food [4]
destroys rich soil						▓	▓	▓	▓	creates rich soil [5]
wastes solar energy						▓	▓	▓	▓	uses solar energy [6]
wastes fossil fuels						▓	▓	▓	▓	stores solar energy [7]
destroys silence						▓	▓	▓	▓	creates silence [8]
dumps its wastes unused						▓	▓	▓	▓	consumes its own wastes [9]
needs repair & cleaning						▓	▓	▓	▓	maintains itself [10]
disregards nature's pace						▓	▓	▓	▓	matches nature's pace [11]
destroys wildlife habitat						▓	▓	▓	▓	provides wildlife habitat [12]
destroys human habitat						▓	▓	▓	▓	provides human habitat [13]
intensifies climate & weather						▓	▓	▓	▓	moderates climate & weather [14]
destroys beauty						▓	▓	▓	▓	beautiful [15]

Score (out of a possible perfect +1500):	**+1500**

Man's work compared to the miracle of wilderness in fifteen ways . . .

Today's City

Left	-100	-75	-50	-25	0	+25	+50	+75	+100	Right
destroys pure air	▓	▓	▓	▓						creates pure air [1]
destroys pure water	▓	▓	▓	▓						creates pure water [2]
wastes rain water		▓	▓	▓						stores rain water [3]
produces no food	▓	▓	▓	▓						produces its own food [4]
destroys rich soil	▓	▓	▓	▓						creates rich soil [5]
wastes solar energy	▓	▓	▓	▓						uses solar energy [6]
wastes fossil fuels	▓	▓	▓	▓						stores solar energy [7]
destroys silence	▓	▓	▓	▓						creates silence [8]
dumps its wastes unused	▓	▓	▓	▓						consumes its own wastes [9]
needs repair & cleaning	▓	▓	▓	▓						maintains itself [10]
disregards nature's pace	▓	▓	▓	▓						matches nature's pace [11]
destroys wildlife habitat			▓	▓						provides wildlife habitat [12]
destroys human habitat					▓	▓	▓	▓		provides human habitat [13]
intensifies climate & weather		▓	▓	▓						moderates climate & weather [14]
destroys beauty	▓	▓	▓	▓						beautiful [15]

Score (out of a possible perfect +1500): **(minus) -1200**

Man's work compared to the miracle of wilderness in fifteen ways . . .

Tomorrow's City

Left	-100	-75	-50	-25	0	+25	+50	+75	+100	Right
destroys pure air						▓	▓			creates pure air [1]
destroys pure water						▓	▓	▓		creates pure water [2]
wastes rain water						▓	▓	▓	▓	stores rain water [3]
produces no food						▓				produces its own food [4]
destroys rich soil						▓	▓	▓		creates rich soil [5]
wastes solar energy						▓	▓	▓		uses solar energy [6]
wastes fossil fuels						▓	▓	▓		stores solar energy [7]
destroys silence						▓	▓			creates silence [8]
dumps its wastes unused						▓	▓	▓	▓	consumes its own wastes [9]
needs repair & cleaning			▓	▓						maintains itself [10]
disregards nature's pace						▓				matches nature's pace [11]
destroys wildlife habitat						▓	▓			provides wildlife habitat [12]
destroys human habitat						▓	▓	▓		provides human habitat [13]
intensifies climate & weather						▓				moderates climate & weather [14]
destroys beauty						▓				beautiful [15]

Score (out of a possible perfect +1500): **+775**

Our Forests Primeval

Arrange a course combining woodland walks with group meetings at the museum, under the guidance of a museum staff member and/or a forester.

Visit (1) an uncultivated woodlot, to observe how nature replenishes the forest and disposes of waste; (2) an arboretum, to survey varieties of trees; (3) a forestry-station nursery; (4) a forest that serves as a watershed for your region. Try to revisit the last in winter, to observe how spacing of trees hoards water, and for a demonstration of how snowpacks are measured.

Invite experts from the forestry service to tell the class what provision your state may make for replenishing trees on private property as well as public lands, and what advice is available to landowners.

Invite an authority to explain how to judge the age of a tree and what its rings tell us about climatic conditions in times past.

Encourage group members to share films, slides or photographs they have made during wilderness camping trips or visits to forests out of your area.

The film *Heritage Restored* is available from the U.S. Department of Agriculture. It shows how forest lands were abused in the past, and how 20 million acres have been restored since passage of the Weeks Law began protection of National Forests in 1911.

The Mark Twain Tree, Giant Sequoia

The first accounts of the size of the sequoias were not believed, but settlers came to realize that they were the oldest and largest living things in the world. The Mark Twain Tree comes from Fresno County, California; it was 331 feet tall, had a 90-foot circumference, and had a root system of 3 acres. It began growing in 550 A.D. and was felled in 1891.

The Mark Twain Tree is situated in the American Museum of Natural History's Warburg Memorial Hall of Man and Nature, one of the first exhibit halls in any museum to demonstrate ecological principles.

Uses of the Forest

Investigate the resources of your area in terms of regional planning, particularly of land use. Does your area have an agriculture agent or a forester? Enlist the aid of these resource people or write to a state county agent to get help in developing an exhibit that will indicate how local forests are used as crops, and show what counsel and assistance the government offers to private owners.

Invite a local TV cameraman to accompany you and the forester (or agricultural agent) on visits to private owners. Let the forester show you how timber is cultivated, and photograph his consultations with local farmers in their woodlots, or with timbermen on larger sites.

Combine the resulting film with a walk-through exhibit showing the many ways timber becomes a cash crop in other states and countries. The objects you assemble may suggest various arrangements:

1. A roll of newspaper pulp, stood on end, with the daily paper tossed on top, and accompanied by photos of timbering and log-floating in northern Maine
2. A ship model whose "mast" is made of Douglas fir, with timbering pictures from Oregon
3. A grand piano whose mahogany came from the Philippines
4. A sample of parquet oak flooring
5. Siding from a shingle or clapboard house

Point out differences in cultivating and timbering techniques. For example, contrast some Maine cutting, in which trees have been planted for young growth and hundreds of acres have been logged off, with a timbering operation in Oregon in which the largest trees have been cut, making room for the smaller ones to grow.

Needs for Energy

Contrast the energy requirements (i.e., water as a source of power and light; wood and other natural resources for heat and light; food for caloric energy, etc.) of a twentieth-century urban family in the United States with those of a colonial family of the seventeenth century, or with those of a hypothetical pioneer family who settled in your region.

Search for Energy

Demonstrate major sources of energy (i.e., fossil fuel, hydroelectric, nuclear, chemical, solar). Show the benefits derived from each source, and also the prices we have to pay in pollution. Illustrate how groups of scientists, technologists and industrialists are working to overcome the problems associated with energy sources. As the final display, build a voting booth where visitors can cast ballots indicating which method they advocate—which one seems to them safest, least expensive, cleanest.

The Balance of Nature

Teachers' guides refer frequently to the resources of museums, and many museum instructors interact with teachers in nearby schools—to the benefit of all young people in the community. In the following curriculum material note how well-explained concepts can be adapted to museums. (This unit is reprinted from *People and their Environment, Teachers' Curriculum Guide to Conservation Education*, with permission of the publisher, J.G. Ferguson Publishing Company, Chicago, Illinois. Copyright © 1968, 1969 by the Department of Education, State of South Carolina.)

Introducing the Concept Field Trip: Students are taken on a field trip to a wildlife preserve, sanctuary, or refuge.

Previous to the field trip, have them study the balance of nature and the predator-prey relationships, and discuss food webs.

On this field trip they are to conduct samplings of the population to establish the predatory-prey relationship in a given area. For methods of population sampling, consult the following: *Field Ecology*, BSCS, A Laboratory Block, p. 51; Benton and Werner: Workbook for *Manual of Field Biology and Ecology*.*

Developing the Concept In the type of forest area recommended, set up experiments for sampling the animal population. (Various groups may take different groups of animals.) Secure the following information for *each animal*:

1. Number of individuals—(a) males; (b) females
2. Name of animal
3. Feeding habits—(a) food; (b) how secured; (c) time of day feeding is accomplished
4. Habitat
5. Means of defense
6. Natural enemies
7. Are there any special management practices needed to maintain their number or keep them from increasing too rapidly?
8. How do they contribute to the balance of life in the community?
9. Relative number in area
10. Does area show balance?
11. What are the predators?
12. What serves as prey?

Consult local game warden for:
1. Local game laws
2. Animals that he knows are to be found in the area

Consult local citizens who are familiar with the area and have them give you the names of animals found there.

Extending the Concept Consider the following:
1. Discuss how the balance of nature was shown in area studied, if it was
2. Discuss predator-prey relationships of area
   a. Develop food web to show these relationships
   b. How are the organisms beneficial to man, nature, soil, water, and wildlife?
3. Discuss game laws of area, and hunting seasons
4. What are wildlife refuges, preserves, and sanctuaries?
5. How is a balance maintained in a preserve?

28

6. Discuss local fishing laws: is it better to fish or not to fish in a pond? Why?
7. How is a balance maintained in the bird population?
8. Discuss various methods of keeping animal populations in balance with available food supply
9. How is overpopulation of a community harmful to the species?

Discussion and Activities:
1. What are some animals which have become extinct due to man's malicious killing?
2. How are predators related to a balance in nature?
3. Is a true balance in nature ever reached? Why? Why not?
4. How are game laws and hunting seasons of importance?
5. Why is "bag limits" rather than "no hunting" practiced?
6. Why are wildlife refuges, preserves, and sanctuaries important? A wide variety of projects and hobbies may evolve from the study of this concept. A few suggestions are:
   a. Furnish nesting and feeding places for birds
   b. Cooperate with U.S. Fish and Wildlife Service in bird banding
   c. Develop wildlife refuges for conservation study
   d. Organize bird clubs and walks
   e. Become familiar with and practice game laws

Instructional Materials

Books

Benton and Werner: *Manual of Field Biology and Ecology*
Black, John D.: *Biological Conservation*
Brandwein, Paul F. and others: *The World of Living Things*
Brown, Robert E. and B.W. Mouser: *Techniques for Teaching Conservation Education*
Dasmann, Raymond: *Wildlife Biology : Environmental Conservation Field Ecology*, BSCS
High School Biology, BSCS—Green Version

* BSCS=Biological Sciences Curriculum Study.

29

Food Webs

To develop the concept that organisms furnish matter and energy for each other, and to help students understand food chains and webs, museum instructors can conduct projects like the one below. (This unit is reprinted from *People and their Environment, Teachers' Curriculum Guide to Conservation Education*, with permission of the publisher, J.G. Ferguson Publishing Company, Chicago, Illinois. Copyright © 1968, 1969 by the Department of Education, State of South Carolina.

Introducing the Concept Select an area such as a lake, pond, field, bog, forest, or desert (nearby, if possible) for a field trip. Plan the trip with students as to:

1. Where they will go
2. What they will bring
3. What they will look for
4. What they will collect for further study
5. Select teams and choose team captains

Developing the Concept Compile observations and record on board. Discuss questions on student worksheet.

Extending the Concept Study litter and soil of area to determine organisms and their place in the food web.

OR

If the study is of a pond, investigate macroscopic and microscopic organisms and the place of each in the food web. Berlese apparatus may be used to find organisms not visible to the naked eye that form a link in the food webs. Simulate a Berlese apparatus by placing a sieve over a funnel set in a preserving bottle. This will separate and preserve the small insects found in the ground litter.

Use film *The Community*, and follow with a discussion of the film.

Use film *A Way of Life*, and follow with a discussion of the film.

Fixing the Concept Construct other food webs that you observe in your backyard or schoolyard using pictures or names and arrows to indicate producers and consumers.

1. What would be the effect of destroying one species in this web?
2. What would be the effect of overproduction of one species in this web?
3. How is the food web a self-sufficient unit?
4. What might happen to the balance of nature in a pond community if one kind of organism suddenly increased or decreased? Would any of the changes that occur be permanent? Would it make any difference if the expanding population were an algae (producer) or a fish (consumer)?

Instructional Materials

Books

Carson, Rachel: *The Sea Around Us*
Smith, R.L.: *Ecology and Field Biology*
Jacques, Harry: *How to Know, Nature Series*

Films

The Community, color, 11 min.—EBF
A Way of Life, color, 28 min.—MOCC

Materials

Berlese apparatus
Microscopes

Chlorophyll and You ("Food Chain")

by Florence B. Schell

Whether your museum is in a city, a suburb or rare rural setting . . . you will be interested in this well-thought-out classroom/field-trip project. Although the guide has been prepared for teaching children, it can be adapted to adults, who may not realize that there is a direct link between chlorophyll and all aspects of their lives, including the issue of law and order!

Following is the text of the teaching guide provided with Carnegie Museum's Ecology Whys Chart No. 10 ©.

Aims

To learn that green plants must have energy from the sun and space for growth, and to appreciate their vital importance as food, primarily, but also, as air-cleansers and for their esthetic value.

Motivation

Write on the board the words *Food Chain*, and explain that the definition is "A series of organisms interrelated in their feeding habits, the smallest being fed upon by a larger one, which in turn is fed upon by a still larger one, etc."

Also write the words *herbivore, carnivore, omnivore* on the board. Discuss these, using the base of the words to make clear the meaning of each—*herb* means plant; *carn*, meat; *omni*, all. Rabbits are a good example of herbivores because they eat only plants. If you have a garden and there are rabbits around, you know they eat your garden plants. Other animals, such as wolves, are carnivores, or meat-eaters, exclusively. Then there are many kinds of animals that will eat almost anything that is available at the moment. There are several of these on our chart; the mouse and the fox are omnivores. The grasshopper eats plants exclusively, so let's say he represents all the animals which eat green plants, and is the beginning link in any food chain.

Green plants are food factories; plants that are not green do not manufacture food. The specific product which makes the green plant unique in our whole living world is chlorophyll, which is the green substance in the plant. Because green plants make

31

the food upon which all animals depend, they are called *primary producers*, and there would be no life on this earth without these. When you go outdoors, look around and see how many green plants—or primary producers—you are able to spot.

If you live in the country, you will see many green plants—in the forests, in marshes and meadows, in farmers' fields where our food products are raised. These may be hay or grain for feeding cows, pigs, or poultry, which we eat. Or they may be crops we eat directly, like spinach, beans, potatoes. While we are discussing what *we* eat, let's find out where we belong in this word picture written on the board. We've talked about meat products we eat, and also about vegetables; so this makes us what? Yes, like the mouse and the fox on the chart, we are omnivores.

If you live in a city, or in a place where there are more people and buildings than there are trees, then you will have to have good eyes, and you will certainly have an interesting time finding green plants. Here are a few clues for places you might look: cracks in sidewalks, corners made by building walls, and sidewalks where dust and moisture have combined to make patches of soil where plants will grow. If there is a vacant lot handy for study, look for green plants where they receive enough sunshine to grow. What animal creatures do you suppose are living in this environment which would make a meal on these green plants and be links in a food chain? Look and see if there are grasshoppers, or caterpillars; maybe rabbits, or rodents of several kinds which need some fresh greens in their diets, as we do.

You will notice that we have a leaf on our chart which represents all green plants. And you will remember that we have called these plants primary producers, important to all life. Let's talk some more about these.

If your home is in a neighborhood where you don't see much plant life, then possibly you have not given much thought to the idea that green plants keep *you* alive; but they do! If you live in an area where there are many green plants, then you have probably taken them for granted and you, too, have never given serious thought to their importance. So this lesson is to learn about this and always to remember it. *Why* should you remember?

The answer is that in your lifetime you will see and hear about forests and fields being chopped away to make room for highways and housing developments. We must have roads and we must have homes, but you know now about the necessity of having green plants, and can insist, as a citizen, that green areas be saved. It has been found that in neighborhoods where there are no green parks and open areas, there often is more violence, rioting, and lawlessness than in other environments.

Let's think about a food chain now—one that *you* are going to make. Start at the bottom of your food chain, with you as a consumer, and work it back to a green leaf or plant. See if you can think of some links in your chain which are not on this chart, by using examples you know about.

Resource Materials

Chart, "Food Chain"

Chalk board, chalk, eraser

Books, illustrated with pictures of animals, insects, plants; any of the reference material listed; Field Guide books

Hand lenses, one for each child if possible, for field trips, equipped with twine or strong string for wearing around the neck

Small notebooks and pencils, for field trips

Follow-up Activities

Discuss the food chains done by children. Many may be garbled, but straighten out where possible. Display any which are at all reasonable.

As soon as possible after this lesson, take the class to any available patch of green. This will be more valuable than any other experience they can have in learning to look and really see. Be sure to have a thorough orientation session before going, as outlined in several references given.

On this trip, have each child make a list of anything he thinks is a link in a food chain. Look up, look down, all around, and under. If a log or a stone is moved, be sure it is replaced; someone lives there.

Back in the classroom, do a second food chain. Use the information gathered in the field and the books given as references, or any others available. (The Buchsbaums' *Basic Ecology* has a typical food web illustration, and their pyramid concept is easy to grasp.) These food chains might be in the form of charts, with drawings; or possibly graphs, depending on abilities and interest. This activity could include art projects as well as essays.

Now have an evaluation session on the food chain graphics, and note the improvements over the first set. Display.

These should make fine notebook material, and should also be an excellent gauge of the value of the in-the-field activities for motivation and learning.

Glossary

Animal: Any living thing that is not a plant.

Butterfly: Any of a group of insects, usually with conspicuously colored wings—diurnal.

Carbohydrate: Any of a class of organic compounds. They form the supporting tissues of plants, and are important food for animals.

Carnivore: The order of mammals, chiefly flesh-eating.

Caterpillar: The worm-like larva of a moth or butterfly.

Chain: A series of things connected, or following in succession.

Chlorophyll: The green coloring substance of leaves and plants associated with production of carbohydrates by photosynthesis in plants.

Contiguous: Touching; in contact.

Diurnal: Active by day, as certain animals.

Ecology: The branch of biology which treats of the relations between organisms and their environment.

Energy: The exertion of activity.

Environment: The aggregate of surrounding things, conditions, or influences.

Esthetic: Pertaining to the sense of the beautiful.

Factory: A place where something is made.

Farm: A tract of land devoted to agriculture.

Field: A piece of open or cleared ground; especially, one suitable for farming.

Fodder: Feed for livestock, composed of rough-cut plants such as field corn.

Food: Anything which supplies nourishment to organic bodies.

Food chain: A series of organisms interrelated in their feeding habits, the smallest being fed upon by a larger one, which in turn feeds a still larger one, etc.

Forest: A large tract of land covered with trees.

Fox: Any of certain carnivores of the dog family; smaller than wolves.

Grasshopper: Any of the orthopterous insects which are terrestrial. Many are very destructive to plant crops.

Hay: Grass cut and dried for use as fodder.

Herbivore: One who feeds on plants.

Lens: A glass device for magnifying objects to be studied.

Livestock: Horses, cattle, sheep, and other useful animals kept or raised on a farm or ranch.

Marsh: A tract of low, wet land.

Meadow: A piece of grassland, used for pasture or for raising hay.

Megalopolis: A continuous complex of urban areas, as contiguous or near-contiguous cities.

Moth: Any of a large group of lepidopterous insects, distinguished from butterflies because of their nocturnal habits.

Nocturnal: Active by night, as certain animals.

Omnivore: Eating both plant and animal foods.

Organic: Pertaining to plant or animal life.

Orientation: Becoming adjusted with relation to one's surroundings, circumstances, facts; orienting one's ideas to new conditions.

Pasture: Ground covered with grass, suitable for grazing cattle.

Photosynthesis: A process in green plants by which plant foods (carbohydrates) are formed from the carbon dioxide and water of air under the influence of light.

Primary: First in order in any series.

Producer: One who creates something.

Rabbit: A small, long-eared animal of the hare family.

Rodent: One of the gnawing or nibbling animals, as mice, rats, squirrels.

Terrestrial: Pertaining to the earth.

Urban: Pertaining to a city or town.

Vegetable: An herbaceous plant, any part of which is used for food.

Wolf: A large, wild carnivore of the dog family.

References

*Brown, R.E. and G.W. Mouser, 1964. Techniques for teaching conservation education. Burgess Pub. Co., Minneapolis. pp. 8-12.

Buchsbaum, Ralph and Mildred, 1957. Basic ecology. Boxwood Press, Pittsburgh. pp. 75, 76.

Curious Naturalist, 1966. Food chains and webs. Mass. Audubon Soc., 5: 5.

Doutt, J.K., C.A. Heppenstall, and J.E. Guilday, 1966. Mammals of Pennsylvania. Pa. Game Comm. and Carnegie Museum, Harrisburg. pp. 172, 185.

Hutchins, R.E., 1962. This is a leaf. Dodd Mead & Co., New York. p. 102.

Miller, Shirley, 1965. The story of ecology for Audubon juniors. Nat. Audubon Soc., New York. 48 pp.

Palmer, E. Laurence, 1949. Field-book of natural history. McGraw Hill Co., Inc., New York. pp. 384, 502, 601.

Parker, Bertha M. and Ralph Buchsbaum, 1961. Balance in nature. Row, Peterson & Co., Evanston. pp. 9-13.

Pettit, Ted S. and G. Don Ray, 1960. The web of nature. Garden City Books, Garden City. pp. 6-17.

Roth, Charles and Verne N. Rockcastle, 1962. Food chains. Cornell Science Leaflet, Cornell University, Ithaca, 55: 4.

Acknowledgments

Doutt, Dr. J. Kenneth, Curator of Mammals, Carnegie Museum

Heimerdinger, Dr. Mary A., Asst. Curator of Birds, Carnegie Museum

Heppenstall, Caroline A., Asst. Curator of Mammals, Carnegie Museum

Netting, Dr. M. Graham, Director, Carnegie Museum

Parkes, Dr. Kenneth C., Curator of Birds, Carnegie Museum

* This will suggest simple classroom and lab techniques for teaching conservation, as well as field trip techniques.

Our Versatile Grasslands

With the cooperation of children in your museum's classes, design an exhibit to show the value as well as the beauty of grass.

1. Open with a freestanding panel of photographs showing people enjoying a grassy lawn or park; Kentucky blue grass, with horses grazing; western range country with its distinctive grasses; Kansas wheat fields, and Iowa cornfields.

2. On a second panel, behind a table, display all the food grasses collected by one group of children on field trips; display samples of the grains on the table.

3. Encourage other children to collect wild grasses, and mount their samples in artistic arrangements.

4. Let a third group of children collect all the things they can find that people make using grass: American Indian baskets, Samoan mats, Hawaiian hula skirts, Chinese rice paper.

5. Still other children might research the Pueblo Indian legend that creation occurred when a grasshopper poked his head up through a blade of grass. This story could be presented in a mural like those the Indians painted in their kivas.

6. Another group might research the western range wars of the last century and other wars that have been fought over ownership and use of grasslands.

7. Another display might be developed showing how grass

makes a home for insects, reptiles, rabbits and other creatures.

8. Allow an older group to develop a display of cutaway earth showing how grass conserves rainfall.

9. Text may accompany any or all of the displays, but the final panel should consist of a listing of all the contributions that grass makes to the well-being of the earth.

10. One or more of the following films might be incorporated into the exhibit, or used in classes during its development:
   The Grasslands—Encyclopaedia Britannica Films, Inc.
   The Dust Bowl—McGraw-Hill Text Films
   Wise Use of Water Resources—United World Films
   Life in Grasslands—Encyclopaedia Britannica Films, Inc.
   The Prairie—International Film Bureau

(See Appendix for extensive list of films, with information on sources, costs, etc.)

The Sea Around Us

Design an exhibit (or series of exhibits) on the ocean depths, emphasizing (1) our need to know about the three-quarters of the earth hidden under water; (2) what is being learned through such programs at the U.S. Navy Sealab experiments about man's ability to adapt to strange environments.

Dramatic two-dimensional settings to illustrate, for example, the composition of the ocean bottom, or the profile of a continental shelf, may be achieved by varicolored diagrams covered with acetate for a watery effect.

If your museum has the facilities —or if you can solicit the aid of stage designers from a little theatre group or from the theatre arts class of a local school — try constructing exciting three-dimensional models. These could either be miniatures or be in walk-through scale. On a scale of one or two feet to a mile, extensive depths could be presented in a room of normal ceiling height. Lath, wire, papier-mache and canvas can be used as materials to build such structures as a replica of the vertical supports the Hawaiian Islands around Honolulu, including the plain to the west and the Molokai Fracture to the east. Topping the pinnacles with greenery, rocks, and sand will show how little is visible above the sea.

Profiles comparing depth and width of undersea canyons with Grand Canyon will reemphasize the vastness of the undersea world.

Surround the major setting of your exhibit with related materials:
. Accounts of Sealab experiments

- The work of Project Mohole
- A model ship, sunken in an aquarium tank and surrounded by fish, to illustrate investigations of fish communities
- Samples of valuable materials found in the sea:

    Oil

    Minerals

    Fossils

    Sea shells

    Aquatic plants that produce oxygen

    Fish and fish products, such as fish flour and fertilizer
- Include an exhibit on ocean farming
- Include an exhibit on desalinization of seawater

The film *The Restless Sea*, available from the Southern Bell Telephone System, might be made a part of your exhibit.

You will find a wealth of additional material on the oceans. Some sources are: the U.S. National Oceanographic Program (NOP) and the Antarctic Research Program of the National Science Foundation; the Scripps Institute of Oceanography in La Jolla, California; the Lamont Geological Observatory of Columbia University; the Osborn Laboratory of Marine Sciences of the New York Zoological Society; the Woods Hole Oceanographic Institute at Woods Hole, Massachusetts. Accounts of work achieved during the International Geophysical Year are also available. The National Geographic Society has published a series of ocean-floor relief maps which are sold by the Society, Washington, D.C. 20036.

Minerals: Treasures Lost Forever

Design an exhibit backed by a large outline map of the world. Using the export-import charts provided in the most recent almanacs, run red ribbons from the United States to other countries, showing the metals which we are still able to export; and run black ribbons to the United States, showing metals we must import. Label each, possibly on ship cutouts attached to the ribbons. Indicate those minerals once abundantly available which are now exhausted or in short supply.

On a nearby table display a series of coins: a new penny and a pre-World War II penny; a silver dollar. Ask the questions "What are these coins made of? How and why are the two pennies different? Why do you never see silver dollars?" Conceal the answers beneath flaps to be lifted.

Display a variety of small articles made of minerals. Ask the question "What is each article made of?" Conceal the answers.

If you have the space bring a new automobile into the exhibit hall. Label each part of the car with the names of all the minerals required for its manufacture. Note which of these minerals the United States must import.

If you do not have an exhibit area large enough to accommodate an automobile use a photograph of an automobile, blown up as large as possible to show the mineral content of each part.

The Endangered Species

Note that, without shifting a case or adding a display, the hundreds of thousands of exhibits already on view can be used to tell the story of man's many roles in the environment and of the need to reexamine our values and actions. All that need be done is to *change the labels* and shift the emphasis so as to relate the contents of the case to the total environment. The use of labels will *not*, as we all know, fulfill the museum's task in environmental education. In fact, as is pointed out frequently in this book, the ecological message calls for rethinking the whole process of exhibition and communication. Nevertheless, the revision of labels does offer one simple, relatively inexpensive interim approach to the development of ecological awareness—an approach that museums can take while planning more imaginative and comprehensive programs of education. Relabeling is particularly adaptable to education about endangered species, but can also be used effectively in relation to many other environmental problems.

Zoos, aquaria, museums of natural history and science, nature centers and national parks, and sanctuaries are the obvious places to foster education about endangered species by means of labels. However, art museums and historical societies may also find interesting opportunities to call attention to the plight of a threatened species when museum collections contain paintings, drawings, sculptures or photographs of such species.

Many museums are approaching problems of endangered species in different ways: displays, participation-learning situations, charts, books. The following have been very successful.

Staff members at the Boston Museum of Science supervised junior volunteers in mounting a simple but effective exhibit on endangered species. Pictures, books, objects, text and live animals were used.

One display case held mounted alligators and caimans, and bore the label "Who's Who?" A second case held books on reptiles and amphibians, and women's shoes made of alligator skin. The third display featured live specimens, in a setting of water and pebbles. A label explained how to distinguish between alligators and caimans, mapped their range, told what they eat and pointed out the danger to the alligator from unlimited hunting.

The Museum of the Hudson Highlands at Stony Point, New York is a small nature museum planned as a participation-learning situation for children. First the children see the animals in environmental displays. Then the children are encouraged to handle the creatures, thus learning how the animals function both independently and in relation to human beings. The ultimate lesson is similar to that of the junior volunteers' exhibit at the Boston Museum of Science: young people are taught about our endangered species.

The New York Zoological Society has made a point of appealing for help for endangered species in a very appropriate place, the inside covers of its book *The Bronx Zoo Book of Wild Animals*. Long before ecology was a by-word, many zoos were conservation-minded, always looking for ways to call attention to the plight of the animals visitors were viewing in more or less natural settings. What better method than sending visitors away with a picture book of animals they might not see elsewhere?

This, then, is a reminder that all publications—whether simple handbooks, major guidebooks, pamphlets, annual reports—should be thought of as potential vehicles of communication about environmental problems; that all museums should employ every means of communication available.

The Bronx Zoo—Book of Wild Animals (front cover)

There was a time, not so many years ago, when a wild animal species could fade into extinction with few persons knowing about it—and perhaps even fewer caring very much. That is not true today. "Conservation" is a concept that concerns Governments as well as individuals, and national and even international organizations have been formed to watch over, collect information about, and urge the preservation of rare and endangered species. Zoos have an important role in these endeavors, for they have the vital interests and skills to maintain at least captive stocks of some animals that are finding it increasingly difficult to survive, and perhaps even to return them to the wild.

A few of the most hard-pressed mammals are mentioned below. The reasons given for their decline make instructive reading.

Going, Going....

Thylacine. This large and rather dog-like pouched animal of Tasmania was hunted almost to extermination because of its attacks on sheep—bounties were paid and 2,268 are known to have been killed between 1888 and 1924. Since then there have been a few "reasonably reliable sightings" in remote districts. Disease and changes made in its habitat by man may also be partly responsible for its decline.

Black-footed Ferret. "On the verge of extinction" sums up the status of the black-footed ferret of the Great Plains of North America. It was closely associated with prairie dogs, using their burrows for shelter and preying on their young. The prairie dogs are going, the original grasslands are being destroyed, and poisoning campaigns have taken their toll.

Asiatic Cheetah. "The last definite report of cheetah in India was in 1951 when three were shot in one night," an investigator reported. "For all practical purposes the cheetah may be considered extinct in India"—and this in a country where cheetahs were trained for sport hunting by the native princes. Besides direct killing, there has been destruction of habitat and a decline in the numbers of blackbuck and gazelles, which were the prey of the cheetahs.

Sumatran Rhinoceros. This is the smallest of the living rhinoceroses but every part of it—horns, hide, hair, blood and viscera—is prized by Asiatic people for supposed medicinal, religious or magical properties. Its future (like that of other Asiatic rhinoceroses) gives cause for "very grave anxiety."

Orang-utan. The name "Orang-utan" means "man of the woods" and at one time this animal was plentiful in the thick forests of Sumatra and Borneo. But the forests are being cut down in logging operations, adults are killed and the babies seized for export, mostly illegal. American zoos have taken the lead in refusing to buy illegally-captured orangs.

Arabian Oryx. The capture of a few pairs of Arabian oryx and their subsequent successful breeding in the Phoenix, Arizona Zoo and elsewhere has had great publicity. "Small pockets" of them may still survive in the wild, but are always in danger of being exterminated for sport by hunting parties using jeeps and machine guns.

The Bronx Zoo—Book of Wild Animals (back cover)

Animals that have recently become extinct, and those now in danger of extinction, are usually conspicuous and restricted in their habitat. Island-dwelling mammals, birds and reptiles have suffered especially severely.

Today man is the primary agent of extinction. He destroys forests, drains marshes, hunts and kills with little thought of the future. And now increasingly he is polluting his environment with wastes from his factories, homes and smokestacks.

Fortunately, many species have great recuperative powers, if the pressures that lead to destruction are relieved. Protection for the few remaining wild places and the creation of more national parks seem to offer the best hope for survival of wild creatures—if they are to remain with us for the education and enjoyment of future generations.

They Need Help

California Condor. "Rare, local and slowly declining in numbers" is the ominous report on the largest (in wingspread) of North American birds, now chiefly confined to the southern Coastal Range of California. Between 50 and 60 were left in 1967. They are protected by law and a sanctuary has been established for most of the nesting sites and winter roosts, but hunters and poisoned bait take a steady toll of the remaining birds.

41

Southern Bald Eagle. The bald eagle is the national bird of the United States and is protected by law, but the southern race is generally decreasing nevertheless. It is the same old story: human population pressure along the Atlantic and Gulf Coasts and in the lower Mississippi Valley, destruction of nesting trees, illegal shooting and perhaps lowered reproduction because of widespread use of pesticides.

Whooping Crane. At least twice a year, at the spring and fall migrations, an anxious watch is kept on the remaining small flock of whooping cranes as they journey between their wintering grounds in Texas and breeding grounds in Canada. Therein lies their greatest hope of survival—national publicity and attention.

Monkey-eating Eagle. This is one of the most striking and imposing of the world's eagles, now confined to the islands of Mindanao and Luzon in the Philippines. Illegal trapping and shooting for the sake of having a mounted specimen in the home (a local fad) are serious threats; probably fewer than 200 remain in the wild. Even zoos are mutually pledged not to import this eagle for exhibition.

American Alligator. Heavy poaching for commercial skins, as well as the usual destruction of habitat, have greatly reduced the number of alligators over most of their range along the Atlantic and Gulf Coasts and in the Mississippi drainage. Federal regulation of the trade in skins might arrest the decline.

42

Galapagos Tortoise. Giant tortoises were once found on each of the main islands of the Galapagos group, but in the 18th and 19th centuries whaling ships raided them so persistently for food that they were all but exterminated on some islands. Introduced rats and goats carried on the work of destruction and now they have disappeared from two islands, are rare on most others, and are still plentiful only on Albemarle and Indefatigable.

How to Score the Environmental Picture

Here is an inexpensive, simple and most importantly, an evocative way to make the community around your museum aware of its changing environment.

The National Wildlife Federation annually publishes an *Index Of Environmental Quality*—the *National EQ* (in *National Wildlife**). It scores air, water and the total environmental situation in the U.S. on a seven-step scale ranging from very bad to excellent; and it rates trends toward loss or gain in wildlife, timber, soil, minerals, living space and population. Each double-page spread on a topic includes quotable text, a dramatic color photo, and highly graphic charts, maps, and tables. An excellent list of suggestions promotes action by the concerned individual. An *EQ* Teacher Kit is available.

Any museum could base an effective display on one or more charts. For example, each of the six fields—wildlife, timber, soil, minerals, living space, and population—could be featured for a two-month display period, and a year later revised figures and other current data could be inserted for a second round of exhibition.

Except for the color photographs, most of the graphics could be easily enlarged to any desired size. The photographs might be handled as projected transparencies or in other ways, by arrangement with the National Wildlife Federation.

In addition, it should be relatively simple to set up a twin display featuring photographs and data evaluating the situation on a local, state, or regional scale.

The schools in your area might cooperate in producing and distributing the local display as a travelling exhibit.

* August-September 1969 and October-November 1970 Reprints available at 15 cents a copy (less in large quantities) from National Wildlife Federation, 1412 16th St. N.W., Washington D.C. 20036.

The Wave Hill Center for Environmental Studies

A cultural institution of the city of New York, the Wave Hill Center for Environmental Studies is devoted to public understanding of man's environment. All aspects of the environment—biological, physical and cultural—are key components in the educational efforts at Wave Hill. Situated on one of the most striking sites in New York, one center has 28 acres of public grounds and gardens open to the public. In recent years specific programs dealing with the urban environment have been developed and implemented.

Students and teachers from public, private and parochial schools schedule field trips to Wave Hill to explore various areas in environmental studies in conjunction with class room studies. The institution concentrates on grades one through six, although programs for all grade levels have been conducted.

New York City children enjoy learning about the natural environment at Wave Hill. Photo: Arline Strong.

Population

The information contained in the first section of this chapter is meant as a general introduction to the problems of overpopulation and necessary urbanization. We have not sought to be comprehensive, since within the scope of this handbook it is impossible to cover all aspects of the problem. Many books have been written on the subject, and the bibliography should be consulted for appropriate references.

The second section, starting on page 61, includes a variety of materials that we hope will be of assistance to you in planning exhibits and programs. We have included suggestions for exhibits, community activities, and teaching programs; descriptions of what other museums have done and are doing to interpret pollution problems; and sample posters and other graphics.

Because the staff of each museum will want to develop exhibits and programs that are unique to their museum and its own geographic region, we are including germinal suggestions as well as structured outlines.

"Whether we are concerned primarily with the present population of the world, with future generations, with man's survival as a species, or with preserving the stability of the entire biosphere, it is absolutely imperative that the human birth rate be curtailed."

J. George Harrar

"Today the articulate cries of the hungry and those who speak on their behalf fill the air channels and there is no escape from a knowledge of the millions who starve today, of the millions more who are seriously undernourished and of the looming famine of tomorrow."

Margaret Mead

"Who is to doubt that the tensions, the frustrations, and the violence which have become part of the urban scene have their roots, to some degree at least, in the environment in which our city people live?"

Russell E. Train

Background

Yesterday 336,960 infants came into the world crying to be fed, even as 34,000 people died of malnutrition, and countless millions went hungry. The 34,000 people who died of malnutrition were among a total of 146,960 who died of all causes. Thus, in a single day, there was a net increase of 190,000 people on the earth.

In the worldwide battle against population growth, it is of no consolation that the human army is 3.5 billion strong. For unless we act decisively, by the year 2000 we will have swelled our ranks to between 6 and 7 billion—and lost the population war.

In few fields are statistics so important as in demography. One could (and many do) write a book about the statistical picture. For the purpose of this report it may simply be said that the population of the world at the time of Christ was one-quarter billion; by 1850 it was one billion; by 1930, 2 billion; by 1962 it was 3 billion; and in less than a decade we have grown by another one-half billion. *Of all the people who ever lived, nearly 5 percent are alive today.*

The climb of the world's population prior to 1800 was attributable to improvements in agriculture and the resulting increases in food supply. The industrial revolution accounted for the sharp increase that occurred between 1800 and 1900. But the growth of the human population in recent decades is a biological development without comparison; there has never been such a threat to the quality of life—and indeed to the survival—of all living species on earth. The growth rate in recent years is attributable largely to the advance of medical science, which by deferring infant and childhood death and by substantially increasing the life span of adults broke the "mortality pattern of a million years."

Photograph of Beach at Seabreeze, Daytona Beach, Florida, 1904. Courtesy, Chicago Historical Society.

Various "solutions" to the population problem have been proposed. Human habitation in the oceans, the frigid regions, the deserts are under discussion and will doubtless take place. Until recently it was common to speak of colonizing the planets. Strangely, since 1969—the year of the first moon walks—such speculation has diminished. Perhaps the success of our space technology served to present the realism of the distance and inhospitality of outer space; fact put a damper on fantasy.

Is our technology adequate to the task of maintaining the world's burgeoning billions: Many authorities feel that it is not, and that technology is likely to remain inadequate until such time as the population growth rate is drastically reduced.

Hunger in the Present

Today enough food is produced to satisfy both the energy and protein requirements of every human being; the underdeveloped countries, in fact, actually have more food than ever before. Yet at least

Benton, Thomas Hart. "July Hay"; (1943). Collection, The Metropolitan Museum of Art, New York; George A. Hearn Fund, 1943.

500 million people are undernourished, that is, suffering from lack of calories; an additional billion are malnourished, deficient in particular nutrients, primarily proteins; and estimates of the number who die every year from starvation range from 4 million to a high of 20 million people.

What of the millions who do not die of starvation but are malnourished? We tend to underestimate the dangers of protein malnutrition. Lack of proper nourishment in childhood, or in the mother's womb before birth, can cause severe mental as well as physical damage. No person of any age who is malnourished is able to achieve an existence of high

48

quality, to live a life in which he is able to realize his fullest potential as a human being.

A recent survey showed that cultural mores can severely restrict the quality of nutrition. For example, people in the Dominican Republic were found to be seriously lacking in protein despite its ready availability in the sea around them: their cultural conditioning precludes the harvesting of fish. Similar mores act in other parts of the world to prevent people from utilizing available, nutritious foods. Who among us Americans would be eager to use flour composed of that highly celebrated fish protein concentrate?

Thus with local failure to exploit potential food resources, and with social customs that prevent certain highly nutritious foods from being acceptable, the need to develop more efficient methods of food distribution is urgent.

....and in the Future

A productive agricultural period, with good weather and without natural disaster and pestilence, has greatly reduced the immediate prospect of famine. Nonetheless, agricultural experts maintain that a tripling of the world's food supply will be necessary in the next 30 years or so, if all the peoples of the world are to be adequately fed.

Hybrid plantings have been extremely successful in escalating production of wheat, corn, and rice for the countries with the worst food problems. In 1970, the Nobel Peace Prize was awarded to Dr. Norman E. Borlaug, an Iowa-born agronomist, for his success in cultivating im-

proved strains of wheat and rice to ease the hunger of the world. Dr. Borlaug is director of the Wheat Improvement Program at the International Maize and Wheat Improvement Center of Mexico, a research organization supported by the Ford and Rockefeller foundations and other American organizations in cooperation with the Mexican government. He has headed teams of scientists from 17 nations, and his extraordinary work has spurred food production in India, Pakistan, Turkey, Tunisia, and other nations as well as in Mexico.

Greek. "Wheat" (4th Century B.C.). Gold. Collection, The Virginia Museum of Fine Arts, Purchase by the Williams Fund, 1968.

Experiments using unusual sources of food also appear to be promising. Great progress has been made, for example, in developing aquatic protein products, including the fish protein concentrate already mentioned and a marine protein concentrate that utilizes plankton. Incaparina—a mixture of grains and bean meal—is an excellent source of high-quality protein, and other advances are being made in synthesizing amino acids and preparing available algae for foods.

Research in agricultural production, the education of farmers, land reforms, the availability of farming equipment, irrigation, and fertilizers are all factors in the future development of food sources. (The new role of insecticides, which in the past have enabled great gains to be made in the production of food, is moot, since their indirect damage to higher animals has made them more of a menace than a boon.) The Population Service of the Office of the War on Hunger, a unit of the Agency for International Development, estimates that a 2 percent per year average increase in agricultural production can realistically be expected from the less developed countries—a rate that would require 35 years to double production.

But the world population will double in 30 years, and in less time than that it will redouble. The situation has its optimists and its pessimists. Professor Paul Ehrlich, a Stanford University biologist, cites, as an example of what might happen, a passage from William and Paul Paddock's book, *Famine 1975*.

A locomotive is roaring full throttle down the track. Just around the bend an impenetrable mudslide has oozed across the track. There it lies, inert, static, deadly. Nothing can stop the locomotive in time. Collision is inevitable. Catastrophe is foredoomed. Miles back up the track the locomotive could have been warned and stopped.

Years ago the mudsoaked hill could have been shored up to forestall the landslide. Now it is too late.

The locomotive roaring straight at us is the population explosion. The unmovable landslide across the tracks is the stagnant production of food in the undeveloped nations, the nations where the population increases are greatest. The collision is inevitable. The famines are inevitable.[1]

Andrew Wyeth. "Nick and Jamie" (1963-64). Collection, The Virginia Museum of Fine Arts, Purchase by the DuPont Fund.

Yet Lester R. Brown, author of *The Green Revolution*, feels that the United States will lead what is, after all, simply another technological struggle (though certainly the greatest one ever) to solve the world's food problems. He believes that global hunger will be dealt with successfully by American foundations and "the largest and best-equipped multi-national agribusiness corporations." Also optimistic are the admirers of the Food and Agriculture Organization of the United Nations, which does not speculate about how long it will be until starvation overtakes mankind but concentrates instead on action for the 1970s and the 1980s. The FAO's Indicative World Plan for Agricultural Development, an integrated, international program, is a broad framework of guidelines for agricultural development intended to close the gap between curves for food production and population growth.

It is inevitable that man, faced with worldwide hunger and malnutrition, should look to the sea as a potential source of food for the future. Much can be done, and is being done, to utilize protein derived from marine organisms. However, with respect to present known fisheries, we are already approaching a maximum yield. Dr. John Ryther of the Woods Hole Oceanographic Institution has pointed out that in 1967 the total world harvest in fish was slightly in excess of 60 million tons. He estimated that this yield might be sustained in the next ten years at present rates of harvest. However, this estimate is based on sound conservation practices and not unlimited exploitation. Yet, the history of fisheries has been one of worldwide exploitation up to the brink of economic infeasibility. The herring industry in the North Atlantic and the anchovy fishery of Peru, both of which have declined markedly from overexploitation, are only two examples.

In the 110,000 square mile area that makes up the northwestern Atlantic fisheries, Dr. Ryther estimated the annual yield at about -1 million tons per year. In the mid-1960s this fishery began to decline sharply as the result of poor conservation practices, overfishing and the pollution of coastal waters long known to be the nursery grounds for many of our food fish.

As a result of the present trend, Dr. Ryther concluded that new approaches to commercial fishing must be considered. The two that he thinks most worthy of serious pursuit are farming the sea and using resources now considered to be sport fisheries. The former appears to offer the greatest hope, providing the potential farming areas are not destroyed by man's discharges of domestic and industrial wastes.

But can increased food production alone solve the population problem? Dr. Borlaug warns that it cannot. In a *New York Times* interview following the Nobel Committee's announcement, he stated emphatically that it can afford only a reprieve, not a permanent solution. "We have only delayed the world food crisis for another 30 years," he said. "The world's population is a monster, which, unless tamed, will one day wipe us from the earth's surface." In a sense, that monster is being nourished by the "green revolution," for the very knowledge that food production can be increased has tended to encourage complacency about the necessity for birth control.

Loss of Elbowroom: Increased Urbanization

Lack of food is only one of the problems arising from excessive population growth. What of the physiological and psychological effects on man himself, on the quality of his existence?

Loss of space, a resource that is consumed in direct proportion to the expanding population and the expanding technology, is especially important. High-rise buildings, the soaring price of industrial real estate, the premium on recreational land, the increasing challenges to private land ownership, and the battles over where to put superhighways are all symptoms of the space shortage. There are still ample open spaces on the earth, but the projected population will make demands on all lands not currently in "use."

Loss of personal space—that which we call elbowroom—also presents problems. What happens to the psyche under the pressure of constant crowding in cities, at recreation areas, in one's own home? Studies on non-human animals have demonstrated some of the relationships between aggression and overcrowding. Current studies on behavior, anthropology, and human ecology are probing the psychological and physiological effects of crowding on human being. The breakdown of essential services, which follows in-

Although the use of space is of great moment in many parts of the world, the most urgent space problems exist in the urban areas. The planning and establishment of open-space systems is finally coming to be regarded with the seriousness that it deserves. Enlightened urban planners believe that most open spaces in urban areas should be devoted to recreation and that the deliberate integration of parks into neighborhood life is a key technique of urban planning. But recreation areas are only one segment of the total urban picture, and it is no longer feasible to plan separately for any single aspect of urban development—space, transportation, housing, waste disposal, to name only a few: the city and hinterland must be considered as a total system.

Cities grow in response to forces, both natural and unnatural. Like art and architecture, cities are expressions of the cultures they serve. The American civilization—our culture— is expressed by the condition of its cities, its land, its society, and its resources.

Honore Sharrer   "Workers and Paintings"; (1943). Oil on composition board, 18-5/8 x 37". Collection, The Museum of Modern Art, New York, Gift of Lincoln Kirstein.

tense urbanization, serves further to frustrate people, and strengthens their sense of individual helplessness.

The profound difference between what is ecologically real and what men think is real is most vividly illustrated in the development of cities. The unreality of contemporary architectural and urbanistic activity has resulted from two human errors and have been described by James Marston Fitch, professor of architecture at Columbia University. One error, he says, is the "lack of comprehension of the absolute inter-relatedness of all the component elements of the natural environment." The second error is "the consistent tendency of modern architects and engineers grossly to underestimate the magnitude of the natural forces of the environment, or grossly to overestimate the magnitude of man-made capacities at their disposal." Professor Fitch cited as an example of faulty estimates the large-scale East Coast power failures of November 1965 and May 1967.

"The contemporary designer," Professor Fitch said, "runs the risk of accepting electrical air filters as a satisfactory substitute for clean fresh air; or feeling that electronically operated louvers are preferable to natural foliage. There are many specific situations for which our synthetic environments are superior to nature's. But this is no adequate basis for the mechanistic conclusion that 'we don't need to pay attention to nature any more.'

"With the complexity of modern building we need nature more than ever before. It is not a question air-conditioning versus sea breezes, of fluorescent tubes against the sun. It is rather the necessity for integrating the two environmental systems— natural and artificial—at the highest possible level.

"The question of a new environ-mental policy is no longer hypothetical. It is a matter of burning immediacy. The task of reintegrating disparate control systems into a viable whole is clearly beyond the capacity of the individual architect or planner. Only a comprehensive national program can possibly meet the crisis."[2]

Richard L. Meier of the School of Natural Resources of the University of Michigan says, "As we become more and more artificial, that is, less and less aware of our utter dependence on the living land, the danger of making greater and greater ecologic mistakes increases. As American cities complete the acculturation of the rural immigrant, fewer problems involving known resource deficiencies can be inferred from our present state of knowledge."

As René Dubos has pointed out, "Modern cities are . . . developing without any regard to physical and biological constraints and only under the influence of economic and political imperatives . . . . Most urban problems derive precisely from such a misapplied interpretation of freedom."

The essentials of an optimal urban environment have been outlined by a number of physicians interested in the subject of human ecology. Dr. Lawrence E. Hinkle, Jr., of the Division of Human Ecology, Cornell University Medical College, said:

I would propose that an optimal environment for men is one in which men are all healthy and all realize their full biological potential. Let me define "optimal health" as that state in which men are free from disability and illness, and live out their full span of life. Let me also define "realizing one's full biological potential" as attaining and fulfilling any social role, any creative intellectual or physical function, which it is within one's biological capacity to fulfill. In concrete terms, this would mean that every man would have an opportunity to attain whatever level of education he can assimilate, to attain whatever occupational position is within his capabilities, and make whatever arrangements for dwelling, marriage, family, recreation and creative satisfaction is suited to his needs. Such an idyllic concept is hardly to be realized, but it does provide a framework in which we can ask ourselves, "To what extent and in what manner does the urban environment today influence the health and behavior of people?" If new urban environments are to be planned and developed, what reason do we have to believe that they will promote the health and welfare of the people who live in them? Indeed, can we develop ways for measuring the effects of the urban environment on human health and behavior?"

Lack of space is of course only one deleterious effect of urbanization—pollution, ugliness, dehumanization, illness, crime, and poor educational opportunities are a few of the others. In New York City recently a venerable and prestigious social service agency announced its intention to discontinue counseling and case work among individuals and families. It is fruitless, the agency said, to attempt to help people who must be sent back into the horrid environment from which their problems arose; henceforth the agency will attempt to correct the social environmental problems of the slums. Increasingly it is recognized that the environment has the prime influence on the quality of life and that life in the inner city is barely tolerable.

An inability to tolerate life as one perceives it is an important factor in the narcotics epidemic that is debilitating so many people today. History is likely to assign a large portion of responsibility for drug use to the loss of the sense of individuality brought about by overpopulation.

Lippitt Homestead and barn at The Farmer's Museum. Courtesy, The New York State Historical Association, Cooperstown, New York. Photo: Le Bel Studio.

Such problems will be exacerbated as the populations of industrial countries continue to shift from rural areas into the cities. Demographers predict that within the present generation 90 percent of the population in industrial countries will live in urban areas. The shift in population distribution toward increased urbanization was pointed up in President Nixon's 1970 State of the Union Message: "For the past thirty years," Mr. Nixon said, "our population has also been growing and shifting. The result is exemplified in the vast areas of rural America, emptying out of people and of promise. A third of our counties lost population in the sixties." Mr. Nixon expressed the hope that this migration could be reversed and stated that "in the future, government decisions as to where to build highways, locate airports, acquire land or sell land, should be made with the clear objective of aiding a balanced growth for America."

But perhaps, modern man, no matter where he lives, tends to regard urbanization itself as the prime evil. It is not. Overpopulation, combined with disregard for the "ecological imperative," is responsible for the thoughtless and hasty development of the cities and suburbs, and most of the problems that follow. Ancient Rome, the Paris and Vienna, the Seattle and Charleston of yesterday are testimony to the fact that cities *can* be comfortable places to live in.

It is clear, however, that any thinking about the future population size of the United States must take into account two propositions: the quality of existence is inescapably related to quantity, and our numbers must be balanced against our ability to provide human services and a human environment for all citizens.

Dr. Richard Allen Chase of Johns Hopkins University School of Medicine states the case this way:

We are responsible for structuring and maintaining the human environment in a manner that optimally supports human growth and development. This responsibility comprehends the physical structure of the environment and the structure of experience . . . . It is suggested that environments that impair behavioral developments should be disallowed in the same way that we disallow dangerous foods and drugs and dangerous pollution of the physical environment. If an infant or child cannot be provided with an environment supportive of his optimal behavioral development within his family and traditional school setting, then it becomes a matter of public concern and responsibility that other options be created and made available. No child should be allowed to suffer preventable retardation of behavioral development because of environmental deprivation. I can think of no more fundamental human right than the right of every child to an early environment that allows him to become a broadly competent human being.[4]

Ecologists such as Professor Ehrlich see the United States population ideally decreasing to approximately 150 million. Says Professor Ehrlich,

With a population stabilized at such a level we could concentrate on improving the quality of human life at home and abroad. And, what a pleasure it would be to work toward an attainable goal instead of fighting the miserable rear guard action to which runaway population condemns us.

The future of mankind, according to some experts on population problems, is dependent upon a growth of *zero* for at least one entire generation.

It is clear, of course, that even a world population one third the present size (the one billion recommended by some experts) would be too high if each individual were to increase his demands on the environment. This is true for the U.S. as well as for the rest of the world. In the words of Conrad F. Taeuber, supervisor of the 1970 United States census,

> Economic and social factors are more important than population growth in threatening the quality of American life. The population problems of the United States are and will be much more a matter of geographic distribution and the way we use our resources than of the rate of increase in our total numbers. [6]

Besides the shift in population distribution, Mr. Taeuber points out that whereas the U.S. population increased by 13 percent since 1960, the volume of goods and services increased by about 60 percent.

Professor Ehrlich agrees that population control is not a panacea; it is essential to the solution of our problems, but it is not sufficient unto itself:

> Our environmental problems involve an interaction between the number of people we have and the way they behave. We have to stop population growth and at the same time change our life style as rapidly as possible. [7]

The Responsibility of Individuals

Unlike other great issues of our time, population control requires individual action. It is literally the people themselves who control the size of the population. Certainly institutions like the government and the church have a role to carry out, but even more important, there must be what Joseph J. Spengler of Duke University calls a "General Will" for reduction of the population. The problems involved in creating a general will are tremendous; they require dealing with such basic human forces as the sex drive, the influence of religion, the pleasures of parenthood, the security that parenthood has traditionally meant for the elderly, the desire for continuation of a family line, manpower for warfare, manpower for the farms, and what has been called the businessman's fallacy—more people, more markets.

Courtesy: Dimensional Communications, Inc.

What is being done to control population growth in the United States? Until recently the private sector has led in population control activities. Among the private institutions best known for their work are the Rockefeller Foundation, which has long supported studies of population problems; the Population Council; the Population Reference Bureau; the Population Crisis Committee; the Hugh Moore Fund; and Planned Parenthood-World Population. The last mentioned is one of the oldest of such organizations and among the newest is one called Zero Population Growth.

Activities of the Federal government, though more recent in origin, are now widespread. Within the United States Public Health Service a number of programs are under way and others are planned, including an institute for population research within the National Institutes of Health. The Agency for International Development, the Department of Agriculture, the Office of Education, the Food and Drug Administration, and the National Science Foundation are among other agencies involved.

Greatly increased motivation will be necessary to stop population growth. Professor Spengler has called for a reorientation of penalties and rewards in such a way as to induce people to replace—in part—the freedom to reproduce by other freedoms. This kind of reorientation must be initiated by national governments. In the overpopulated, underfed countries, even as in the United States, the challenge is similar: highly motivated individuals will have to act wisely; the partici-

pation of each individual is called for. As the National Academy of Sciences has stated: "Either the birth rate of the world must come down or the death rate must go back up."

Dr. Frederick C. Robbins, Nobel Laureate and dean of Case Western Reserve University School of Medicine, states the case succinctly:

It is hard to conceive of any subject that is more important today or more international in its scope than that of family planning, or population control. In fact, until population growth is controlled, there is little likelihood of solving other critical problems of our civilization. The majority of the people of the world will not secure the adequate food, housing, health care and education for which they are now striving. The deterioration of our environment due to unplanned exploitation and pollution will not be halted, and there will be little prospect of easing the tensions among peoples and nations which pose the constant threat of war.

Many experts believe there is one goal upon which all meaningful government and private activity must focus: the universal establishment of conception control. The conception control methods that are now available are well known—rhythm, physical barriers to sperm such as condoms and diaphragms, spermicidal chemicals, intrauterine devices, and the pill. Suffice it to say that each of these has its advantages and its drawbacks—some psychological, some physiological, and some purely mechanical.

Voluntary sterilization of both sexes, but particularly of males, is seen as a hopeful trend in this country, especially among educated, professional people. But ignorance and perhaps indifference still abound. A recent survey on the desirability of family size taken among the faculty and students at Cornell University showed that the majority wanted three children or more. Only 6 percent favored vasectomy as the preferred form of contraception once full family size had been achieved. Further answers disclosed a general ignorance of the effects of sterilization on sexual performance. This student body and faculty, already in the adult state, may have been hopelessly hampered by an inadequate or distorted childhood sex education. Their responses raise the question as to whether the vital issues of population control can be learned effectively only when begun in childhood. The introduction of this material into the curriculum of many schools will undoubtedly lead to greater public understanding.

It is unlikely that any one of the conception control methods now available can solve the population problem; what is needed is something that is safe, cheap, and does not require continued motivation. Millions are being spent on research to find a method or methods that will fulfill these requirements.

The necessity for vast additional research and education on methods of birth control was emphasized at a national Institute on Medical Education and Family Planning conducted in Washington in March 1969 under the auspices of the Association of American Medical Colleges. Dr. Margaret Mead, the noted anthropologist and curator emeritus of ethnology of the American Museum of Natural History, told the conferees:[4]

I think that we are going to have an ethic on the subject of population control, an ethic that is worldwide, an ethic that includes everyone from the tiny island of Mauritius to the Soviet Union. We cannot have policies that say in effect that *those* people are too undeveloped, or their agriculture is too backward, or their harbors are too poor, or they like to go to sea so why shouldn't they go to sea and stay away for twenty years, and then advocate a special and different policy for them, but not for us, not for the other countries of the world. We have to recognize that the population explosion is as serious a problem for the most developed country as for the least. . . . We are all part of an interdependent world so that if one country blows up through starvation and social disorganization it affects us all . . . .

McGeorge Bundy, president of the Ford Foundation, in concluding an address to the same assembly, reviewed the prognosis for population growth and declared:

What matters most is what happens *after* the year 2000. For if present trends continue unchecked, the 7 billion would become 14 billions 25 years later. The consequences of that kind of growth are no subject for the last moments of a long speech, so I leave them to your imagination . . . .

It isn't just that there is a scientific problem which needs to be attacked and a teaching problem from which it would be folly to turn back. It isn't just that there is a partnership to be forged between medical men and all the other kinds of men and women who must commit themselves to this problem. We contemplate those massive numbers, and as we look at the political and social complexities of this question, we run the risk of thinking about it in mechanical terms, in managerial terms, in terms of control, in terms of statistics, and in terms of technology. There is a danger that we may forget that the impelling cause of concern here is not the numbers themselves, but the millions of human situations which those numbers represent. We are talking about the human reproductive process; we are talking about the life of the human family; we are talking about the closest, most intimate, and most sacred choices human beings can be asked to make. We are talking, therefore, about a problem of *man*, and not merely a problem of resources and management.

Clearly, the rate of population growth confronts us with one of the great crises in man's history, and it is a crisis that museums can help to recognize, evaluate, and contend with in practical and humanitarian terms. The need for the development of a population ethic has been clear for some time; museums with their vast resources of materials and ideas can help create that ethic and determine the kind of world in which we can continue to live.

Summary

A human population explosion has resulted from advances in science and technology. Unless the rate of population growth is sharply reduced overpopulation will, within a few decades, destroy much of the environment that makes the earth habitable for man and other organisms. Hunger and malnutrition are widespread today, but even with better distribution and use of food, and with technological innovations that will increase the food supply, we can expect increasing mass starvation. Apart from the questions of sufficient food and water, the physiological and psychological effects of increasing urbanization and overcrowding detract from the quality of life. Action to stem the population tide, ultimately an individual responsibility, is being supported by research and education in conception control. Success will require the universal acceptance of a new population ethic.

exhibits and projects / population

Overpopulation
A Group of Exhibits
and Projects

As we have seen in the background material, overpopulation, until recently, usually occurred within limited areas, such as a single nation, or a major city. The problems caused by too many people living in too little space could be "solved" through drastic actions or natural catastrophes. Pestilence, starvation, disease, floods, earthquakes and holocaust *eliminated* the people—and thus restored a balance of food and natural resources. For centuries, overpopulation has been recognized as a basic cause of wars, and to complete the vicious cycle, wars have been recognized as a basic way to get rid of people.

on public understanding of the problem. The task of restoring natural balance must be shared by every individual.

Museum presentations may be made in different ways and take different forms. The path may be through the arts, the sciences, or history.

Illustrate the hazards of overpopulation in a pertinent exhibit built around one or a combination of the following suggestions and graphics:

* Artists have chosen the violence of this and former centuries as the subject for paintings and prints. Works that can be effectively related to the theme of overpopulation include Goya's series, "The Disasters of War;" Callot's series, "Great Miseries of War"; Picasso's mural, "Guernica."

* You might contrast paintings and

Pablo Picasso, "Guernica", (1937). Oil on canvas, 11' 5-1/2 x 25' 5-3/4". On extended loan to the Museum of Modern Art, New York, from the artist.

Now, however, because overpopulation has become a worldwide threat, the old violent solutions—particularly wars—are no longer acceptable. They, too, would endanger the entire human race—and probably the Earth itself.

The success of new methods of controlling population will depend

photographs of crowds of people having fun (at rock festivals, beaches and ball games) with artwork depicting the misery of people in overcrowded environments (e.g., migrant-worker camps, Indian reservations, Black or Puerto rican ghettos, Asian cities, subways and highways).

Population — Human

This unit is reprinted from *People and their Environment, Teachers' Curriculum Guide to Conservation Education*, with permission of the publisher, J.G. Ferguson Publishing Company, Chicago, Illinois. Copyright © 1968, 1969 by the Department of Education, State of South Carolina.

Concept Given sufficient natural resources, a population will continue to increase in size, unless some limiting factor is imposed.

Purpose of Lesson To help students understand the influence of the human population explosion on natural resources and human survival.

Introducing the Concept BSCS Green Version (pp. 24-48; 689-695) BSCS Blue Version (p. 50 and Chapter 28)

"American Forests," *Conservation and the Population Explosion*

The teacher should read the above information and background information at end of lesson before introducing the concept. The concept should be introduced by presenting the students with the following information for discussion.

Assuming that you have a normal pulse beat, it will not quite keep up with the increase in world population. Every time your pulse throbs, the population of the world will have added one more human being.

In 20 years from now:

Thirty-five per cent of all people alive will be less than 15 years old. Even today, China has more children under 10 than the total population of Russia.

In the United States there will be 62 million families in place of the 48 million today.

Almost nine per cent of those who are heads of households will be under 25 years old, almost double the number of young householders today.

About three-fourths of all people will live in urban areas. Half of all Americans will live in three great metropolitan areas. Even today, an airplane flying from Boston to Washington, D.C. can no longer distinguish separate communities; the whole area is one continuous megalopolis.

Developing the Concept

1. Why are we studying conservation, if before long the increased human population will have resulted in vast metropolitan areas and modified land for food production with a resulting destruc-

IT TOOK FROM—		OR—	FOR EARTH'S POPULATION TO REACH
The beginning of man to the Neolithic age	7,990,000 years		10 million
Neolithic to the birth of Christ	10,000 years		300 million
Birth of Christ to the days of Columbus	1,500 years		500 million
Columbus era to 1850 A.D.	350 years		1 BILLION
1850 to 1925 A.D.	75 years		2 BILLION
1925 to 1962 A.D.	37 years		3 BILLION
1962 to 1975	13 years		4 BILLION
1975 to 1982	7 years		5 BILLION

63

tion of wilderness, wildlife, and forests, leaving nothing to conserve?

2. How has the increasing human population affected man's use of natural resources? (Rather than emphasis on management and respect for nature's laws, the emphasis has become focused on saving a remnant of wilderness, building more campgrounds, more roads to streams and through forests, and compromising the demands of multiple use. Instead of positive goals, we are diverted into stop-gap measures.)

3. Hunger stunts the health, vigor, and mental capacity of two-thirds of the world's population, thus retarding the development of whole nations, according to the U.S. Department of the Interior. Thus we can see that food is a limiting factor in human population. What other factors may have a limiting effect on human population? (Space, disease, war, pollution of water and air, human wastes, sociological factors, psychological factors.)

4. With what major water problems do metropolitan areas present us? (Collection and disposal of sewage; pollution control; adequate water supply.)

5. What are some of the main causes of air pollution in highly populated areas? (Increased numbers of automobiles; burning of fuels in the homes and places of business; increased numbers of industrial plants giving off waste fumes.)

6. Three forces—population growth, the trend toward urbanization, and the horizontal expansion of cities—have been gobbling up land at a prodigal rate. What, if anything, can be done to obtain maximal use of the space available?

7. Supply of natural resources is reduced by: increasing the level of living and consumption; sharing resources among more people; natural and man-induced catastrophes. Can we maintain our standard of living without drastically depleting our supply of natural resources? How? Lead class to understand that there are limits beyond which the level of living can't be lowered or production from resources increased.

Extending the Concept Discuss:

1. Based on our studies of animals, how may human behavior change due to overcrowded conditions?

2. Is there a relationship between the increase in heart disease, ulcers, and other stress diseases and overcrowded conditions?

3. What behavioral problems do you associate with the overcrowding in cities?

4. How can a population explosion result in the loss of our democratic freedoms? (Overcrowded communities cannot provide enough of the means for satisfactory individual development. Government must exert increasing control. Socialism, therefore, is not entirely political, but results from social stresses of overpopulation.)

5. Can the individual do anything about controlling population size? What can be done on state and federal levels?

6. How can man stabilize populations and plan long-range conservation?

Fixing the Concept Debate:

Resolved: Unless man can maintain some measure of individual freedom and dignity and avoid the frictions of crowding, he will destroy himself by shock or increasing strife resulting in nuclear oblivion or depletion of resources.

How does the spread of starlings in America illustrate the effect of no limiting factors?

Instructional Materials
Books

The Yearbook of Agriculture

Magazines

Huxley, Julian: "Are There Too Many of Us?" *Horizon*

Fowler, H. Seymour: "The Population Explosion and Education," *The American Biology Teacher*

Silvan, James: "Food, Space, and Survival," *Science World*

_____. "How Many People? How Much Food?" *Science World*

Background Information for Teacher

Our current population crisis is now costing us heavily in money, social problems, and lost liberty. This crisis is becoming more and more critical each day.

In 1900: U.S. produced 15 per cent more raw materials than we used.

In 1950: U.S. was consuming 10 per cent more than produced. Also, 33 vital minerals were on a critical shortage list, according to a Presidential committee.

Foreign nations face the same shortages because of their population gains. We, therefore, cannot depend on them very long to supplement our shortages.

Results of work done at the Albert Einstein Medical Center, Philadelphia, with mice, rabbits, and other mammals, indicate that endocrine feedback mechanisms exist in mammals. These internal mechanisms can regulate population growth in response to increases in population:

1. Reproduction functions lessened in both sexes.
2. Sexual maturation was delayed or, at higher population densities, totally inhibited.
3. Weights of accessory sex organs delclined.
4. The female's egg cycle was extended.
5. Death of fetuses in the uterus increased.
6. Inadequate lactation (milk secretion) in mice—mouslings were stunted.
7. Increased susceptibility to infections and parasitism.
8. Increased fighting and aggressiveness.

Human resources include the abilities and capacities with which we are endowed—our physical, mental, social, and spiritual capabilities. But the human capital of a region may be dissipated by natural resource depletion.

World population has been slowly increasing for a long time. But through modern medical technology, which has increased the life span and decreased the death rate in younger people, human populations are increasing at accelerating rates. At the present rate of increase, world population will be doubled by the end of the 20th century.

In every animal population studied, numbers increase until the carrying capacity has been reached and the environment can sustain no higher population. At the point where population pressure equals the environmental resistance, the population levels off with varying degrees of fluctuation. Not withstanding man's ability to modify his environment, there is no reason to expect that these same biological principles will not apply to human population.

Man is developing the technical knowledge needed to control his population growth. As yet, this knowledge has not been applied to any considerable extent. Wide sociocultural concern about the problem and acceptance of the means of control must prevail if population growth is to be curbed.

Without the imposition of checks on population growth, either by nature or by man himself (cultural resistance), population will increase beyond the capabilities of man and natural resources to sustain a high level of living.

The Security of Change

"Cultural shock" and "future shock" are catchy terms recently added to our language in recognition of the hardships imposed on man by rapid technological change.

A useful exhibit would demonstrate that although man is adaptable to changes in nature, drastic or sudden changes in the environment might require such far-reaching changes within the species that only a small percentage of the human race might survive.

For such an exhibit, a series of small dolls might be dressed to represent humans in specific situations. These would be set against illustrative backgrounds, such as maps or dioramas, listing the more common traits. Alongside would be instructions to the visitor for moving the dolls from place to place, with accompanying commentary on the resulting changes. In a sophisticated format, the instructions and comment might be taped. But in either case, the visitor would move the dolls.

For example, a doll dressed as a Bolivian miner, noted for possessing adaptations of an enlarged heart and large lungs, is set against a background of high mountain peaks. The visitor is instructed to move the doll down to a background showing a rain forest at low altitude, with its emphasis on other adaptive features.

Conversely, a Cajun doll from the levees of Louisiana is moved to the mountaintops of Colorado, with the appropriate conditions noted on the place dioramas.

As a third step, either or both of the dolls may be moved to the interior of a model representing an air-conditioned, windowless, controlled environment such as an urban office building, where work is sedentary and entirely mechanized. What adaptations are emphasized here?

If man ever becomes adapted to manufactured climates and living conditions, what will happen to his metabolism?

Reproduction and the Continuity of Life

In developing programs on the problem of overpopulation, some museums—particularly those of science and natural history—may wish to present exhibits on population in all the species. Many different treatments are possible; following is one suggested outline for a major exhibit:

Script Outline

Reproduction is Nature's provision for the continuity of all species; it is a universal attribute of living organisms. Reproduction in a given form of life takes place by one of two methods: asexual (fission, budding) or bisexual.

If conditions for fertilization and subsequent survival were optimal, a very limited number of sex cells, properly spaced in relation to the life span of the organism, would provide the requisite continuity.

But since the hazards to reproductive success are almost always very great, each organism has become adapted to much more than minimal sex-cell production, and most organisms must produce many millions of reproductive cells in order to yield a relatively few new individuals. And this new generation may suffer still further attrition before its members, in turn, have attained reproductive maturity.

Thus, all organisms, in the absence of reproductive and of postnatal wastage, are *capable* of expanding their numbers astronomically in a short space of time. In practice this does not happen, because reproductive wastage is always high and a balance of postnatal factors tends to

Suggestions for Exhibit

Diagram contrasting continuity of successive generations with examples of extinction.
Models or diagrams of two methods of reproduction.

Pictures or models of reproductive hazards: "seed on stony ground" and eggs as food for other animals.

Baby birds as prey; young animals as food; lack of food for progeny.

Diagram showing equation of natural increase.
Diagram showing effect of maximum production.

67

limit the survival of individuals capable of reproduction. In this balance, death, aging, predators, and other natural factors, such as limited food supply, offset birth rate.

Although in nature most organisms maintain a fairly stable balance, with their numbers remaining fairly constant, some species occasionally exhibit episodes of great expansion when conditions are favorable for germination and/or individual survival. After such periods of expansion, a balance is restored. Occasionally a species finds a particularly favorable niche and expands until it again meets natural restrictions.

Lemmings, rabbit cycles in Arctic, **shown in photographs or drawings.**

Some of the factors that serve to limit the survival rate, and hence the natural increase, of a population are:

Distribution maps.

1) Supply of food. As a species increases in number, its demands on the available food supply grow commensurately. When, for whatever reason, this supply is inadequate, the species is directly affected. Islands denuded of their cover by goats overgrazing them provide an example of the inherent limitations on population imposed by an insufficiency of food.

Aquariums of different sizes and containing different population densities, showing effects of various factors.

2) Predators. As animals increase in number, they become more susceptible to natural predators. The relationship between wolves and hares in the Arctic is an illustration of this factor as a regulator of population size.

Pictures of areas that have been overgrazed.

3) Susceptibility to disease. This factor becomes increasingly significant with greater population density. Disease may decimate a population and thereby severely curtail its reproductive potential.

A series of small dioramas illustrating this restrictive factor.

4) Effect of crowding or increased density. Much research is yet

to be done here, but it seems apparent that crowding affects the endocrine system of animals subjected to it, and that reproductive behavior itself may be influenced by this condition.

Human populations and their reproductive potentials and performances reflect these basic considerations. Man produces many more reproductive cells than are strictly necessary for population survival. The male produces billions of spermatozoa in a lifetime, and even though some may be defective for reproductive purposes, most of them are inherently effective.

Each female in her lifetime produces hundreds of ova. The disparity in number is a function of the fact that physiological hazards operate in greater degree against spermatozoa. But even with continuous exposure, no female is capable of bringing each of the ova in her ovaries to fruition. And very few bear the total number of offspring possible to them physiologically. Thus reproductive potential is always higher than actual procreation.

The fertility of a given population will depend on several variables: 1) maternal health; 2) exposure; 3) cultural conditions that affect sexual patterns; 4) available food supply.

The other requirement for reproductive success is survival to reproductive age. In human populations, as in other populations, low survival rate, offsetting high fertility, will serve to prevent rapid increase and contribute to maintaining a balance.

In the course of human evolution, the rate of population increase was

Models or diagrams of male and female reproductive cells and relative numbers.

Shettles' photos of many thousands of spermatozoa around one ovum.

Diagram of relative numbers in relation to potential in natural survival.

Population curves showing losses through infant mortality.

Demonstration of causes of increase in relation to increase.

relatively low throughout most of the history of mankind. This was because early man as a simple hunting-gathering creature was more directly exposed than modern man to environmental hazards comparable to those affecting animal populations. High infant-mortality rates and exposure to risks during the growing stage kept natural increase low. During possibly two million years, mankind increased to a total population estimated at about one million. In the last 10,000 years this number has increased to three and one-half billion.

The slow, steady increase all through the Paleolithic Age has been modified at two critical points:

1) The neolithic revolution about 10,000 years ago freed man for the first time from a direct dependence upon the natural produce of nature. Agriculture and domestication of animals yielded an abundance of food many times greater than any population could find by simple hunting and gathering, particularly for agriculturalists who necessarily became sedentary and village-living. Human population shows a considerable and rapid expansion following the introduction of neolithic culture. The increased rate of growth on this new economic base brought world population from one million to about 500 million in the course of less than 10,000 years.

2) The other notable expansion has occurred in modern times. It was ushered in by the Industrial Revolution, the first striking consequences of which are to be observed in the rapid growth of European populations since 1650, and, now, of most of the populations of the world.

Displays illustrating the Industrial Revolution; with small dioramas; and with charts and maps showing the growth of population.

In part this is the consequence of a massive increase in economic productiveness, but contributing equally are advances in medicine which have sharply reduced the death rate and, in particular, the infant mortality rate. Although the birth rates of western European countries during this period dropped to about half their former level, the death rates dropped, relatively, even more. Thus, despite falling birth rates, natural increases were greater than ever during the period of transition to the Age of Industrialization. Only recently has the balance between births and deaths returned to the lower levels characteristic of an earlier age when population grew less rapidly.

In the nonindustrialized countries, however, the drop in death rates achieved by the relatively recent introduction of western medicine has not been accompanied by a drop in birth rate as was the case in western industrial nations. Therefore, the natural increase, or the growth rate, has been far greater.

Increase in food supply through scientific advance makes possible the support of far greater numbers than could have been maintained in former centuries.

The fact remains, however, that these technological advances are not universal and are least understood in areas where population pressure is becoming greatest—in areas of underdevelopment and/or of limited natural resources.

At present an estimated one-third of the world's population is living on substandard nutrition. To provide

Diagrams or models showing increase of population at various rates; showing the growth of world population from Paleolithic times to present.

Diagrams showing the growth rates of India, Brazil and China.
Projection of current rates.

Pictures showing new crops, research teams working on development of hybrid plants. Displays comprised of samples of newly developed products.

71

adequate food for the anticipated population in the developing world, the food supply in these nations would have to be doubled within the next ten years. The actual improvement during recent years has been encouraging, but not sufficient to meet the expected population increases in the developing world.

But even if the food supply can be increased in the regions where it is most needed, there are other factors to be considered. These include the economic and political consequences of overpopulation, and the physiological and psychological effects of overcrowding.

Thus the problem of human overpopulation is so immediate that, regardless of what can be done to increase our food supply, what is imperative right now is a slower rate of human growth in all regions of the world.

Graphs, charts, pictures illustrating the consequences of overpopulation. Graphics from government agencies, foundations, news agencies, and paintings from museum collections.

Posters and other Graphics

"I GUESS WE'LL HAVE TO FALL BACK ON YOU OLD EXPERTS!"

MINNEAPOLIS STAR

"Will it come to this?"

By Fred O. Seibel
Courtesy Richmond Times-Dispatch

An effective panel in the Carnegie Museum's conservation exhibit features "All over the Map," a cartoon treatment of population increase in Pennsylvania from 1800 to 1950.

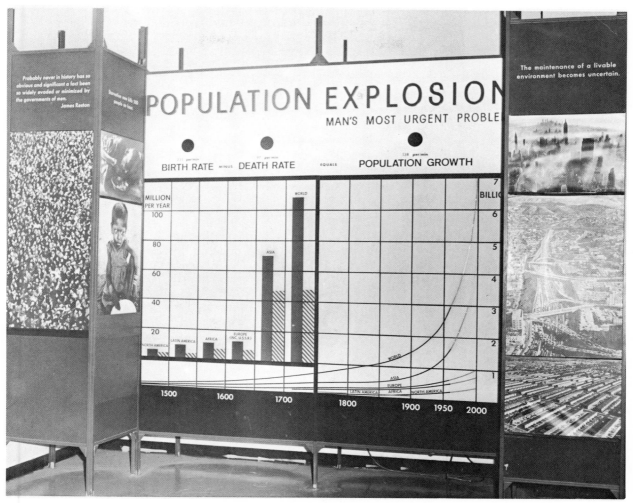

"Population Explosion" is an exhibit from the Museum of Science in Boston, Mass. The left panel carries a quote from *New York Times* editor James Reston: "Probably never in history has so obvious and significant effect been so widely evaded or minimized by the governments of men." The right panel carries the heading "The maintenance of a livable environment becomes uncertain."

Every 8.6 seconds someone dies from starvation. Think about that for a minute.

Courtesy of the Hugh Moore Fund

76

Population Trends in the U.S.

Using the United States Census Reports and Immigration Reports as factual guides, plan an exhibit to demonstrate population growth and trends in the United States from 1790 (the year of the first decennial population census in the United States) to the present. Prepare large outline maps of the continental United States (in natural green, with brown for mountainous areas) as backgrounds for population pictographs of each significant period. Accompany each of these with prints, sketches or photographs to illustrate circumstances at that time. For example, show Chicago and St. Louis in 1830; early pioneering and westward expansion; San Francisco in 1850; waves of immigration on both east and west coasts; industrialization; flight to suburbia; no escape from megalopolis.

Problems of the City: A Study on Population and Pollution

The congested city is a microcosm of problems stemming from overpopulation. You will note from the following exhibit ideas that awareness of a bad situation can result in the discovery of a healthy solution; that cities and their people are not necessarily doomed.

Show how population densities are related to: supplies of natural resources, creativity, aggressiveness, productivity and consumption, mental and physical health.

Set up a chamber in which the noise levels of a city can be reproduced by means of audio-tape and then measured. Are sounds in various parts of your own city above acceptable levels?

Set up a display showing the vast regions of land needed to supply a city with food.

Set up a display showing what might happen if cars were barred from the heart of the city and the people in your area had to use mass transit. Would the results be favorable?

Present various planning proposals for housing and open space.

Set up a pictorial display, accompanied by significant artifacts where possible, to trace the history of cities. Show how each city was constructed to conform to its natural location and environment, and show the effect of the city upon the environment. It might be interesting to choose some cities slightly off the beaten track, such as ancient Jerusalem or Alexandria; Byzantium long before it became Istanbul; Timbuktu in the fifteenth and sixteenth centuries; or Essen, Germany in the twentieth century.

Creating a Film-Strip on Over-Population

The subject of overpopulation is one that might be presented very effectively in a filmstrip. By the use of acetate overlays on original art, cumulative effects can be gained. This might be valuable in presenting problems of crowding, traffic, increased air pollution, and the other mounting stresses of civilization. Modern automatic sound filmstrip projectors can now make "flips" from frame to frame in fractions of a second, thus approximating animation. The film can be backed with recorded music and sound.

Creating a Motion Picture on Overpopulation

In many cities there are groups of young filmmakers who are learning the craft of motion-picture making by experimenting. Some of them are sponsored by schools, others by such organizations as settlement houses. Often they do photographic work of exceptionally high quality. Usually, too, the young people involved are deeply interested in social problems. They bring a creative, fresh approach to their work. If there is such a group in your community, you may be able to enlist their talents in the production of a fine film featuring your own city. (Please see Chapter 5 for further information.)

Concrete Deserts: The Growth of Urbanization

Wherever land is covered by concrete it loses its capacity for conservation of water and reconstitution of the air we breathe. It may also lose its potential for beauty. It becomes a desert.

Massive constructions, such as highways, parking areas, large business buildings, industrial parks and housing developments, must be the concern of all museums. To educate the public about the necessity for preventing the needless spread of concrete deserts:

Select study areas for which "before" and "after" pictures are available.

A former rural area, now covered with mammoth highway clover leaves

A former green area, now occupied by a large shopping center, housing development or other major construction in which paving and rooftops have replaced earth

Show pictures of slums or other old buildings as they were before reclamation. Contrast these with pictures of the same site after construction which allows for green belts.

Show pictures of children playing in a concrete-jungle type of playground contrasted with pictures of children playing where greenery abounds.

Sponsor "town meetings" to discuss proposed constructions. If community action results, good!

In any event, your museum will be helping to bring important issues before the public while there is still time for action.

William Birch. "New York from Brooklyn Heights"; (1802). Colored engraving. Engraver: Samuel Seymour. Courtesy, Museum of the City of New York, Bequest of Mrs. J. Insley Blair.

1970 photograph of lower Manhattan from Brooklyn Heights, matching the 1802 engraving by William Birch. Courtesy: Museum of the City of New York. Photo: George Roos.

Street Museums

As the article by Zora B. Martin on "The Inner City Museum" says so effectively, the environmental message can sound a little hollow to the man who must live near a refinery or spend his life in the very worst part of the city.

As one such person said to a museum official, "To you the issue is pollution; to us it's survival!"

Now that we know the facts of the crisis, we know that it is truly a question of survival for *all* Americans. We know that rich and poor alike share the same fate, as the environmental clock ticks closer to the day of decision. We know, above all, that if that decision is to be "life." then everyone must be made aware of the facts as quickly as possible.

The Anacostia Neighborhood Museum, the Muse, and other storefront and neighborhood museums are rendering superb service to their communities. Another valuable type of museum could come into existence readily. Without paving another inch of the cities, it would be relatively cheap and fast to convert a city block of derelict houses or factories into a relevant museum of ecology. If such a conversion were properly done, it could lead each visitor—subtly, compellingly, cleverly and compassionately—in and out of sagging doorways, through old warehouses and shops . . . and deposit him—years wiser, but only an hour or two older—a block away from where he started, and he would have gained a basic understanding of the interrelationship of all things.

As a follow-up exhibit, the next block might be made a wonderland of the city restored. Not shiny new buildings in the same dead environment, but ordinary city places brought to life again: wildflower gardens, parks and ponds, coexisting with urban people in a city reborn.

Parts of this street museum concept have been used. But the potential is so great that the surface has hardly been scratched.

Restoration by the jobless; a neighborhood museum, preaching the gospel of life and hope in the city . . . urban transit and dinosaurs; the whole story of life on a dying planet. A story of hope.

From Maine to California . . . dying cities bursting with promise. Every block a potential showplace.

Disaster and Urban Renewal

When a city is hit by disaster, the widespread destruction often forces the town fathers to come up with large-scale plans for rebuilding. Using historical photographs and old newspaper articles, your museum can show how disaster has led to urban renewal in: Chicago after its great fire, San Francisco after the earthquake, cities in Texas and Louisiana following hurricanes, and towns along the Mississippi, Allegheny and Ohio Rivers following the floods of 1937.

A related exhibit might demonstrate how industrial calamities, such as the Triangle Fire in New York and steel mill accidents in Gary, Indiana, caused legislation assuring safer working environments for man.

Historic Landmarks in our City

The historical society and the local landmarks preservation committee can cooperate effectively in sponsoring a tour of sites that may be threatened by "progress." This could be followed by publication of a booklet depicting the landmarks and their cultural value. Emphasize the importance of diversity in city planning. One dramatic effect might be achieved in the booklet by inserting opaque acetate sheets in strategic places. On these would be traced the exact locale (block, park area, etc.) but with the old structures or open space replaced by glass-and-chrome office buildings, highways, etc.

Adler Planetarium

Adler Planetarium. Planned as an underground facility under the present mall, the Astro-Science Center was designed to preserve the exterior setting and character of the existing building and landscape, while meeting the new demands of Space Age education and information.

The Contemporary Art Center of Cincinnati

On a highly-sophisticated, adult level, the contemporary Art Center in Cincinnati stresses improvement of the city's architecture in relation to total environment.

To alert local citizens—and tourists who visit Cincinnati—the Center conducts a variety of tours in which special attention is directed to the role of building design in urban living.

Members of the Center also work with city planning groups when new construction is being considered.

The Center's own building—recently opened in the heart of Cincinnati—serves as an example of the best in current design.

Cityscapes

The quality of urban life affects not only the physical well-being of a majority of our people, but also their emotional health and their ability to function successfully in our society.

Cities contain both beauty and ugliness. In setting up an exhibit of cityscapes, contrasting images should be juxtaposed in such a way as to make the good and the bad self-evident.

If floor space permits, this exhibit in particular should be set up on freestanding panels, with as little clutter and congestion as possible. The visitor should be able to walk through, absorbing one idea at a time. Scale models and miniatures might be displayed to provide relief from the flatness of two-dimensional photographs and paintings.

The variety of suitable subjects is infinite. Here, a dozen:

The inner city
The underground city
City spaces
City "links"—within the city, to the suburbs, and beyond.

Ferries	Tunnels
Bridges	Highways
Trains	Boats
Airports	Trucks

Subways—including master plans and maps, paintings, tile decorations, and advertisements
Skyscrapers
Historic buildings
Skylines
Smog
Industrial areas
Apartment developments
Parks and play areas
The use of air rights

Subjective views of city life may be made a part of the exhibit if the work of twentieth century painters are included—especially those of the "Ashcan School."

City rooftops are a subject in themselves. When buildings were not so high, rooftop "paintings" added color to city living. Today people are not often in a position to look down on roofs.

The sterility of city facades is another subject of importance. Contrast the faceless, anonymous, inhuman monuments of glass and steel that have become common in cities with some buildings incorporating imaginative new architectural concepts. You might include both illustrations of beautiful period architecture that has not been torn down and those of architecture that has been demolished.

The city at night becomes a fairyland, from a distance. In contrast, it might be shown in blackout, as a portent of the future.

The Drug Scene in New York City

Early in 1971, The Museum of the City of New York opened the first major exhibition dealing with the problems of drug abuse and addiction to be presented in the United States. This educational exhibition is primarily concerned with the drug problem as it relates to the City of New York.

The pictures at the exhibition (see following pages) were so shocking that no one passed by unmoved. To reach all visitors, particularly the ghetto victims, the Museum printed all display labels in Spanish as well as English. There was also a most effective give-away pamphlet printed in both languages. Simply, but dramatically, the pamphlet revealed the scope of the drug abuse problem:

Drugs know no economic or social boundaries and show no discrimination

Drugs are the Number One killer of persons between the ages of 15 and 34, and one-quarter of those deaths are of people under 20 years of age

What treatment is available

How to obtain immediate help (including a list of agencies with treatment facilities)

In addition, at the end of one pamphlet, there was a fine chart citing the most-used drugs, their slang names, medical uses, potential for psychological and physical dependence, short- and long-term effects, withdrawal symptoms and potential for overdoses and fatal accidents.

"The Drug Scene in New York City," made possible by a grant from the New York State Narcotic Addiction Control Commission, was the first such major show in the United States. Hopefully it will be the model for many similar presentations across the nation.

"From the Drug Scene in New York City"

The Architectural Vision of Paolo Soleri

The problem of over-population is desperate, but not hopeless. You have seen how helpful it is to keep citizens informed, how healthful it would be to increase mass transit and ban cars from the hearts of cities. Museums of all types can make increasingly effective, positive contributions to life in beleaguered cities; street museums can help improve their communities—but some architects and urban planners think that the best solution of all might be to start from scratch with completely new cities. Consider "The Architectural Vision of Paolo Soleri" . . .

During 1970, two major American art museums presented exhibits consisting of room-sized models and 100-foot-long scroll drawings of the "arcologic" designs by Paolo Soleri for future cities. In March, the Corcoran Gallery in Washington, D.C., with sponsorship by the Prudential Insurance Company of America and the United States Department of Housing and Urban Development, filled most of its exhibit space with his work. Through the summer, the Whitney Museum in New York made a similar presentation. Both exhibits attracted record attendance.

Soleri, who works from his studio in Arizona, is an Italian-born architect who came to this country as a young man to study with the late Frank Lloyd Wright. His proposed cities, which have such fantasy names as Babel Canyon, Hexahedron, Stonebow, Arcosanti and Arcube, are conceived to provide all urban needs for a population as large as that of San Francisco—under one roof, on a land area approximating one square mile. His structures reach down into the earth, and up into the air to as much as three times the height of the Empire State Building. Some are suspended in space. Others float upon water. Some are incorporated into bridges. Their architectural forms stagger the imagination.

"Arcology," the word Soleri coined to describe his work, is a combination of "architecture" and "ecology." It defines the passion and purpose which inspires his designs: to accommodate humans in urban environments in which pollution and other conditions are completely controlled, yet which occupy so little space that 90 percent of our land area could be consigned to agriculture or allowed to return to its natural state.

Automobiles would be unnecessary in such a city, since a resident could reach any part of it—or the wilderness outside his door—within 15 minutes on foot.

Soleri envisions "rivers" of such cities spanning the nation, connected by smog-free, uncluttered transportation arteries through open country.

"Man is eminently an environmental animal," says Soleri. "If one adds that man is also a social animal, then one sees that environment comes close to being predominantly the city . . . . Architecture redefined may open a door to the quest of the city for a new life. Architecture is the physical framework for the life of man . . . . The city is a human problem that has to find its answers within ecological awareness."

Soleri's work is one example of ecologically-oriented architectural thought. See "Museums and the Ecological Imperative" for further thought-provoking views on architecture and ecology; and consult the appendices for books and films on the problems of the cities.

chapter 3 / environmental pollution

Environmental Pollution

The information contained in the first section of this chapter is meant as a general introduction to the problems of overpopulation and increasing urbanization. We have not sought to be comprehensive, since within the scope of this handbook it is impossible to cover all aspects of the problem. Many books have been written on the subject; the bibliography may be consulted for appropriate references.

The second section, starting on page 103, includes a variety of materials that we hope will be of assistance to you in planning exhibits and programs. We have included suggestions for exhibits, community activities, and teaching programs; descriptions of what other museums have done and are doing to interpret population problems; and sample posters and other graphics.

Because the staff of each museum will want to develop exhibits and programs unique to their museum and its own geographic region, we offer germinal suggestions as well as structured outlines.

"Technology is at once our blessing and our bane, the well-spring of our aspirations yet the threat to our well-being, Technology is both social benefactor and social calamity."

Howard W. Johnson

"It is hard to suppose that penultimate Western man, stalled in the ultimate traffic jam and slowly succumbing to carbon monoxide, will be especially enchanted to hear from the last survivor that in the preceding year Gross National Product went up by a record amount."

John Kenneth Galbraith

"Man has lost the capacity to foresee and to forestall. He will end by destroying the earth."

Albert Schweitzer

Background

The modern environment, which is increasingly artificial and man-made, poses a twofold threat to human health: in the first place, it contains elements which are outright noxious; secondly, it is undergoing rapid, drastic, and often irreversible changes which more and more endanger the delicate balance of the ecological system and outrun the human capability for adaptation . . . Man has seriously depleted the world's surface. The waste products of his technology and of his own biological processes have grossly polluted the land, air and water.[1]

Charles C. Johnson, Jr.
U.S. Public Health Service

When materials are released in quantities greater than natural forces can assimilate or cleanse without damaging the environment, the result is pollution. The word comes from the Latin, and means to soil or defile. We, the human species, have done plenty of both—in most cases unintentionally or unknowingly. However, we cannot escape the fact that today man-made forms of pollution have created alarmingly serious and widespread conditions.

The word pollution has gained wide use as an indication of signs of insult to the environment. Pollution can result from a variety of causes and sources. We may have natural pollution, as when a volcano erupts and scatters sun-obscuring dust for miles; or we may have man-made pollution, as when dust from cultivated fields spreads over a wide area. Technological man has built vast cities and made his goals "bigger is better" and "more, more, more." But in his concern for achievements he has not, until very recently, questioned the unwanted by-products of his gains or thought about how to cope with them. Indeed, whenever these became troublesome he put them out of sight and out of mind by one means or another. He dumped

Richard Oelze. "Expectation" ("Erwartung") (1935-36). Oil on canvas, 32-1/8" x 39-5/8". Collection, The Museum of Modern Art, New York, Purchase.

them in the water, buried them underground, blew them into the air, or just left them where not too many people would see them. The consumer was to be served and nourished, and no one worried about disposing of the leftovers. This short-sightedness has produced an abundance of non-biodegradable wastes such as aluminum cans, glass bottles and plastic packages and containers. Our hardware has been developed with built-in obsolescence, but when it becomes junk it is indestructible. Until the human population exploded, the clutter and contamination did not seem too much of a problem. In our eagerness for the benefits of technology and the comforts and luxuries it gives us, we ignored its by-products, and as our technological ability has increased, so have our demands.

We have permitted personal interests to blind us to the price we will all have to pay for our "improvements." We want the electric utility companies to stop polluting our air, but we continue to demand more electricity to power our "essential" electric toothbrushes, can openers, and pencil sharpeners, as well as our air conditioners and heating systems. Our demands for rapid transportation by air are unabated—but unless a jetport is in our own neighborhood, we lose sight of its potential to disrupt the environment.

Today, the most common pollutants or contaminants (for the purposes of this handbook the words may be considered interchangeable) are waste products from industrial plants, mines, power plants, agricultural operations, transportation facilities, and human dwellings. These are the pollutants that we can and must control.

"From Sea to Shining Sea". Courtesy of The American Institute of Architects.

In the United States we are annually dumping into our environment:

360 million tons of garbage

  48 billion cans

  26 billion bottles and jars

  1.5 billion tons of solid wastes from mines and factories

  1.3 billion tons of agricultural wastes and manure

142 million tons of air pollutants

50+ billion gallons of liquid sewage

Dr. Glenn Seaborg, chairman of the U.S. Atomic Energy Commission, estimates that by 1980 we will be producing "enough sewage and other waterborne wastes to consume, in dry weather, all the oxygen in all twenty-two major river systems in the United States."

What does pollution of this scope and extent mean? What does it mean to each one of us? To our community? To our environment?

We do not know all the answers to any of those questions, but we know enough to realize we had better start learning the answers as fast as we can. The first steps must be analysis, measurement, classification, and determination of the scope of the problems. This procedure requires time and money. What we cannot afford is procrastination or diversionary half-measures.

The Cost of Pollution

We can measure the cost of pollution in different terms: destruction of life; hazards to health; damage to the physical environment; economic costs. The total price can probably never be assessed accurately.

Air pollution killed 4,000 people in Greater London in 1952. In 1967,

95,000 tons of oil from the Torrey Canyon destroyed countless numbers of marine organisms and birds. In 1969 pesticides killed 40 million fish in the Rhine River.

Death may occur slowly, as when hundreds of thousands of plants and animals succumb to intolerable qualitative changes in their environment. Recent investigations on the reduction in fertility of eggs of several species of birds exposed to chlorinated hydrocarbons (DDT, dieldrin) demonstrate how a species may slowly die off.

In the San Bernardino National Forest, east of Los Angeles, some of the country's finest stands of Ponderosa pine are being killed by smog.[1] In the past five years, 10 percent of the trees—nearly 46,000 acres—have died or begun to die.

In the mountains of Maryland, some 300,000 coniferous trees are suffering from severe sulfur dioxide damage caused by smoke from a coal-fired power plant.

In New Jersey and southern California, truck and commercial flower farming have been seriously curtailed because of air pollution, and in many urban areas the variety of ornamental shrubs and trees that can be planted has been drastically limited by the same noxious blanket. These are only a few of many examples that could be cited.

Classification and Occurrence of Pollutants

The enormous complexity of the pollution problem does not permit easy description or generalization. Man-made pollutants may be classified in numerous ways, generally on the basis of their source: motor exhausts, industrial fumes, sewage and other waterborne wastes and chemicals, noise, heat, and radioactive materials.

Because the environment is a continuum, a specific pollutant may often be found in all of its components. Thus, most pollutants in the air wash out in rain and snow, settling on the land and in the water, often far from the original source.

DDT or radioactive isotopes may be dispersed in the atmosphere, in water or soil, and in living organisms; the extent of their pervasiveness is dramatically illustrated by the fact that DDT has been found in the flesh of polar bears in the Arctic and penguins in the Antarctic, both far from places where the pesticide was originally applied. We know, too, that since the testing of nuclear devices was begun, the worldwide concentration of strontium 90 has greatly increased.

A complete summary of the more than 500 different substances that pollute the environment would be far too long to include here. Those we have chosen to discuss as examples can best be considered in relation to the part of the environment in which they are most prevalent.

The Atmosphere

Our atmosphere, estimated to contain 5 million trillion tons of air, used to be adequate to accept and neutralize most air pollutants. Now even this vast receptacle is becoming clogged. In 1966, over the United States alone, approximately 125 million tons of pollutants were discharged into the air.[2]

POLLUTANT	MILLION TONS PER YEAR	PERCENT
Carbon monoxide	65	52
Oxides of sulfur	23	18
Hydrocarbons	15	12
Particulate matter	12	10
Oxides of nitrogen	8	6
Other gases and vapors	2	2
Total	125	100

SOURCE	MILLION TONS PER YEAR	PERCENT
Transportation	74.8	59.9
Industry	23.4	18.7
Generation of electricity	15.7	12.5
Space heating	7.8	6.3
Refuse disposal	3.3	2.6
Total	125.0	100.0

By 1968 the Department of the Interior estimated that the total volume of pollutants discharged into the air had increased to 143 million tons per year, with the relative occurrence of primary atmospheric pollutants remaining approximately constant. The total is probably even larger now, although there are regions where pollution control systems have been effective in reducing some pollutants, among them the oxides of sulfur.

Internal combustion engines are mainly responsible for the carbon monoxide, the oxides of nitrogen, and the hydrocarbons in the atmosphere. Electric utility plants powered by fossil fuels are the principal producers of oxides of sulfur. Industry is the primary source of the particulate matter and of miscellaneous pollutants.

Pollutants carried in the air damage a wide variety of materials used by man. They corrode metal and concrete, and discolor and erode stone. They cause paint to discolor or peel off; glass to become brittle; leather and rubber to crack; cloth to become stained and weakened.

Other air pollution damage, although less easy to see, is far more dangerous. It is the harm done to living things.

The extent of the effect of air pollutants on human health has been the subject of considerable study and debate. Much research remains to be done on the long-range and cumulative effects of certain of these substances. It has already been demonstrated, however, that positive correlations exist between increase in the quantity of some air pollutants and a rise in the number of deaths from respiratory ailments such as chronic bronchitis, bronchial asthma, lung cancer, and pulmonary emphysema—which is the most rapidly increasing cause of death in the United States.

Nor is the effect of air pollutants on human health limited to respiratory ailments. For example, at very low levels some photochemical pollutants, such as ozone, produce irritation of the eyes; at slightly higher levels—0.8 parts per million—they can cause a temporary decrease in mental capacity; and in concentrations of 2.0 ppm or higher they may interfere seriously with the ability of a healthy person to function normally and comfortably.

One of the most familiar pollutants, the carbon monoxide produced by automobiles, trucks, buses, and other internal combustion machines, accounts for one-half of all air pollutants. At high levels such as those encountered in heavy urban traffic, carbon monoxide produces headache, loss of visual acuity, mental impairment, and decreased muscular coordination. With 101 million motor vehicles in the United States alone, we need to know the effects of dumping something like 70 million tons of carbon monoxide into our atmosphere annually.

Another carbon compound, carbon dioxide, is not generally considered to be a major air pollutant. It

Industrial air pollution on the Merrimack River at Manchester, New Hampshire, 1971. Photographed by Miller/Swift.

is a harmless, odorless, invisible gas, and a normal constituent of the atmosphere. Plants require it to manufacture food. However, the activities of man, especially his use of fossil fuels for creating energy, have generated quantities of this gas vastly in excess of the amount the environment can absorb. Since 1880 the carbon dioxide content of the atmosphere has increased about 12.0

percent, causing concern about the effects it may have on our global weather. Increasing amounts of carbon dioxide in the atmosphere may be associated with a worldwide increase in temperatures through a phenomenon known as the "greenhouse effect." The gas is able to absorb infrared radiation (heat energy) emitted by the earth and allow it to return to earth, where the trapped heat produces an increase in atmospheric temperature. A 10 percent increase in carbon dioxide, it is estimated, will cause the temperature to rise an average of 0.5° C. This is enough to produce significant modifications in climatic patterns, such as the gradual warming of the seas, with consequent ecological changes. Some scientists have even predicted that the polar ice caps would melt sufficiently to produce such a disastrous rise in the sea level that the major metropolitan coastal centers would be flooded, but this seems unlikely.

We do not know enough about modification of climate and its relationship to the carbon dioxide and excess man-produced heat radiation in the atmosphere. Their effects are influenced by several other phenomena, and more research must be carried out on the changes in the climate resulting from man's activities. There is evidence, however, that the vast amount of excess heat dumped into the atmosphere in the vicinity of industrial cities has produced increases in atmospheric temperatures, increases in cloudiness and fog, decrease in wind, and increases in precipitation—all in easily measurable amounts when compared with the surrounding rural areas.

Water

The pollutants we dump into our waters and onto the land are as varied as those intruded into the atmosphere. There have been dramatic examples recently of what can happen when water is severely polluted by petroleum leakage: the flesh of Hudson River shad has acquired a "harbor flavor" that has made this valuable food fish unmarketable; both the Cuyahoga River at Cleveland, Ohio, and the Kill Van Kull in New York Harbor have actually caught fire; and thousands of waterfowl have died as a result of massive leaks either from tankers at sea or from offshore wells. The uncontrolled flow of thousands of barrels of oil from wells in the Pacific Ocean near Santa Barbara, California, and in the Gulf of Mexico has been sad testimony to the hazards of offshore drilling operations. Recently the government tightened its regulations of the petroleum industry in order to curtail oil pollution.

Normal physiological functions of fish and wildlife can be disrupted by a single chemical element which may in turn produce harmful effects in humans who eat the animals as food. Lead, cadmium, mercury, and fluorine, when they are accumulated in sufficiently high concentrations, will produce harmful results. In 1970 Canadian and American officials discovered that fish in the Great Lakes area and in Lake Champlain contain a dangerously large amount of mercury—more than an allowable 0.5 parts per million. The U.S. Water Quality Administration, once alerted to the widespread dumping of industrial wastes high in mercury, acted vigorously to reduce this type of pollution. Dumping in Lake Erie alone was reduced from 280 pounds a day to 10

Aerial view of the harbor of Cleveland, Ohio.

pounds. Similarly, the Department of Agriculture took steps to reduce mercury compounds used in agricultural pesticides.

Mercury is now so widespread in the complex environmental networks that it has been reported in dangerously high quantities in drinking water systems, shellfish, fish, and fish-eating birds. Scientists of the Department of the Interior have reported finding dead bald eagles that had lethal amounts of mercury —as high as 130 parts per million—in their kidneys.

The U.S. Department of the Interior, in a recent survey, concluded there were dangerous levels of mercury in the lakes and streams of at least 33 states and 16 of these instituted sanctions designating mercury pollution a hazard to public health.

Toward the end of 1970 mercury was found in large amounts in tuna and swordfish. The Food and Drug Administration confiscated large quantities of canned tuna and frozen swordfish from market shelves and discovered that the confiscated food contained more mercury than 0.5 parts per million. It is difficult if not impossible to determine the sources contaminating these pelagic and migratory fishes. It is clear that tests will have to be made on fish meal and the animals that are fed fish meal in order to determine the safety of other links along the food chain.

Water pollutants also lead to an increase in disease—producing viruses and bacteria, including such common pathogens as those of typhoid, paratyphoid, and salmonellosis. In the latter half of the twentieth century we are still dumping enormous amounts of untreated human wastes into our waterways. As a result shellfish have become carriers of hepatitis; aquatic-borne viral diseases of unknown source have increased; and the waters of many beaches have been declared unsafe. In 1970 a Federal government survey of drinking water in the United States reported that several million Americans were drinking water of a "potentially dangerous quality." More than half of the 969 representative water systems surveyed were found to be inefficient and archaic. It is not surprising that in August of the same year the New York State Health Department ordered chlorination of all public water supply systems.

Raw human sewage and even partially treated sewage, aside from endangering human health, contributes to direct disruption of the environment. When discharged into ponds, lakes, and waterways, nitrogen and phosphates from human and agricultural wastes (including detergents and fertilizers) produce a tremendous increase in the nutrients of the water. This in turn results in the growth of vast numbers of minute, aquatic plants, principally algae and phytoplankton. Eventually the increase of the plants produces a condition termed eutrophication, the ecological process of enrichment and aging of water bodies.

The acceleration of what is normally a slow ecological process has become so widespread that Dr. Arthur S. Hasler, a noted limnologist at the University of Wisconsin, terms it "cultural eutrophication—an aberration—a natural process running

Scene near East Haven junk yards and Quinnipiac River, Photo: Miller/Swift, East Haddam, Conn.

amok." More than one-third of our lakes are showing signs of cultural eutrophication: surface waters are covered with algal scum; long filamentous strands are formed, rocks and logs become enslimed; waters turn murky and fetid under the summer sun; excess algae die and drift to the bottom; decomposing matter uses up the small amount of oxygen left in the deeper waters; trout, whitefish, and other deep water food species die from lack of oxygen and are eventually replaced by trash fish. As sediments and muck fill in the lake, the shoreline vegetation moves out, filling the area formerly occupied by water. The unpleasant odor, the unsightly mats of algae, the dead fish, and the vanishing shoreline are the despair of all who cherish the beauty of natural waters.

Dr. Hasler writes:[2]

It took the visual (and olfactory) impact of a huge body of water, Lake Erie, suffocating as a dump for industrial waste, sewage, and urban and rural runoff, to bring the problem of water pollution dramatically to the public eye. Some now pronounce Lake Erie "dead"! We, however, extend hope for recovery. For if communities and industries in Lake Erie's drainage basin cease polluting and fertilizing its waters, and if a cleansing flow from Lake Huron is permitted to reach and "flush out" the lake via the Detroit River, Erie might show signs of recovery within a decade. True, our hope is contingent upon many 'ifs'. However, it cannot be too strongly emphasized that these situations are reversible—that bodies of water will respond when the right steps are taken.

The tragedy that befell Lake Erie is being repeated on a smaller scale in virtually all parts of our country, both in fresh waters and the coastal estuaries. Even the disposal of treated sewage—the "sludge dumping" that is practiced by most large cities along the Atlantic seaboard—is causing depletion. When dumped into the ocean, sludge, which is the solid residue from sewage treatment plants, produces so-called "dead seas" in areas immediately surrounding the dumping sites.

Land

Where pollution of land is concerned, we tend to think first of paper litter, garbage, bottles, tin cans and worn-out cars. The disposal of the solid wastes that litter our landscape is very serious not only for economic and aesthetic reasons, but also because of the health hazards that develop in connection with despoiled conditions. These wastes give protection and encouragement to rats, mice, and other rodents that harbor disease vectors. The problem of efficient disposal presents a great challenge to the cause of land preservation. Dumping, burying, incinerating, compacting are all processes of disposal currently practiced—at the expense of our environment. The most promising developments are in methods of refuse; in the recapture of separate elements by recycling; and in the hydrogen Fusion Torch.

The last method, hydrogen fusion, may bring many new technological benefits, including greater efficiency in reusing many solid wastes. Dr. Glenn T. Seaborg foresees a most optimistic future for this new development:[3]

The list of things that can be accomplished with these Fusion Torch processes reads like the answer to both the conservationists' and technologists' prayers . . . . In a broader sense all waste could literally be transformed back into potentially useful resources. The ultra-violet radiation created by the plasma could be used for large-scale desalting, bulk heating for many applications, the sterilization of sewage, food production through the production of ozone, the Fusion Torch might be used to sterilize drinking water, revive 'dead' lakes and rivers by reducing their excess organic matter and to help eliminate industrial air pollution.

This new technique involves the use of the ultra-high temperature plasma of a thermonuclear reactor. It creates power by fusing and utilizing the nuclei of light elements, such as deuterium, tritium, and lithium. The major fuel resource for fusion is the deuterium (heavy hydrogen) found in seawater.

Dr. Seaborg cautions that the wonders he enumerates will not be available for a while. First scientists will have to develop in a single fusion facility all of the required steps for fusion, including high temperatures, plasma density, and adequate confinement time. He believes that we will succeed in solving these problems, but "just in the nick of time."

Considerable damage is being done by the chemicals man is adding to the land in the form of fertilizers, insecticides, herbicides, fungicides, growth enzymes, and plant hormones. The accumulation of many of these toxins is so detrimental that in some places the land will no longer grow agriculturally important plants. Widespread concern has also developed over the destruction of wildlife resulting from DDT and other pesticides. First highlighted by the late Rachel Carson, this form of poisoning has been increasingly well documented. Accumulations of the pesticides occur in the body tissues of each creature in a food chain, culminating in the death of the top animal in the sequence. Recently it has been reported that DDT (and the substance into which it is metabolized, DDE) are reducing the oxygen production of certain marine phytoplankton. The accumulative and long-lasting nature of the so-called "hard" pesticides is now acknowledged by the Department of Agriculture and other governmental agencies, and the use of these products is being banned on an increasingly wide scale. Still there are agriculturists who continue to press for their use.

Radiation, Thermal Pollution, and Noise

Concern grows about the effects of radioactive materials on human genes and human embryos. The germ cells appear to be more sensitive to radiation than are other body cells.

Radioactive pollutants are produced from sources other than nuclear power plants and atomic weapons testing. The earth is continually exposed to short-wave radiation, and many of our so-called "conven-

tional" sources of energy, such as fossil-fuel power stations, emit radioactive products. These pollutants are distributed throughout the

Charles Sheeler. "American Landscape"; (1930). Oil on canvas, 24 x 31". Collection, The Museum of Modern Art, New York, Gift of Abby Aldrich Rockefeller.

environment, but they usually present a potential problem only near a test site or reactor. Since the 1940s, however, the presence of certain radioisotopes has increased to proportions large enough to cause concern. Many studies are being conducted to evaluate accurately the extent and seriousness of radioactive pollutants. Because of widespread fear by the public of alleged dangers from radioactive materials, few people want to have a nuclear powered electrical plant located close to where they live or work. This creates serious problems for an expanding economy, and ways are being sought to meet the growing demands for power with a minimum disruption of the environment.

Another aspect of the nuclear problem is the disposal of radioactive wastes. So far no method has been proposed that does not in some fashion involve disposal in the environment, either deep in the earth or deep in the oceans. Nuclear wastes currently amount to about 2.4 million cubic feet per year. The AEC is planning to bury the wastes in old salt mines at depths of between 500 and 1,000 feet. Because these wastes will be active for hundreds of years, and the containers will probably not last anywhere near that long, it is clear that much research needs to be done on safe disposal methods.

Thermal pollution is a relatively recent form of contamination commonly associated with the development of nuclear power plants. Most of these plants are located on rivers, lakes, or estuaries because they need large quantities of water to cool their steam condensers. The heated effluent water mixes with and raises the temperature of the natural waters into which it pours. The increase is greatest near the outfall, where the ecology of the receiving water can be grossly altered. Depending upon a variety of factors, the effect extends to a greater or lesser degree from the outfall. A particular plant may have minimal effects, or it may contribute to ecological modification of a whole river system.[4]

The ecologists' concerns about the dangers of thermal pollution are based on the forecast of a tenfold increase in power generation in the next few decades. This large increase in excess heat (utilizing half of the total annual runoff water of the United States by A.D. 2000) could have any of the following effects if not properly handled: rapid increase in eutrophication; alteration of the balance of aquatic communities in favor of undesirable species; interference with migrations of anadromous fishes; alteration of bloom successions so that larval stages of valuable fishes and invertebrates are out of phase with their planktonic food sources; decrease in the feeding efficiency of fishes; increased susceptibility to diseases; and decrease in dissolved oxygen. In brief, what ecologists fear is not dramatic and visible kills, but an insidious undermining of the ecological *balance* of the waterways of the country.

Field studies to date have given uneven results. For example, studies done in the Chesapeake Bay and the Columbia River show clear evidence of damages; but in a Connecticut River study the ecological effects appeared minimal.[5] The Connecticut River study involved a plant discharging a modest 372,000 gallons per minute (one twentieth of the average flow) into the tidal part of the river, heating it to a temperature 20° F. above normal. Bottom life in the affected part of the river (4.2 linear miles) did not appear to be adversely affected. Anadromous fish appeared able to pass the plant by swimming up the opposite side or under the heated layer. Effects on zooplankton and resident fishes remain to be estimated.

Heated water often attracts fishes, particularly during the cold season. Although this phenomenon can provide a temporary increase in fish catches, it also causes problems. When the generating plants are shut down, the warm-adapted fish suffer shock, sometimes fatal. Another problem is that the heated zone around plants on lakes or estuaries attracts young fish, which may be drawn in with the intake water and killed. In the winter of 1969-70, for example, many millions of young striped bass and white perch were killed at the Indian Point plant of Consolidated Edison on the Hudson River. As these cases demonstrate, a certain amount of heat can be assimilated without extreme damage, but thermal pollution is always an ecological threat. The answer lies in advance ecological planning rather than last-minute crisis level before-and-after studies. One fact *is* clear—plants located on the coast discharging into the open sea will be the least harmful because of the immense quantity of heating water available in the ocean.

Noise is another kind of pollution that has recently increased and we are threatened with more noise and a rise in its intensity. Once thought of only as a disrupter of peace and quiet, noise is now known to produce definite and serious physical effects. Prolonged exposure to noise may damage hearing, and some authorities maintain that exposure to very loud noise may produce cardiovascular, respiratory, and glandular disturbances.

Sounds above 45 decibels are considered disturbing. The average home is estimated to have a background noise level of about 40 decibels, but a food blender may produce 90 to 95. A heavy truck or subway train at a distance of 25 feet produces about 95 decibels; an outboard motor or motorcycle, 100 or more. A rock-and-roll band at its peak can burst into the 120 decibel range, and a jet aircraft at close range may give off 150 decibels. We have recently been accumulating evidence that noise in the 85-90 decibel range may cause irreversible damage to the autonomic nervous system, and that noise may be a factor in diseases related to stress.

Since noise is a form of energy radiating outward in waves, loud explosive noise can actually break the eardrum—as many servicemen have learned. Jet aircraft, flying faster than the speed of sound, create destructive noise radiations when they break through the sound barrier. Windows and fragile structures have been shattered, and even delicate geological formations in some of our scenic national parks have been destroyed by the sound waves emanating from jet aircraft. The question of how much damage will be done by the supersonic jet transport planes flying on regular schedules remains to be answered.

Thus we are learning that pollution can take many forms, may

A grouping of pipes.

appear in any part of the environment, may develop quickly or slowly, visibly or invisibly. We know, too, that the abatement of pollution requires wise and prompt action and that this action must be taken if we are to preserve beauty or quality in our world. The dilemma here is how to have the benefits of technology while avoiding unwanted, undesirable effects: giant earth-moving machines gulping up rich forest and farm lands; industrial plants spewing waste products into the air and water; herbicides, pesticides, and fertilizers poisoning fields and water courses and all that live in them; trucks and high-speed automobiles racing over superhighways through an ugly, littered landscape.

There seems no question that we will have to make important changes in our way of looking at the world around us. The judgments that will determine the future of our planet will have to be based on the whole network of relationship among all living things and the environment. They will have to take into account not only scientific and technological criteria, but humanistic and aesthetic values. Otherwise our environment will not be fit for life.

In *The Future of the Future*, John McHale, Director of the World Resources Inventory of Southern Illinois University, offers a set of priorities for "redesigning our ecological undertakings." Dr. McHale says, "we may sum up our more urgent objectives as follows":[6]

1. *To recycle the metals and materials in the system*, so that there is a swifter turnover with the least lag in scrapping and processing cycles. In high-grade technological process, each use cycle tends, through overall development, to achieve more, not less, performance per invested unit of materials.

2. *To employ increasingly our income energies* of solar, water, wind, tidal, and nuclear power, rather than the hazardous and depletive fossil fuels. The latter represent major capital investments, hich once used are not replaceable. They are too precious to burn up in our currently prodigal fashion, but they may be more efficiently—and more fractionally—employed in indirect conversion to plastics, foodstuffs, and other essentials.

3. *To refashion our food cycle* so that we may more swiftly augment the present starvation diets of more than half the developing world. We need, however, to go also beyond emergency satisfaction of immediate needs toward the more extensive ecological redesign of our whole agricoindustrial system; employing the most efficient natural means of food conversion through the plant animal chains and the possibilities inherent in microbiological, biosynthetic, and other processes.

4. *To set up ecomonitoring and control centers* that will act as early warning systems in relation to our large-scale scientific and technological undertakings, analyzing and evaluating their immediate and largest range effects on the overall ecological matrix and their positive and negative implications for the quality of the human environ.

The future of our ecological maintenance depends on such redesign of our presently chaotic undertakings and on their coordination into more directly advantageous relationships within the larger planetary ecology.

Summary

Man has been polluting the environment since ancient times, but with modern technology, his vastly increased pollution has begun to destroy whole areas of the environment. The benefits of technological gains in industry, power generation, transportation, agriculture, and human habitation must be balanced against their unwanted by-products in the form of pollutants. These can be classified according to the part of the environment where they are discharged or where they remain to cause damaging effects—the air, the water, the land, at times all three. Sometimes they even pervade the food chain on which all life depends.

If we are to preserve or in some way re-create an environment fit for life, we must develop new ways to reduce all forms of pollution; to do this we must recognize that the primary source of pollution is man's own carelessness and greed.

exhibits and projects / environmental pollution

Changing Values

An exhibit can set forth the choices every consumer must make if our environment is to become habitable again. It should stress the hard facts involved in three questions:

Factories: Production or Pollution?

Advertising and Packaging: Necessary or Frivolous?

Cars: Conveniences or Contaminants?

One-half of the exhibit might be focused on a series of graphs illustrating the old "conservation index" idea. It might feature paintings of the 1930s, when that idea was popular. The other half of the exhibit could feature contemporary paintings (or clippings and photographs) which relate to air pollution and pollution by automobiles and trash.

Contrast glossy full-color advertisements, showing pristine factories, cars and packages, with photographs showing the pollution resulting from production:

Smoke and particulate matter from factories

Paper and plastic trash blowing across a landscape

Trees festooned

A car dump

In one exhibit hall, juxtapose a brand-new car with a sculpture constructed of car parts or pressed cars.

A steel plant in the middle west.

"This? Or That?"

Here is a suggestion for another fine exhibit that offers choices, implying but not forcing the idea that there is a better alternative:

The Sky: National Dump? or
A Bit of Heaven?

The Rivers: National Dump? or
Sparkling Waters?

The Future: More Artificial? or
More Natural?

Education: Greater Knowledge? or
Greater Wisdom?

Resources: Desalt the Sea? or
Conserve the Rain?

Attitudes: Conquer Nature? or
Learn from Wilderness?

Love Man? or
Love All that Lives?

Manage Nature? or
Give Nature a Chance?

More Highways? or
More Walking?

G.N.P.? or
Real Wealth?

A Million Species? or
One Life?

Photo: Miller/Swift, East Haddam, Connecticut. Roadside junk yard on the outskirts of New Haven.

Albert T. Bricher, "Monhegan Cliff, Maine". Oil on canvas. Collection, The Virginia Museum of Fine Arts, Gift of Mr. Eugene B. Sydnor, Jr., 1970.

This is Progress?

Show how mass acceptance of such "necessities" as electric toothbrushes and can openers increases air pollution by tracing the power back to smokestacks or thermally-polluted water.

Create a greenhouse chamber through which visitors walk. Use it, not to grow plants, but by means of various measuring instruments to interpret "the greenhouse effect." Have an exhibit demonstrate how CO_2 causes a greenhouse effect, and how careless modern architects can create unfavorable indoor climates through overuse of glass.

A Good Life or a Life of Goods?

Catherine Pessino

A.   THE AIR WE BREATHE

The Look of the 70s

Prepare an exhibit simulating a store window display of mannequins (men, women, and children) wearing face masks and sporting other paraphernalia for fighting air pollution.

What's in the Air?

1. Build a small diorama of a city covered with moving smoke and gases, buildings barely discernible.
2. Grit, grime, dirt, and dust are not always seen. Set up a microscopic projector or use enlarged micro-photographs to show particles of soot on a tree leaf, clothing, etc.
3. Filth pours. Use a kinetoscope. Start out with sky-blue screen and end up with gray-black screen. Begin with the smoke from one cigarette and build up.

Nearby, under the heading "Come Out of the Fog," place a dispenser with giveaways from various agencies containing information on what the individual can do to help.

B.   THE WATER WE DRINK

This Is the Way It Should Be

Diorama of balanced pond or river with a faucet at one end. Clear water flows from faucet into cup.

But This Is the Way It Is

Diorama representing the same pond or river, now polluted. Diorama contains beer cans, plastic bags, oil slick, detergent suds, styrofoam cup, etc. Murky water flows from faucet and goes down the drain.

The Rivers We Know

Use slides, film, or photographs of well-known rivers (Mississippi, Hudson, Suwannee, Columbia) with which the viewer is familiar. Show how pollution has affected them.

Nearby, under the heading "Join a Scrub Team," place a dispenser with giveaways containing pertinent information on steps the individual can take.

C. THE FOOD, CLOTHING, AND SHELTER WE NEED

We Buy the Food, Clothing and Shelter We Need

Set up an exhibit against a backdrop of store counters (supermarkets, hardware, etc.). Shopping carts filled with groceries, clothing, lumber, sand, brick, etc., pass by on a conveyor belt.

Mount a related display on revolving sections. On one side, under a heading of "It All Comes from the Land," show large photographs of a farm, ranch, forest, mine, etc., each with an accompanying panel illustrating the same products as those seen in the shopping carts. On the other side, under a heading "If We Misuse the Land," use photographs showing a wasted farm, ranch, forest, etc., and show no products on the panels.

Under a heading "Our Minerals, Once Used, Are Hard to Regain," a shovel scoops out coal, sand, copper ore, and so forth, until an empty hole remains.

Using the title "What Is Essential?," show a shelf covered with everyday items. Next to each item present a list of its mineral content.

Start with a bobby pin and end with a chrome fender. What are the priorities?

In conjunction with photographs of junk piles and scrapped cars, ask "Can we afford a one-way ticket for our junk?"

Place a dispenser nearby containing appropriate giveaways.

The Automobile

The automobile has had such a tremendous impact on us—our mobility, our economy, our health—that you might want to devote a whole hall to the subject of the automobile in American life, with exhibits on:

the space it occupies

the space its accessories occupy

the effect parking lots and roads have on water supply

the pollutants the engine causes

the oxygen the engine consumes

the influence of the auto on architecture and city plans

the cars effect on sexual mores

the auto as an instrument of "rite of passage" in American male society

Museums with limited space could prepare one or more of the following less-ambitious exhibits on one of the most, if not the most, dominant artifacts of American culture.

A presentation of the history of the automobile illustrating its role in shaping America's physical and social environment

An offering of tape recordings of automobile accidents and traffic sounds

A demonstration of the production of pollutants by combustion engines in automobiles—perhaps by showing damage to vegetation along heavily-traveled routes

If there is an antique car club in your community, consult with its members to secure models of early steam and electric cars. Set up an exhibit contrasting these with present-day cars. Stress the comparative amounts of pollution discharged by each. In addition, photographs or models of varius types of trains, boats and planes might be exhibited for similar comparison

A Group of Exhibits and Projects, Easy to Execute

The urgent necessity to preserve our air, land and water resources is crucial to survival. Stimulating projects and exhibits may be built around a number of subjects:

Using a glass wax-pencil, outline major landscape features on a window—trees, clouds, rivers, etc. Put in arrows and labels indicating the water cycle. Everyone who looks at the window will be shown the importance of this continuum.

The same technique can be applied to the glass sides of a terrarium or aquarium.

Set up a display showing how insecticide residues damage beneficial soil organisms and affect the growth of plants. This may be illustrated by means of potted plants.

Illustrate case histories of damage resulting from overuse of detergents and biocides, and from improper disposal of containers.

Illustrate how industrial processes affect vegetation.

Set up a program which consists of a series of visits to:
Landfall sites
Sewer outfalls
Abandoned-car locations
Ghettos
Suburban dumps
Highway-construction sites

Mobiles
Make mobiles which illustrate:
The variety of raw materials used by an average North American and an average South American
The creatures of a clean stream in contrast with those of a polluted stream
Predatory relationships as illustrated by a charging lion and a herd of impala, a peregrine falcon and a flock of doves, an otter and a school of trout
Perhaps you could commission a local artist to design these in a form

that would facilitate reproduction; such reproductions could be offered for sale in your gift shop.

Using simple three-dimensional dioramas, create before—and—after scenes of the environment as it is affected by air pollution, water pollution, solid-waste disposal and similar destructive practices.

A display showing that political and ecological boundaries do not always coincide may cause surprise to many viewers. For example, the Great Lakes, oceans and some major rivers are the joint property and concern of more than one nation. Within our country, rivers often cross state lines. Responsibility for them must be shared.

The high wilderness watersheds in our country are, in large proportion, public lands. They provide most of the clear water draining to lower areas. A display pointing out the issue "sale of natural resources versus depletion of scenic value" should be easy to set up and enlightening to the viewer.

One-Step Air Pollution Exhibits

Major exhibitions related to air pollution may be reinforced or supplemented by single, simple exhibits which each convey just one thought:

Show the composition of industrial gases, indicating their effects on humans and stating the limits which can be tolerated.

Contrast smog and smoke (Man-made) with Haze and Mist (Natural Phenomena).

Illustrate visible emission, by means of photographs of the skyline of your city taken each day for a week.

Present a treatment of the phenomenon of temperature inversion and show how it affects people. Enlist the cooperation of a local Camera Club in preparing this exhibit.

A Closeup View of Stream Pollution

Set up an exhibit showing the organisms that live in polluted waters. Encourage visitors to go out and obtain samples, from local streams, which can be viewed under microscopes to determine the extent of pollution. Excellent references for the planning of such an exhibit may be found in *The Biology of Polluted Waters*, by H.B. Hynes, and *Biological Field Investigative Data for Water Pollution Surveys* published by the United States Department of Interior Water Pollution Control Administration.

Save the Bay for Life

The exhibit by the California Academy of Sciences calling attention to the damage being done to San Francisco Bay attracted widespread attention. Following is the complete text of the exhibit and 3 of the handsome photographs that accompanied it.

"San Francisco Bay". Photo: Diane Beeston, San Francisco.

San Francisco Bay is the reason for San Francisco

One truckload at a time
we have extended thin line dikes
to capture many square miles of Bay surface.
More than one-third of the original Bay
has been surrendered already.

Tandem truckloads quickly fill diked shallows
and another expanse of Bay is lost forever.
It is unlikely that any of this new land
will ever revert to open water,
and still the fills continue.

Scavenging gulls thrive on garbage-filled tracts
which appear to suffocate the graceful bridges
with unstable new land.

Salt-evaporation ponds and unfilled diked pools
preserve great expanses of water surface
where oxygen exchange occurs.

Both air and water undergo drastic changes in quality
as open water surfaces diminish.
Salt ponds breed a rich supply of crustaceans
to feed our wildlife population.

Mill Valley vigilance stipulates "clean soil only"
to guarantee that the fill can consolidate into stable land.

Relentless filling with trash may dispose of one waste problem
temporarily
while wasting priceless water surface
permanently.

Even unfilled stagnant pools
may disrupt natural water currents needed to flush the Bay.

This Berkeley waterfront fill resembles an earthquake disaster
and could serve to warn us of the unstable nature
of fills composed of progressively-deteriorating material.
As the garbage fouls the water
the "Athens of the West" adds its bitter cup to the Bay.

Domestic, industrial and agricultural wastes from most of Central California
flow into the Bay and out to sea.
Disrupted currents and backwaters created by poorly-conceived fills
may retard the flushing function of the state's giant sewer.

Airborne pollutants also find their way into the Bay
as this great blotter absorbs the residue which settles on its surface.
A diminished Bay becomes an inadequate filter
when lethal dust collects on the new streets
which replace old waterways.

San Francisco Bay is the reason for San Francisco.
One of the world's great natural harbors,
it attracted a cosmopolitan population who built dynamic cities.
As regard for the Bay diminishes
so does that quality of life generated here.

As international airports filled parts of the harbor
developments levelled orchards and fields.
Now the crop being dusted every few minutes is human.

Great ships have learned not to blow out their wastes
in exhausted port waters.
When will we exhaust the seas?

When will people learn?

Crowded freeways overload the air with pollutants
while depriving the Bay of the surface required to absorb them.

The fertile delta thrives on a delicate balance
of fresh- and salt-water flow.
This gentle country is little understood
as an integral part of the Bay system.
A threat to this fresh water supply
could endanger the delta and affect the salinity in the Bay.

"Delta". Photo: Diane Beeston, San Francisco.

Stagnant pools made by man collect pollutants
which should have been flushed by Bay currents.

A thin film of scum
seals off the oxygen-exchanging water surface.

Open water allows tidal currents and prevailing winds
to cleanse the Bay Area's atmosphere and waterways.
Filling the Bay is like slamming shut the Gate.

Unsightly trash floats off deepwater piers
like surface buoys marking sunken accumulations
of human indifference to water quality.

The organic beauty of a ship's hull and keel
is just one of the many delights
which abound in a Bay-oriented culture.

Opening Day of the regatta is a million-dollar extravaganza
shared free by any landlubber with enough imagination
to look beyond his "bay window."

"Opening Day of the Regatta". Photo: Diane Beeston, San Francisco.

These abandoned foundations
with the stark beauty of a modern "Stonehenge"
picturesquely frame the jet liners
which daily strew the waters
with black exhaust to be flushed to sea.

"CONTAMINATED"
A poison slough
dying at the foot of dramatic land forms
which really should crown
a pool of beauty.

Harbor seals live where they do because they can.
So do people.
When the Bay can no longer support wildlife,
how well will we live?

Sport fishing will become poor sport
when the prize catch is unfit to eat.

Bird-watchers are not strange people
who endure all weather to document the passing migrations
of birds along the Pacific flyway.
We may all become bird-watchers after all the birds have gone.

Against an industrial background flocks of birds still thrive
on the remaining, nourishment-rich mud flats.

Dead anchovies strew the beach
and tax the scavengers to keep up with the lethal water.

Today's babies survive the sewage
but what will their babies' playground be?
A larger population can smother a smaller Bay.

The virgin mud flats of Marin
are a giant incubator for wildlife nourishment
and a great source of oxygen.
This living foreground is as vital
as the great white city across the Bay.

Outraged students demonstrate
against the overwhelming tide of human indifference
by "policing" the Albany mud flats.

Living mud flats
are as ugly as we make them.

No community of cities is so richly endowed
that it can afford to squander
a treasure of such magnitude.

By tearing down the hills to fill the depths
we can create a new low in beauty.
Progress need not produce monotony.

No matter how stable is the earth used to fill the shallows
it represents a permanent loss of priceless Bay.

"Baghdad" is an enchanting backdrop
for a flock of international visiting birds.
May the city that knows how
learn to share its survival.

Herb Caen of the San Francisco Chronicle refers frequently to San Francisco as Baghdad.

How to Kill or Cure a Lake

Here is a subject of vital interest in many parts of the nation.

Show the factors involved in natural eutrophication, and how organisms adapt at various stages of this condition.

Show how man hastens the lake's aging process.

Show ways we can apply technical development, to reverse the process or slow it down.

The History of a River

Select a river in your area and follow its course downward from its source.

What are its natural characteristics (i.e., vegetation in the stream and on the bank; types of material that form its banks and bottom; length, breadth and depth)?

How has man made use of the river in the past?

What is the present condition of the river?

Why does man turn his back on the river?

Can the river be improved? By what steps?

"Clearwater" —A Hudson River Sloop Restoration

Led by folksinger Pete Seeger, a group of conservationists has reconstructed a replica of a nineteenth-century Hudson River sloop, the *Clearwater*. The ship and the activities centered around it bring people back to the abandoned banks of the Hudson. The major objective of the project is to focus attention upon the urgent need to clean up the waters of the river.

Young people and adults from communities along the Hudson have been recruited as crew for the *Clearwater*. Local celebrations have been organized in communities where the boat has docked.

The sloop began its operation during the summer of 1969. In September of 1970 it was a feature at the South Street Seaport Museum in New York City. It is expected that its visits along the river will become annual reminders of the need to abate water pollution.

Activities such as those centered around the *Clearwater* can be adapted for use in other regions.

Folksinger Pete Seeger helps other conservationists dramatize environmental problems.

The Depletion of Minerals

In the history of our country irreplaceable mineral resources have been owned and mined by private industry.

Set up an exhibit featuring pictures of the '49 Gold Rush, the Aspen, Colorado silver rush, iron mining in Pennsylvania and copper mining in Montana. Accompany this with a large bar graph showing the extent to which we have depleted our resources of important metals, and such reserve as experts estimate is now remaining

Set up a pictorial exhibit showing how mining and quarrying change the face of the landscape

Query university schools of mines for information on companies now including land-reclamation in their plans

Contrast old and new concepts of responsibility to the public

Pollution in Food

Some of our most critical problems in the pollution of food can be set forth in exhibits which illustrate food chains, focusing on such topics as:

. Radioactive fallout in milk supply
. Pesticide residues in and on food
. Fish-kills by inorganic chemical pollution (and the resulting changes in bird population)
. Estuarine pollution causing the destruction of fish breeding grounds

A separate subject, but one in which housewives have a special interest, is that of the use of chemical additives by the food-processing industry. This can be the subject of a simple case exhibit.

An Exhibit at OMSI

An exhibit on pesticides at the Oregon Museum of Science and Industry makes use of small glass bubbles containing insects that create problems in agriculture.

OMSI says the exhibit attempts to tell the story as it is, without editorializing; advice has been obtained from outstanding experts thoughout the nation.

The Noise Factor

Set up a series of carrels (desks with headphones). At each desk provide a set of tasks to be done—a crossword puzzle, reading matter, a picture book to color. Pipe a variety of sounds into the headphones at different decibel levels, thereby impressing upon the visitor the extent to which noise influences his ability to perform the tasks.

No Place to Play

This is a traveling exhibit from Cranbrook Institute of Science. The title suggests the urgent message this exhibition conveys as it explores growing population, urban sprawl and contamination of the environment. Dramatic changes in land use in several areas are documented through the display of matching illustrations contrasting the past and the present. Other illustrations show some corrective measures, and note agencies active in bettering the human condition. The Michigan scene is emphasized. A list of recent publications is included for the convenience of the exhibitor wishing to set up an accompanying book display.

Hanging: The 32 masonite panels (maximum 42" x 48") are complete with grommets to facilitate hanging, either on hooks or by picture wire. Panels are numbered in a suggested sequence. Some panels may be hung back-to-back on freestanding frames (not provided). Space requirement is 100 linear feet.

Weight: 500 lbs. (crated)

Reprinted here are two of the photographs from a press kit prepared for the traveling exhibit, which also includes a press release and a list of suggested readings.

Cranbrook Foundation. Photo: Harvey Croze.

Cranbrook Foundation. Photo: Harvey Croze.

The Museum of Science in Boston has introduced a number of exhibits on pollution. Several are described here:

An Air Quality Monitoring Station

In Boston an Air Quality Monitoring Station has been placed in operation on the Science Museum's garage roof. It provides continuous monitoring of sulphur dioxide, nitrogen dioxide, oxides of nitrogen, photochemical oxidants, carbon monoxide and total hydrocarbon content in the air.

The station is part of the statewide air surveillance network of the National Air Pollution Control Administration. It is administered by the Massachusetts Bureau of Air Use Management, and is one of only two automated units in Massachusetts; there are 45 manually-operated units in the state.

Smog in a Big Way

An aerial photograph of smog over a city was enlarged to gigantic proportions and used as a mural facing the entrance of the museum. The label beside it was printed, in large letters, to read: "Boston's air ranks among the nation's dirtiest. Is this what you want to breathe? Population and pollution—everybody's number one problem today."

A Breath of Air

Actual human lungs are a dramatic illustration of the ravages of disease, in a major exhibit at the museum. Entitled "A Breath of Air," the multi-unit display, contributed by the Massachusetts Division of the American Cancer Society, drives home its point with the subtitle "What Kind of Lungs Do You Want?"

Courtesy: Museum of Science, Boston, Massachusetts.

Three real human lungs—one healthy, two diseased—are mounted in large cases. According to the museum's news release, "each presents compelling evidence for reduction of air pollution and discontinuance of cigarette smoking. In full-color diagrammatic representations and explanatory material, the process of air intake and exhalation, the entire respiratory system, and the inroads of emphysema and cancer are powerfully demonstrated," the news release states.

The four-unit display makes use of vivid drawings, huge photographic blowups and detailed expository material as well as the authentic human organs.

The diseased lung is shown against a photographic backdrop of a smog-blanketed city. Behind the cancer-damaged lung is a picture of cigarette butts. The photo in the unit containing the healthy lung has full, straight trees against a clear sky.

"Lung tissue," the exhibit label states, "once destroyed, cannot be repaired."

Posters Carry the Message

Many problems related to solid-waste management can be brought to public attention through distribution of posters in the community. The following chart showing gross national pollution suggests how a number of subjects might be presented with great impact, yet by simple means. Such posters might be designed by the museum staff, or selected from contest entries.

Apart from their direct educational value, posters circulated in the community can be used to call attention to your museum's activities in regard to environmental concerns.

Nature does it naturally—we **MUST**, and soon

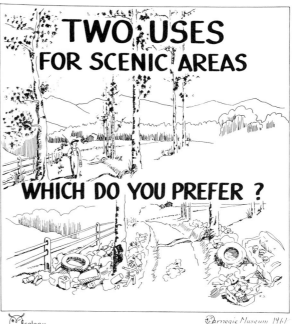

"With Power On Wheels He Scarred The Earth." Power-shovel cartoon superimposed on aerial photo of unrestored strip-mined area. Carnegie Museum's Conservation Exhibit. Photo: Leo T. Sarnaki.

The Power of Museum Publications

Museum publications can be potent forces for environmental education, both on their own and as backup for exhibits, courses, symposia and other means of communication. The article from *Smithsonian*, reprinted here with permission, is an excellent example of a simple but forceful message which will appeal to art historians and antiquarians as well as to individuals whose concern is limited to narrower, everyday aspects of pollution.

For a listing of some of the other museum publications that carry articles on environmental issues see Appendix.

A Sad Monument to Air Pollution.

"Cleopatra's Needle" may have survived three millennia in the Nile Delta, but 90 years in New York have done it in

Standing on a knoll in New York's Central Park is a tall granite obelisk, two of its sides covered with hieroglyphics and the other two blurred by erosion.

A timeworn object, you would say. But time had little to do with it. The obelisk and its twin, now in London, were erected in Heliopolis, Egypt, about 1500 B.C. and moved to Alexandria in 14 B.C., where they eventually acquired the name of "Cleopatra's Needles" (erroneously —she had nothing to do with them). There they stayed until the early 1880s, when the Khedive of Egypt sent one to London and one to New York, both in mint condition, as goodwill offerings.

New York's rains and frosts are hard on objects preserved by the aridity of the desert. But if that were all, the wear and tear on Cleopatra's Needle would be uniform. Instead, its south and west sides are worn away. These are the directions of prevailing winds in New York, and the inescapable conclusion—supported by experts—is that wind-driven chemicals have eaten away the surface.

"Ninety years in New York," says a park official, "have done more damage than 3,500 years in Egypt." The Needle is an unwitting monument to pollution.

Cleopatra's Needle, Central Park, New York. Detail of East Side. Photo: Morris Warman New York.

121

Cleopatra's Needle, Central Park, New York. Eroded West Side.
Photo: Morris Warmar, New York.

Cleopatra's Needle, Central Park, New York. North Side left
and eroded West Side. Photo: Morris Warmar, New York.

122

Destruction of Art at Home

Flood-damaged statues in Florence, Italy . . . an air-eroded Cleopatra's Needle in Central Park . . . what has been lost is irreplaceable. To bring the message home, have your art restorer develop an exhibit showing how outdoor sculpture or other works of art owned by your museum are being damaged by pollution. Indicate measures your museum is taking for protection, and the cost of these.

Plants and Human Ecology

Plants are the earth's source of oxygen and are the consumers of carbon dioxide. Green plants use the carbon dioxide produced by both natural respiration and combustion, and the ever increasing amounts of it produced by man's fuel burning and incineration. Plants also absorb other gaseous pollutants into their leaves and collect particulate matter on leaf and stem surfaces. Unlike carbon dioxide, however, these other pollutants are not used by plants in photosynthesis but rather are harmful. In excessive amounts they cause damage and death.

Displays can be designed to dramatize the processes of oxygen production and carbon dioxide consumption by plants. For example, growing grass on a 50 by 50 foot plot produces enough oxygen to meet the needs of a family of four, whereas it would require one to two dozen trees to produce enough oxygen to remove the CO_2 produced by one automobile.

The similarities in the ways that plants and air conditioning machines condition and clean air can be graphically shown in museum exhibits. The superiority of plants over commercial air conditioners should be stressed; plants, unlike air conditioners, remove gaseous pollutants and condition the air efficiently with no drain on overburdened electrical power sources which are, themselves, sources of pollution.

Design an exhibit to show that plants generally have a lower tolerance to air pollution than do humans, and that plants are, therefore, used to monitor pollutants. Because different gases produce distinctive symptoms visible on leaves, the presence of these often colorless and odorless gases can be detected, identified, and their sources located. Museums can exhibit plants damaged by pollution, preferably plants grown in the community at or near the building. Petunias are ideal for monitoring demonstrations; they are highly sensitive to a wide spectrum of pollutants, easy to grow, attractive and familiar to everyone. They can serve a dual role as a colorful component of museum landscaping and a dramatic exhibit of atmospheric deterioration.

"There's Cash in That Trash"— (A Symposium)

Call on economists and businessmen in your neighborhood to help develop a program to examine pollution and ecology from the economist's point of view. Consider this dual theme: "The High Cost of Pollution" and "The Profitability of Cleaning up the Environment." A seminar, lecture series, debate, or workshop could bring a new audience to your museum.

Discussion can include evaluation of steps being taken in the community to improve the quality of the environment. Specific examples can be cited to show that it is economically, as well as ecologically, sound to develop anti-pollutant systems and take corrective measures.

Perhaps not, if...

It has been hypothesized that the decline of the Roman Empire was due in large part to lethargy and inertia brought on by lead poisoning: the wealthy rulers used lead pipes and lead dishes — and under the effects of the resulting low-grade poisoning, guided a mighty nation to its demise. An environmental pollution story for a history museum? — yes. A parable for our own future? Perhaps not, if . . . .

chapter 4 / creating and building environmental exhibits

Creating and Building Environmental Exhibits
Principles of Environmental Exhibition

G. Carroll Lindsay
Director of Museum Services
New York State Museum

From the last decade of the nineteenth century until the middle of the twentieth, large, well-managed museums generally agreed upon the function of the museum as described by George Brown Goode, first director of the United States National Museum: collection, preservation, research, and interpretation. Each of these four elements of the museum function received about equal emphasis.

Research included the publication of research results. Interpretation included the interpretive exhibition of collections and various educational activities. The museum's efforts followed the descriptive and quantitative approach that characterized nineteenth-century academic endeavor. Research into scientific specimens dealt primarily with the description of scientific objects and their identification in forms of genus, species, provenience, and the like. Research into historical, cultural, or aesthetic objects also centered upon their description, origin, and use. Comparative studies generally extended only to the discussion of physical similarities or differences. The emphasis of research was on investigating the inherent characteristics of the object.

The interpretation of objects also concentrated upon their inherent characteristics. Thus, labels in museum exhibits dealt with such information as length, width, weight, material, place of origin, scientific name, and where possible, with the history of a given object. Only secondary attention was given to the relationship of one object to another, to a group of objects, or to ideas.

During the period between 1870 and 1940 museum interpretive practice did develop two significant devices aimed at presenting objects in relatively broad perspective. These

Life group of American Moose. New York State Museum.

devices, the full-size life group or habitat group and the so-called "period room," allowed related objects to be exhibited together in a manner emphasizing their relationships rather than their disparity. Both of these simulations of actual environments have proved useful and exceedingly popular with museums and their visitors.

However, the life group, the period room, and similar representations of a given environment are not adequate as devices to explain the interaction of human and natural forces affecting the total environment. A life group or habitat group must isolate a particular segment of time and space, but the conditions obtaining in that time and space are often influenced by actions that occurred far distant from the space in question. A habitat group may, for example, display the animal and plant life at the mouth of a river. The condition of the river at that point and its effects upon the life it supports may have been seriously affected by pollution that took place far upstream. Such a habitat group is adequate to describe and quantify the conditions at a given moment at the river mouth; it is not adequate to explain the relationships between those conditions and other conditions obtaining in another space and time.

The matter of space and time relationships is critical to the understanding and interpretation of many phenomena of human activity and natural forces. Objects and specimens, the unique resources of museum interpretative programs, also represent a particular time and space. For this reason it is seldom possible to use an object or specimen alone as the device for explaining its relationship to other objects or to abstract concepts. In the past the

127

museum relied upon the printed label to convey information the object itself could not communicate. But since the amount of printed material the visitor will absorb is limited, explanations of the kind necessary to relate an object to other objects or concepts could not be satisfactorily communicated. This fact, plus the traditional museum orientation toward merely descriptive and quantitative interpretation, limited the effectiveness of exhibits that had to depend primarily on the printed label. Thus the message of

Life group of Beaver. New York State Museum, Albany.

the life group or habitat group, reduced to its essentials, was simply that all the objects or specimens seen in such a display occurred in spatial and chronological proximity.

It is critical to the success of exhibits on the subject of human ecology and environmental pollution that the concept of exhibition be expanded beyond description, quantification, and the isolation of time and space.

Since 1950 museums have made ever-increasing use of other devices that can be helpful in demonstrating relationships between things, peo-

ple, and ideas. Among these devices are films, slides, tape recordings, and a variety of combinations of these, often used in association with actual objects. The ability to use these sophisticated audio-visual and multi-media devices is limited only by the museum's budget and the imagination of its staff. It is essential, however, that museums recognize that, like the older life group and period

Mastodons. New York State Museum.

rooms, the new forms of presentation are no more than vehicles for the communication of information. Even the most innovative applications of audio-visual and multimedia presentations are not necessarily adequate substitutes for other forms of communication.

In determining the communication device that will most effectively convey a given message, primary attention should be given to the content of the message and the audience toward which it is directed. Museums do not always fully appreciate that in their interpretative role they are essentially in the business of communication, and that as communicators they have the opportunity (if not always the funds) to use almost every means known to the

128

communication industries: print, broadcast, film, or various combinations. In addition they have a unique opportunity to make creative use of actual objects in their communication efforts.

The remarkably wide choice of media at the museum's disposal makes its decision about which one medium to use, or which combination of media, especially complex. Whatever the choice, be it an individual object, habitat group, slide, motion picture, or any combination of these, the message the museum wishes to communicate must be well conceived and of interest to the audience. Even the most interesting media can convey a message the audience will find dull, unimportant, or irrelevant. It may surprise many museum managers to learn that there are a number of expensive, sophisticated, and very dull audio-visual and even multi-media presentations to be found in museums. The fact that there are also many dull presentations of this kind to be seen in industrial and trade shows should remove doubt, if any exists, that electronic sophistication alone can guarantee good communication. Only when the message, the media, and the audience are considered together does the presentation achieve outstanding success. An example is seen in the American Museum of Natural History's Centennial exhibition "Can Man Survive?" a multi-media presentation using films, slides, sound, printed labels, graphics, and objects, provocatively describes the threat facing mankind through the destruction of our natural environment. This presentation represents major innovations in museum interpretation; the technological advances, although significant, are quite secondary in importance to the innovative philosophical concept which is the basis for the entire presentation. Here, for the first time, a major museum has devoted a significant portion of its interpretative activity to a non-descriptive, non-quantitative program of interpretation. Nowhere in "Can Man Survive?" does one find a single object described by sound or label in descriptive or quantitative terms! Equally remarkable for a museum presentation, even the subject itself, environmental pollution, is nowhere discussed in a precisely descriptive or quantitative manner. The presentation opens with a simple yet dramatic statement that man's survival depends upon an adequate supply of food, water, and air. Not a word about how much of these a man requires—how many gallons of water, pounds of food, and cubic feet of air we consume in a given time. Simply and directly the opening film sequence states that man depends upon these three essentials for survival. Precise description and quantification are entirely unnecessary to the communication of this message. Indeed description and quantification would vitiate the effectiveness of the message. Visitors are not interested in, nor would they be likely to remember, any information about calories, carbohydrates, protein, vitamins, or minerals. Instead the simple message, "man needs food, water and air," immediately produces interest among the audience, for each person relates instantly to this highly personal need. The remainder of the presentation shows

129

the effects of pollution upon air, water, and food and indicates that the visitor himself is responsible for both the pollution and for its prevention. The presentation nowhere describes or quantifies the precise kind or amount of pollution, nor does it undertake to discuss the effects of particular pollution in a particular place or upon particular air, water, or foodstuff. None of this is necessary to a ready comprehension of the message that man is now polluting his air, water, and food at a dangerous rate.

the environmental pollution problem. The exhibit technique has become an essential element of the message to be conveyed. The urgency of the environmental pollution problem is conveyed by the manner and technique by which the problem is presented, rather than by mere factual statements that the problem is critical and urgent.

It takes twenty minutes to view the exhibition. One goes first into a cool spacious environment with pleasing films showing the interdependence between animals and their

"Can Man Survive?" Centennial exhibition, American Museum of Natural History. Courtesy: Dimension Communications, Inc.

The design of the exhibit and its extensive use of motion pictures, slides, and sound create an atmosphere of movement and immediacy that emphasizes the critical nature of

natural surroundings. The next scenes depict the development of man's technology and progressively, his intrusion on the natural environment. The sounds accompanying the scenes get louder and the space in which the visitor can move gets smaller. With an atmosphere of increasing tension, the exhibition shows the horrors of an already overpopulated world and the disgusting intrusion of man-created wastes. The visitor is bombarded by shouts, cries, slogans, flashing lights, discordant music, unrelenting noises, and a feeling of stuffiness. He finds himself bumping into other visitors; the path appears to be blocked by junk. Since up to 300 people an hour can, and often do, go through the exhibition, there is a feeling of herding that reinforces the visual and auditory messages of too much garbage, too many pollutants, and above all, too many people. At the end of the tunnel the visitor is told that the solution to the problems he has experienced depends on him.

"Can Man Survive?" which opened in the spring of 1969, took two years to prepare and cost $650,000. The exhibition area is suspended without interior support in a Japanese-built Takanaka Truss, a clear-span frame that was used for the first time in the United States for this purpose.

Six films, 800 slides, some of which are used repeatedly, and eight sound tapes are used. A staff of six persons is required to operate the exhibition. The admission fees are $1.00 for adults, 50 cents for children, and 35 cents for members of school groups. Teachers are encouraged to visit the exhibition before bringing classes, so that they can provide orientation in advance of the class trip.

"Can Man Survive?" represents several new trends in museum exhibition. First, it deals not with an object or group of objects but with a condition. Second, it deals with this condition (environmental pollution) in abstract rather than descriptive or quantitative terms. Third, it not only uses contemporary multi-media devices not only as elements of its presentation, but relies upon the overall effects of these devices for the communication of part of its message. Fourth, and as a result of the three foregoing, it escapes the limitations imposed by displays that isolate space and time.

These four characteristics are necessary for the success of any museum exhibit that sets out to deal with conditions rather than simply with three-dimensional things. Since the subject of human ecology is a condition rather than a thing, exhibits on human ecology must be planned along the following guidelines:

1. That the condition, rather than the things that exist under the condition, is the central theme of an ecological exhibit.
2. That the exhibit deal with the condition in the abstract and not with materials that attempt to describe or quantify the condition precisely.
3. That the design of the exhibit and of its various individual units serve to aid in communicating the message the exhibit attempts to convey.
4. That individual displays within the exhibit avoid the presentation of isolated space and time unless the space-time relationships between disparate displays are inherently obvious.

The process of planning and designing exhibits following these guidelines will be different from the planning and designing process that produces descriptive and quantitative exhibits dealing primarily with things. This difference may be compared to the difference between the written essay and the photographic essay. Too often exhibits take the form of a written essay using things as illustrations. A photographic essay, on the other hand, uses pictures not to illustrate points but as the vehicles by which the points are stated without recourse to any written text. This means that the photographs must be chosen with extreme care for their inherent capability to communicate on their own, unaided by text. Similarly in planning the kind of exhibit that will dramatically convey a message about human ecology and environmental pollution, the components must be chosen for their ability to communicate by themselves. If the visitor's interest is consumed in identifying the object rather than in receiving its contribution to the message the exhibit is attempting to communicate, the exhibit will not succeed. Thus objects that must be described or quantified before the visitor can understand them fail as devices to communicate an ecological message. Museums, which traditionally deal in the descriptive and quantitative presentation of objects or things, can learn to use three-dimensional things in other ways. Some museums have already begun to do so.

The potential of museums to create exhibits dealing with the conditions affecting human ecology is very great. The realization of this potential requires a new look at how three-dimensional objects and specimens can be used to communicate ecological messages. Once the technique is clear, the display of three-dimensional materials supported by other communications devices available to the museum can place museums in the vanguard of ecological education.

Conceptual Exhibits on the Problems of the Human Environment

Charles E. Roth, Director of Education, Hatheway School of Conservation Education, Massachusetts Audubon Society

As an educator, I am interested in the uses of museums. Over the years I have been concerned about some of the things I have seen, and have hoped that some changes perhaps might be made. Despite the sophistication of many museum exhibits, the casual visitor—not the person who comes in with a group, but the individual, casual visitor—still comes to a museum as if it were primarily a freak show; he comes to "ooh" and "ah." We don't like this, but it tends to be true.

We have to do some thinking, therefore, about how we are going to reach out to this audience, particularly in the field of environment. Museums generally exhibit objects, but we need to help people find meaning in the objects, and we need to think about the composition of the audience for whom we are designing exhibits. In my own organization, when we argue from time to time over the preparation of a new exhibit it is because we are designing it for our peers instead of for the people who are going to view it. The arguments are not about how it is going to be received by the public, but about what our colleagues think of it; and the question becomes "If I simplify it a little bit more, will it somehow diminish my professional respectability?"

There must be a balance, I think, a play between the objects to help the viewer see the meaning of those objects. Many of the objects we show have meaning to *us* after many years of experience in the field, but a viewer who does not have a wealth of prior background needs a great deal of explanation. Some people feel that we should put the exhibits together with long labels, put chairs in

"Winterfest". Massachusetts Audubon Society Display, 1967. Photo: Calvin D. Campbell.

front of them, and let people sit down and read. I don't agree with that view. People will not read lengthy labels, because that is not what they came to a museum to do. A museum should not be an extensive textbook, although many of the exhibits I have seen are just that. Rather, we must look at what we can do in a slightly different way. We must narrow what we are attempting to something that is manageable and comprehensible, even if some people would call it a ridiculous minimum.

In teaching ecology, for example, we need exhibits on environments that tell not only about the Arctic and the tropics, but that tell about the world just outside the door of the museum. There have to be exhibits that tell us not only about the unusual and the far away, but that tell us about the here and now as well. Moreover they must tell us about it in such a way that, beyond the factual information they give, they change our perception of the world so that it is different when we leave the museum. This takes some doing, and perhaps the best way to explain is by examples.

The first is a very simple exhibit, one that many of the nature centers already do. Stand at a window, take a wax crayon, and outline the trees, plants, buildings, and other objects that you can see. Then draw in arrows and words to indicate the cycles that are going on out there, demonstrating the exchange of oxygen, the water cycle, the nitrogen cycle, perhaps a simple food chain. People looking through your window are suddenly confronted with what is happening outside, and, hopefully, when they go out of doors they will retain the impression of what is happening and will look at the world in a new way.

133

For an example of an exhibit that will show ramifications of actions, we can take a simple act, such as the purchase of an automobile. First we can trace back all the materials that went into it. Then we can consider all the ways in which automobiles are shaping our environment, all the ways in which they are consuming oxygen, all the ways they are polluting. We might end up with a whole museum devoted to the automobile. It would be doing considerably more than exhibiting antique cars, although we might attract antique car buffs who would learn about the changing effects on the environment of the automobile through time.

We can look at art and air pollution. Many outdoor sculptures in our museums are already suffering from the effects of chemicals in the air. We can call this to people's attention and ask them to begin to look at the buildings they pass every day. What is happening to them? Where are the damaging chemicals coming from? What are they doing to other objects? To people?

Andre Derain, "Three Trees"; (1923?). Oil on canvas, 36 x 32-1/8". Collection, The Museum of Modern Art, New York, Gift of Mr. and Mrs. Sam A. Lewisohn.

We can also, in some of our museums, show how art has influenced our perception of the environment. For instance, the English landscape painters shaped what people visualize when they think of a "nice landscape." A wild area is not a nice landscape for most people because it hasn't become normative to them. The idea that people have of landscape has been formed by our artists instead of the other way around.

We need simple exhibits on interactions that will give people the technique by which they can look for interaction in their environment. I suspect that people know more about lions and tigers than they know about cockroaches and rats. They may have had more experience with the latter, but they don't understand them. A simple exhibit on pigeons can help us look at the world around us by showing that the pi-

Jacob Van Ruisdael, "Wheatfields". Oil on canvas, 39-3/8 x 51-1/4". Collection, The Metropolitan Museum of Art, New York, Bequest of Benjamin Altman, 1913.

geons' food supply results largely from man's slovenly habits, and that the answer to the pigeon problem is not poisoning them but rather changing the environment of pigeons, which of course means changing some of our habits.

These are the kinds of things we need. They are simple. In fact they are so painfully simple that you usually find them in small museums that don't have enough money to build big exhibits and so end up doing this kind of thing.

Another type of exhibit that may be potentially useful in this field is the comparative exhibit where we set up examples of things that are going on in the environment. We might have an exhibit of the kinds of pollution, or of life in polluted waters, and people who are interested can go out and look at their own environment, find materials,

Miriam Dickey, Urban Conservation Center, 1969. Photo: Ted Polumbaum.

and actually bring them to the museum to compare with the things on exhibit to find out more about what is going on in their environment. It is to be hoped that this type of exhibit and the exhibits already mentioned will also lead people to books, because the exhibits will have stimu-

lated, created concern, and given the museum visitor some conceptual frames with which he can look at the world in a new way, and go on to explore and grow.

I hope, also, that this type of thinking will permeate some of the new museum concepts. For example, as an educator I would like to see a museum get away from the idea of a hall of fishes and a hall of anthropology that talks about fishing peoples and put them together to show how the life history of the fish is re-

Stony Brook Nature Center Day Camp, 1967. Photo: Robert Bernath.

lated to the techniques that must be used to catch it, how the fish shapes man's perception of the environment, the kind of art work that comes out of it, and the life styles that emerge from it. The result would be a hall on the relationship of man to a particular area of the environment. I would like to see museums look at the way in which dif-

135

ferent cultures have reacted to the same problems, and I would like to see them come up with something that ties man together with his environment, instead of artificially pulling them apart and placing the separated parts into little pigeonholes, as we have done for all too long.

All our museums can change their emphases slightly to put more emphasis on the environment, and they can do it simply. It just takes a little imagination. One of the simplest and most effective exhibits I have seen, and I have seen it duplicated several times, was a small exhibit in the Bronx Zoo that asked you to look into a cage to see the most dangerous animal in the world, and when you did you saw your own image in a mirror. This, of course, is the crux of the whole matter. Man is indeed the most dangerous animal in the world. He is dangerous, first of all, because he doesn't recognize that he is, in fact, an animal. But he is. He is an animal with his own species' specific traits that make him unique, just as a gazelle or a cheetah is unique. We do have the uniqueness of cultural heritages which also shape our environment, but because we have the potential for maneuvering and manipulating environments, of increasing our populations by decreasing our death rates, we are indeed— beyond any doubt—the most dangerous animal in the world. Think of that and ponder it the next time you look in a mirror.

Practical Exhibit Materials and How to Use Them

Prepared by the Exhibit
Department of the California
Academy of Sciences

Textural Materials

Textural materials mixed with a water-base paint may give a unique and pleasing surface, especially useful when a particular exhibit is subject to handling by the public. Grease and smudges do not show.

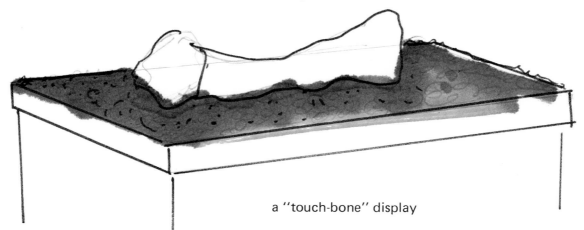

a "touch-bone" display

Crushed walnut shells; broken cork, and similar light-weight materials are recommended; simply mix into desired paint and brush on surface.

Rubber Cement

Rubber cement is a handy tool for masking surfaces that cannot take tapes—afterward, simply rub off with a finger, or use a hardened patch rolled into a ball to "pick up" excess cement.

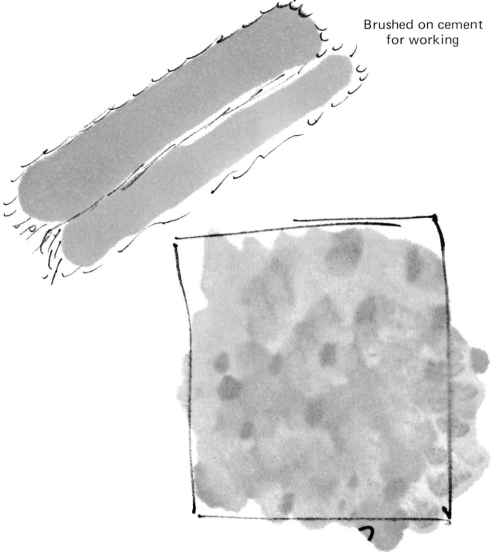

Brushed on cement for working

You can achieve interesting effects by using rubber cement with paint; apply some cement, then paint over it (water-base paints work best). Apply the cement in a "spotty" fashion to allow some of the paint to reach paper or surface. When paint is dry, pick up this cement, and either apply a fresh patch and paint again or simply apply more paint. Experimentation will result in many interesting effects.

Slides

A slide projector may be used to produce large graphic-drawings, silhouettes, etc., of whatever subject is desired . . . subject slides are available commercially yet personal satisfaction may be greater if you use amateur slides in your own collection.

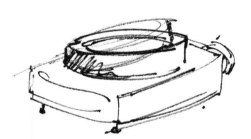

Letter forms, Symbols Numbers, Logos may all be blown up in this way. Slides may be either photos taken of these items or hand-drawings.

139

Self-adhesive paper

Self-adhesive paper, readily available at hardware, variety, or stationery stores, offers easy, fast, clean display usage at low cost. It can be drawn or painted on; even cut-outs from self-adhesive paper are easy. Use self-adhesive paper or floor plans, directories; use it on plastic or painted wood panels—care should be taken in cutting . . . a number 11 x-acto knife and a steel rule are recommended. A wide range of colors and patterns is available.

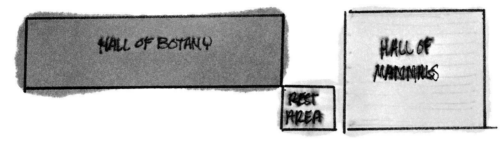

Use self-adhesive paper for artwork "masking" when irregular or curved shapes are desired; it will sometimes be more adequate than tape. Remember to be aware of the surface being washed; when contact paper is peeled off, it may pull up a papered surface behind it. Best use on enamel-painted wood, on plastic, or on glass.

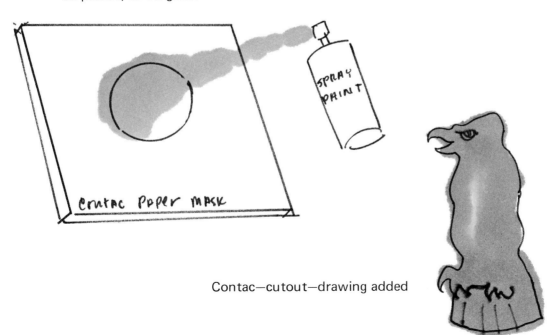

Contac—cutout—drawing added

Acetate

Thin sheets of acetate are available at most art-supply or stationery sotres, and are available in various widths, lengths and colors—the exhibitor may find them useful in such ways as these:

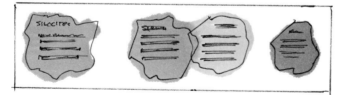

Clear or translucent sheet

Cut-outs mounted on plastic, back lit; since acetate is transparent, overlaps of color may yield some interesting effects.

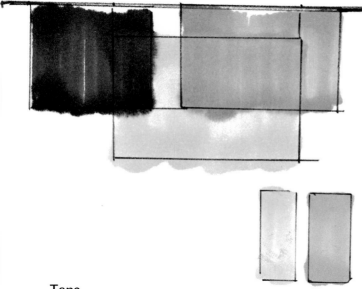

Sheets of acetate hung at varying distances from each other; the free flow of light is an asset in the effective use of acetate.

Clean, sharply-defined areas of color for graphs, charts, etc.; quickly achieved with the aid of a razor knife.

Tape

Many varieties of tape are available commercially which can be put to use as display elements in addition to their functional uses as adhesives.

Colored tapes used for large Letter Forms

The range of available widths (from 1/32 to several inches) and colors of these commercial tapes adds to their functions.

Thin tapes for framing panels, body of type.

— as design elements to precede areas of copy or text.

A line of tape may be just the touch needed to finish a temporary exhibit with a crisp, sharp, clear design element.

Transfer Type
Transfer type is easy to use for amateur "Do-It-Yourself" and traveling professional exhibits alike.

It can illustrate points, dramatize words, or make precision presentations. The result is worth the expense.

Plastic Letters
Plastic three-dimensional letters in many sizes are now available in art stores. They can be used for mounting with glue or as pin-ups.

Do-It-Yourself Projects
Mobiles
"Balance of Nature"

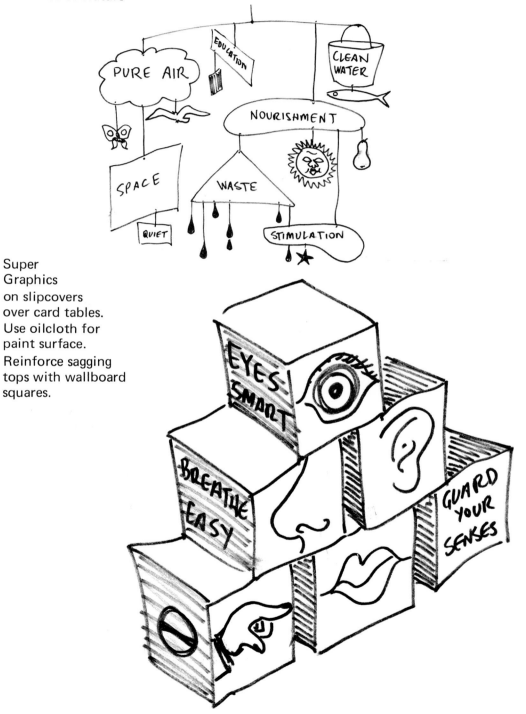

Super
Graphics
on slipcovers
over card tables.
Use oilcloth for
paint surface.
Reinforce sagging
tops with wallboard
squares.

Use wallpapers and self-adhesive papers to illustrate points .

Colorful seamless paper is available for exhibitors who want to become involved enough to do the project themselves. Magazines have a wide variety of ecological photos which make great collage material for elementary schools.

Magazine photos cut out and pasted on to "color" the monster.

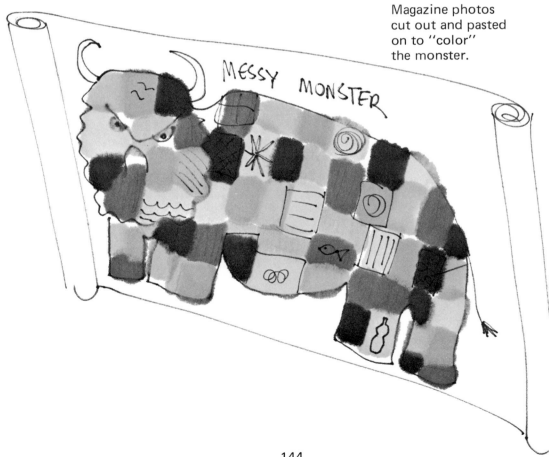

Panels
Set of flat panels, easy to assemble.

Traveling Exhibit

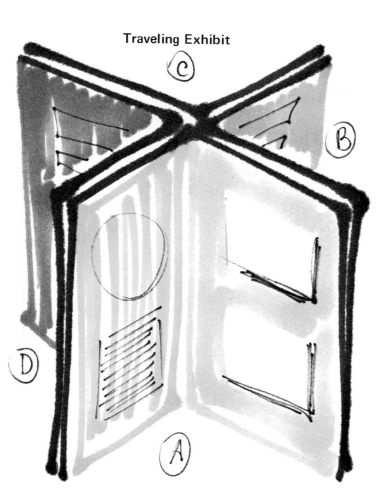

Four folded panels could travel together and when opened and displayed back-to-back, their rough shipping exteriors would be concealed.

Traveling Exhibit

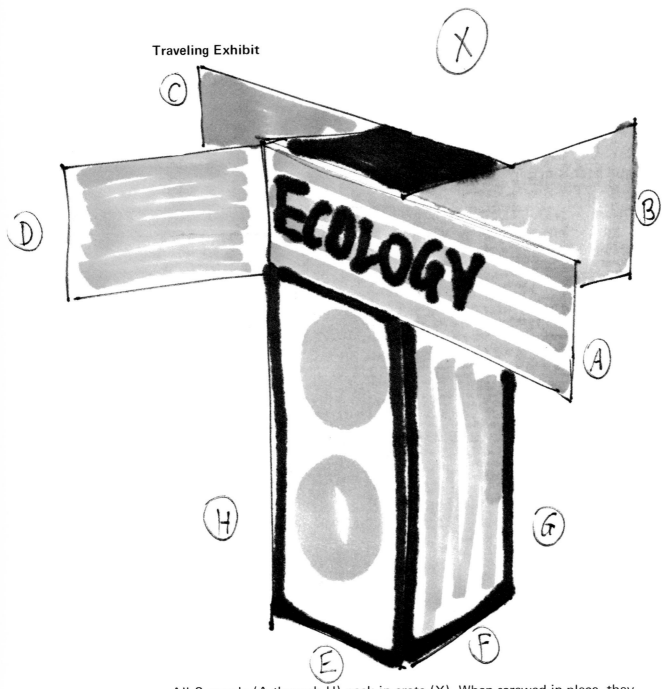

All 8 panels (A through H) pack in crate (X). When screwed in place, they completely cover the "travel-weary" crate (X), which serves as a free-standing pilaster. Total exhibit could include as many units as required. No lighting provided.

**Traveling
Exhibit**

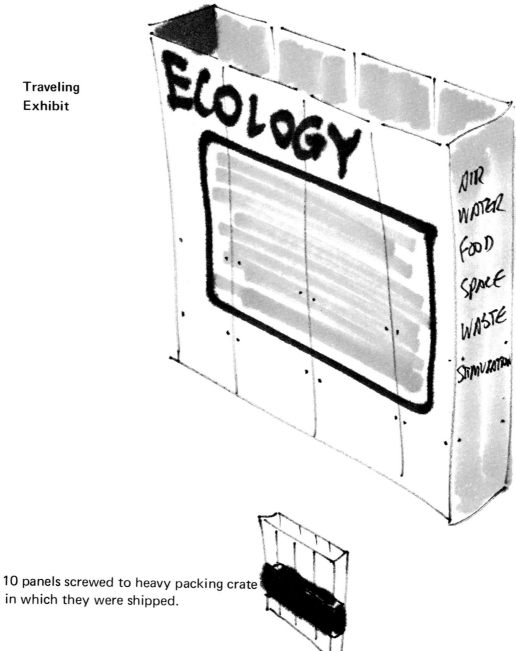

10 panels screwed to heavy packing crate
in which they were shipped.

Plexiglas and Acrylic

The properties of acrylics are similar to those of plexiglas.

These materials come in a variety of thicknesses and shapes, and in colors and textures. They may be purchased in sheet or block form.

Most sign companies have bins of discards from which samples can be obtained for experimentation.

Plexiglas has many uses. It can substitute for glass as covering for cases. It can be used to diffuse or manipulate light. It can be glued together like wood, or welded and sawed into shapes. "Scratch-proof" sheet plastic (clear) is now on the market. It can be heated in an ordinary home oven and bent into organic shapes. (See illustration) It can also be vacuumated or pressure-formed, although this requires special equipment.

Combined with other media, plexiglas is most useful. It can be silk-screened upon; etched (chemically or by hand); used as a mounting plate for objects such as hanging arrows, coins, rocks, tools, virtually anything requiring a suspended look.

Translucent panels make excellent diffusion panels for packing photos, labels, etc. These are available in many colors.

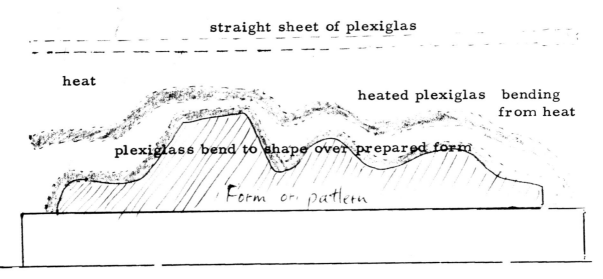

straight sheet of plexiglas

heat

heated plexiglas bending from heat

plexiglass bend to shape over prepared form

Form or pattern

Resins:

Clear coating resins, for general-purpose casting and laminating

Laminating resins—for use with glass cloth, and for creating thin sections with strength

Flexible impact resins—for making flexible castings or sections that have durability

Finish resins—for castings or coatings

Polyurethanes—for light-weight castings when organic or artistic effects are desired

Specimen-embedding plastics—to be used in displaying insects and small specimens

These resins may be combined with one another to obtain the desired plastic properties. They may also be colored, using special pigments made for polyesters.

Filler and Strengtheners for Resins:

Glass cloth, which comes in weaves, mats, or strands

Asbestos fibers

Thixotropic agents

Adhesives:

White glues

General epoxy glues

Quick-set epoxies—for strong glueing in minutes

Rubber cements and contact cements

Casting and Molding-Making-Materials

Rubber latex is available in various types, but a white latex with gelatin added is recommended. It cannot be reused, but its cost is moderate. It is suitable for making flexible molds. It may be painted into prepared plaster molds to make castings for such forms as snakes.

Polysulfides (collectively, sometimes called black tuffy) show little shrinkage, but are quite expensive and not reusable.

Silicones are also expensive and not reusable.

Moulage is useful for making life masks. It is very gentle, and renders good details. It is reusable.

Polyvinyl chloride is also reusable. However, it must be poured in a vacuum chamger, or on non-porous masters.

Plaster of Paris or hydrocal are the cheapest materials for making non-flexible molds of organic or perishable specimens. Burlap or straw may be added to the mixture to give strength.

Polyester resins—useful in flexible or non-flexible molds

Epoxies—for flexible or non-flexible molds

Hydrocal—a super-strength gypsum casting plaster

Plaster of Paris

Cement or concrete

Swedish hardware

These plastic bolts and washers can join corrugated panels quickly—no tools needed. From ARKIVA in Sweden. 25/mm polyetenstift med brickor.

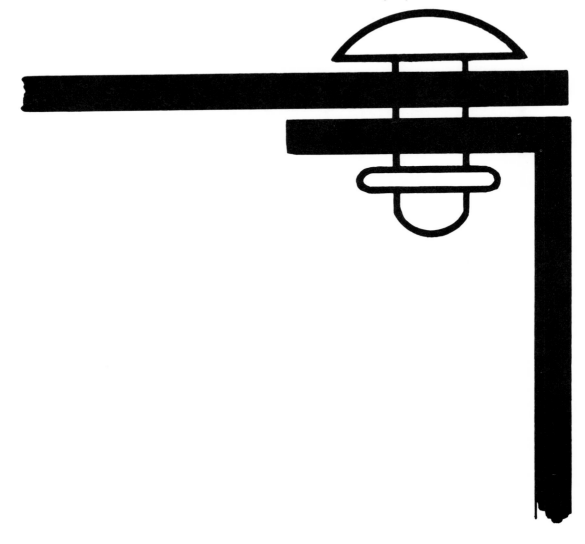

chapter 5 /added dimension through the use of films

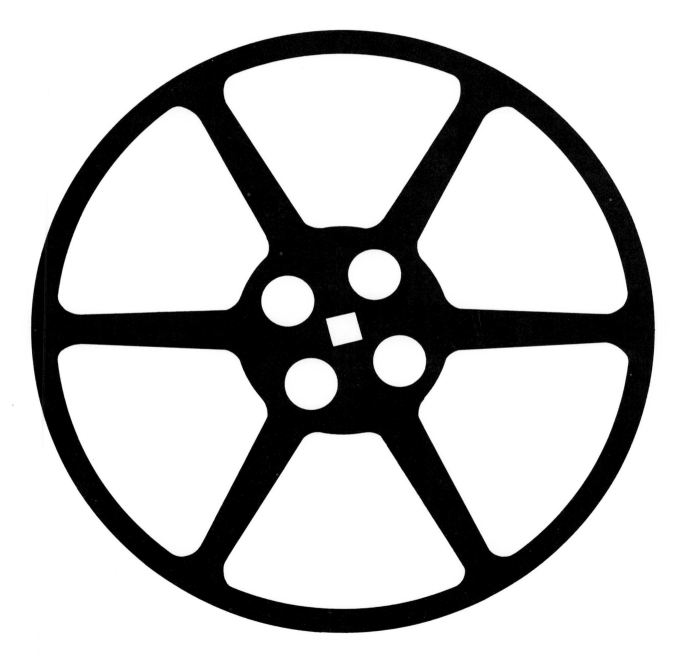

Added Dimension Through Films

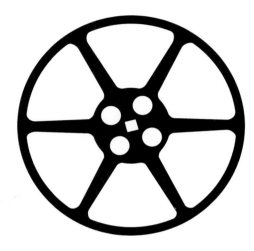

Wise use of various types of films can enrich many exhibits, from the simplest to the most complete.

In the past two decades great advances have been made in the development and automation of multimedia presentations. However, these spectacular achievements should not lead us to scorn less complex uses of films, or to overlook the contribution that new, relatively inexpensive equipment can make to everyday programs.

Traditionally, many museums appear to have regarded films—especially motion pictures—as an entity in themselves. For a long time their use was restricted largely to auditorium showings at specified hours. Audiences came to see a film as they would attend a play or a concert; or because they were interested in seeing one film as part of a series that dealt with film history or techniques.

This limited approach to the use of films is no longer valid. From the single slide through experimental motion pictures, films have much to offer in combination with other exhibit techniques.

A well-designed, simple multimedia presentation, for example, can be extremely effective, and can be produced at a remarkably low expense of time, money, and effort.

A simple exhibit might involve no more than slide projectors, a continuous-loop cartridge-loaded tape recorder, an amplifier, screens (or other surfaces), and speaker enclosures. (For more complex exhibits, motion picture projectors, 3-D slides and films, and horizontal slide projectors, for example, can be added.)

Excellent portable projectors, some of whose screens can be viewed in almost normal light, make it possible to set up a film as part of almost any exhibit. Some of them operate continuously and automatically. Others operate on insertion of cartridges, in a procedure so simple that a child can run them.

Slide film projectors, and most portable automatic projectors, are best suited to individual use, or for groups of classroom size. For this reason they are adaptable to use within an exhibit.

Certain film techniques may be more suitable than others for your exhibit. For example, many educators feel that when facts are to be conveyed, still pictures in the form of 35mm. slides, or filmstrips, are effective and least expensive. Presentations can be designed locally. Processing can be done by local laboratories or through the neighborhood camera store.

35mm. slides are the favorites of most amateur photographers, who often can be helpful in securing material. The film fits many small cameras.

Narrative for slide presentations can be recorded on tape or discs. However, except in highly sophisticated projection systems, it is usually necessary for an operator to make the necessary switches of

individual slides manually. This means that switches cannot be as rapid as on automated equipment, and there is more chance for error.

Individual slides also have the disadvantage of being highly susceptible to mistakes. They are easily dropped or mixed up, inserted upside down or backward. However, they have the advantage of flexibility, in that they can be arranged and rearranged to serve different purposes.

The *filmstrip*—either with titles printed on each frame, or with accompanying sound—is an economical and satisfactory method of still picture presentation.

Filmstrips may be made from original artwork, diagrams, acetate overlays to achieve an effect of animation, or transparencies. They can be photographed from miscellaneous materials, but it is more efficient and economical to use material that is all the same size. (If you are preparing your own material, take pains to compose it so that the elements of interest lie within the central two-thirds of the frame. The hoods of many projectors mask out edges. The ratio of artwork or photography should always be 3-vertical by 4-horizontal.)

Filmstrip frames must be photographed in sequence on an uninterrupted length of film. This requires professional equipment and expertise. However, a number of excellent laboratories specialize in this work, and in processing and printing filmstrips at reasonable cost. Once a printing master is made, duplicate prints are very inexpensive.

Filmstrip prints should always be especially coated for durability. Care should be taken to handle them only by the edges, never allowing the hands to touch the face of the film. Each print should be cleaned before and after showing. Use a fold of velvet, dampened with a film-cleaning fluid, and run the film through the fold. Also be sure to clean the gates and other parts of your projector before use. These precautions will avoid scratching and other damage to the print.

Filmstrips are easily stored in small cans and can be shipped by first class mail.

Legends to be imposed on filmstrip frames should be typed separately and sent to the laboratory along with the original artwork or photography. Do not attempt to photograph these yourself. This should be done at the same time as the sequential photography.

Legends should be at most three lines long, with no more than 35 characters to a line, including punctuation and spaces between words.

For automated equipment, the original tapes must be taken to a professional sound studio for insertion of signals.

Today sound studios are equipped to synchronize magnetic signals, along with original narration, on dual or 4-track tape. This combination is then transferred to a disc or duplicate monaural tape.

In planning filmstrips for use on modern automatic machines, you can change frames at intervals of only a fraction of a second, if desirable, making it possible to achieve an illusion of motion. Rapid flipping is valuable when you wish to achieve cumulative effects through superimpositions and in creating mood.

Articles and advertisements in such magazines as *Business Screen* and *Audio-Visual Education* will acquaint you with many models of projectors, including some of the more recent experimental types. Both magazines bind in postcards that can be checked for free literature about products.

These publications also list companies which produce filmstrips commercially and review new programs that are available.

A significant development in audiovisual education is the introduction of cassette television. It is said that these systems will convert any standard television set into a "phonograph for the eye." A cassette is placed on a player much the way a record is placed on a phonograph. Cassettes can be purchased individually and played back through a television set which has been equipped with a video cassette player. A cassette will play continuously as in a motion picture, or in the case of at least one model, will play frame by frame. A single cassette can contain a full hour program.

Players and cassettes are being introduced this year. The next model will make it possible to film programs directly from a television set. *With permission of the copyright owner* programs appropriate to environmental education might then be added to the resources of your museum direct from newscasts and documentaries. It is too soon to judge the full impact of this medium but it will add an exciting new dimension to the creating and building of exhibits. For information on ordering cassettes, please see Appendix.

In general, 16mm. prints have become the norm for educational use. Their quality is now so good that they can be projected on large screens, yet they are adaptable for small spaces.

There is an amazing wealth of 16mm. motion pictures available. Some have been made by industries or organizations and are loaned free or at low rental costs. Others have been reduced from television network documentaries or from theatrical films. See Appendix for information about sources.

Employment of 16mm. sound films within the floor-space of an exhibit may present two problems:

(1) cutting down the light so that images on the screen will be clear; 2) keeping the sound low enough so that neighboring exhibits are not affected.

One possible solution is the use of draperies to form a "walk-in" area and to cut down on both light and sound. Another possibility is the construction of folding screens made of the pegboard-type insulating material used for regulating sound in broadcasting studios. If these are constructed with sufficient stability, their outer side can be used for hanging exhibits.

In recent years the improvement in the quality of 8mm. film has made this economical size increasingly popular for school and institutional use. Projectors are small, self-contained, and suitable for individual use and small-group viewing.

155

The Fairchild Mark IV is the most widely used. It costs about $400.00, and film for it is mounted within cartridges which are practically fool-proof for handling. The duration of the film in any one cartridge may range from 3½ up to 30 minutes. Once inserted, it plays continuously. The image is rear-projected onto a small television-like screen.

Technicolor Inc. makes a similar machine, but with a separate screen. It costs about $200.00 and the cartridges for it are cheaper than for the Fairchild. Both machines include sound. They are particularly desirable for the utilization of "single concept" films of short length.

Another highly interesting recent development in educational procedures is the wide use of *filmmaking* as an educational tool. Children as young as kindergarten age are capable of using 8mm. cameras to make

their own films. The technique is used for teaching, reading, and writing, as well as for teaching science and other subjects.

Raw materials children may use for photography include direct drawing on film; animation, stop-motion photography, and other techniques that were once considered the exclusive province of the professional.

The Communications Center, Teachers College, Columbia University, New York has produced a fascinating film on these techniques.

Results emanating from many young filmmakers' groups are remarkably good photographically, relevant to social problems, and exceedingly fresh in concept.

Finally, fascinating ideas can be drawn from close observation of some of the "Teaching Machine" techniques used in schools and industry. Some of these depend on hardware and may combine films and other media. A number of companies (General Learning; Analearn) are producing materials of this nature. Of course, no teaching machine can be any better than the "software" with which it is supplied.

Multimedia Presentations

Mark out one area of your exhibit space, and set up:

1. 3 slide projectors
2. a continuous-loop cartridge-loaded tape recorder
3. an amplifier
4. screens (or surfaces) strategically placed for each projector
5. 2 speaker enclosures.

Such a system is capable of displaying a five-minute presentation with a minimum of attention and servicing. Its operation should be within the scope and capability of staff or volunteers.

As visitors proceed through the exhibit, they come upon the multimedia area. Without warning, display lights begin to dim, and images begin to appear on surfaces designed as screens. They dominate the attention of the visitors, and as the sound track carries the presentation along, the synchronized slide story unfolds. When the placing of screens has been geometrically planned for informal viewing, and the program is of short duration, it can have an impact out of all proportion to the effort involved. It need not be expensive, and it offers a very high yield per dollar invested.

As the staff grows increasingly adept in handling multi-equipment, more complex systems can be attempted, such as the addition of movie projectors, 3-D slides and films, and horizontal slide projectors.

There are no hard-and-fast rules for writing such a script. In the beginning, you may wish to use a horizontal format, with a column for each projector, and a righthand column for sound and narration. Timing can be shown effectively by spacing downward, as in a documentary motion picture script.

Many fine motion pictures have been made, showing the natural wonders of our nation. There are also excellent films centered around the arts.

It is not necessary to screen films in a large theatre. A small area of your exhibit space can be allotted as a "walk-in" theatre, and the film projected onto a portable screen.

By separating the area from the rest of the exhibit with draperies or portable screens made of the type of acoustical board used in broadcasting studios, you will be able to darken the area, and also keep sound at a level that will not disturb neighboring exhibits.

Showings can be scheduled for exact times, or the film can be run continuously during exhibit hours.

A Multimedia Show

America! Where Are You Now? has been described by environmental specialists as one of the best multimedia shows of its kind. Produced for Strategies for Environmental Control (a National Conference sponsored by the Association of the Junior Leagues of America, Inc. and the Junior League of Chicago), it is multi-image bombardment of the rape of the land.

The show contrasts unspoiled scenic beauty with smog-obscured skies, dead water and the chaotic urban development of debris-strewn cities, to the accompaniment of folk singers, jack hammers and hard rock.

Materials: 864 slides in 12 carousel trays (to be used with six dissolve units) for rear or front projection and audio tape. Running time: 28 minutes.

The Junior League of Westchester-on-Hudson has donated a copy of this presentation to the Hudson River Museum of Yonkers, New York, where it was shown beginning in the spring of 1971. Plans for future use include museum programs, town meetings and national conferences. For information write: Mrs. Donald E. Nick; Consultant on Communications; Association of the Junior Leagues of America, Inc.; 825 Third Avenue; New York, New York 10022.

chapter 6 / the emerging role of museums in environmental education

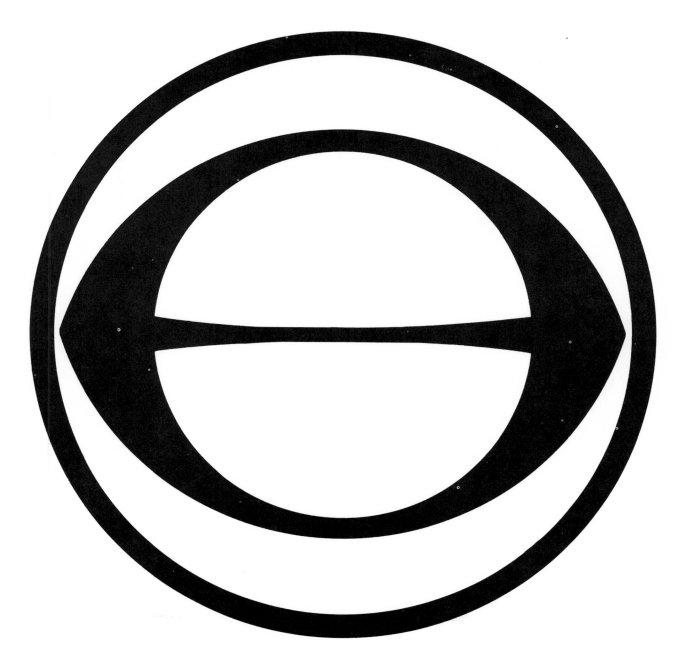

Emerging Role of Museums in Environmental Education

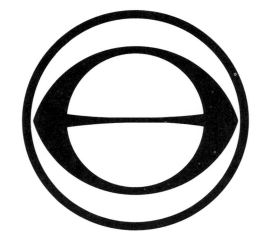

To an infant, the environment is a mixture of being hungry and fed, of being wet and dry, of feeling softness and warmth. Sights, sounds, odors, and touch are not distinct from one another but are interrelated. At first, in fact, an infant does not know what is *he*, and what is not. Adults have long since learned to distinguish the myriad sights, sounds, odors, and feelings by which they are bombarded. They have learned to separate them, and in doing so have lost the infant's capacity to perceive himself and the world around him as one.

If museums can help their visitors see that all elements in the environment—*all* elements—are interrelated, they will indeed perform a vital service.

Science and natural history museums are by definition engaged in an exposition of the natural world, but other types of museums can also reveal the environment—as it is, as it once was; as people saw it or made it; as living things evolved in it; as it could be, as it should be, as it will be.

The essays that follow speak to the specialized roles of museums in reminding man that the world is one—interrelated and finite.

Art Museums and Environmental Education

Charles Parkhurst,
Assistant Director,
The National Gallery

If the word *ecology* is to assume its fullest meaning (the entire house, the *oikos* in which we live), art museums become involved *de facto*.

The role of art in environmental considerations can easily be seen as an essential one if we construct our world view on a tripod. If the first leg is biological and the second technological, then the third certainly must be related to accomplishments in the visual world that man has made, remade, and, in many instances, unmade. Nomenclature is difficult, but since we refer to an organization of the environment in terms of sensory apprehension and perception, perhaps we can speak of the biosphere, the technosphere, and the aesthetosphere. It may be significant that in this return to the ancient Greeks some conceptual tendency of mind is inherent. In any event, our concern here is that man is causing pollution in all three areas of the environment. If we accept this as fact, and also accept that the problems of pollution already threaten to overwhelm us, we should propose immediate steps and offer practical devices to further our point of view. Among the leaders should be the art museums.

Since art is fundamentally anthropological, all man-made environments can be considered suitable areas of concern for artists and therefore for art museums. The part of the environment created and expressly organized out of chaotic matter is of special significance in containing and making visual man's essential tendencies of mind. Art is, in other words, a formulation in striking symbols—forms, shapes, colors—of what is *real* to man. The organizer is the artist, the reality so manifested is the art.

Art museums must point to and develop an awareness of the broader ecological significance of all artistic endeavor. Without detracting from their focus on art as art, they can also stimulate day-to-day awareness of the aesthetic rewards, or their deplorable absence, in each person's environment.

Art museums, like all other museums, educate subliminally through their exhibitions and overtly through their catalogs, public relations releases, and labels, and through the spoken word. The overt aspects are perhaps the ones that should be dealt with most immediately but let us mention here a few nuclear notions in the subliminal area of exhibitions.

Part of the energy of contemporary art has gone into the literal creation of *Environment* and *Things*. The works of such artists as Nevelson, Lichtenstein, Krebs, Gilliam, and many others are examples. There is no doubt that their creation has been a response to a deeply felt need on the part of many people. Some of these environments actually respond to activity, specifically to the activity of those entering the scene. Robert Rauschenberg, for example, has created an environment that responds with flashing lights to the sounds of persons passing it; by their presence, the people illuminate the environment he has made. Nature is excluded generally in this man-made world. It is, one can say, a techno-aesthetosphere.

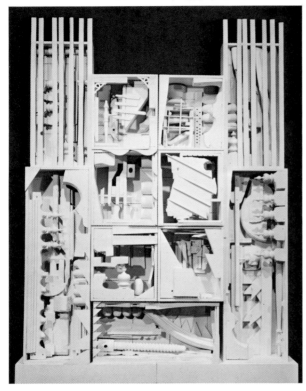

Louise Nevelson, "Dawn's Wedding Chapel II"; (1959). Painted wood. 115-7/8 x 83-1/2 x 10-1/2". Collection, Whitney Museum of American Art, New York, Gift of the Howard and Jean Lipman Foundation, Inc.

A wider overview of artistic activity might consider, as a broad ecological question, the concepts and ideas of man's relation to nature as manifest in art: man opposed to nature, for example, as in Romantic art; man reduced to nature's scale, that is, man naturalized, as in Roman art and the art of some other periods; nature remade by man, as in the Enlightenment Rococo where man appears in charge of nature; and finally man in charge of nature in the Merzbild and in Dadaism, from Schwitters onward.

A ubiquitous but often ignored environmental art form is the fountain. In its creation, sound and substance, light, motion, and color are imaginatively controlled. The philosophical premises and the meanings of fountains in our environment have probably never been dealt with, at least not adequately, although clearly they have both environmental and political implications.

Naturalism exists in all pictorial arts, including photography. First, art as an analog of nature. Next, there is man from nature, the biology of art, the pre-figurative or proto-art; one comes eventually here to Disraeli's question, "Is man an ape or an angel?"

And there are art and science together in the environment; a case in point is a series of exhibitions on the importance of color in our environment.

Also, historically speaking, several artists have dealt with the development of man—in particular, in the stages or the ages and cycles of man.

Thomas Cole, "Voyage of Life: Old Age"; (1840). Oil on canvas, 51-3/4 x 78-1/4". Courtesy, Munson-Williams-Proctor Institute, Utica, New York, Purchase.

Thomas Cole, Piero di Cosimo, and others all made ecological interpretations long before the word *ecology* was popular. These have been widely studied, but for educational purposes they might bear reexamination in the contemporary ecological context.

One element of environment that is dealt with frequently in art in various ways is the concept of time. Whether it be durational, ephemeral, past time, timelessness, or whatever, time as environment always rewards consideration.

In an art museum the designed environment—city planning, the linear city, the skyscraper, transportation and communications, the piazza and the square, urban sprawl, the typology of buildings, suburban fallout, and many more—are legitimate subjects for environmental exhibitions.

What about the effects of pollution on art, or that have been manifest in art. What, for example, is the meaning today of Monet's "Waterloo Bridge, Grey Day," or Turner's

Claude Monet. "Waterloo Bridge, Gray Day." Collection, National Gallery of Art, Washington, D.C., Chester Dale collection.

"Rain, Steam, and Speed," or the paintings of the Ashcan School? Much has been done with the images of pollution by our great photographers; and that is pollution as art. The visual images devised by the artist soon extend into other fields, however, such as commercial design, and in debased form, they batter our senses daily from all sides. As a major part of our environment, they are perhaps the prime example of art as pollution.

To some degree all art is ecological in character. To say this is not to suggest that ecological enthusiasm should supercede all other meaning in art, for the historical and philosophical implication of art is the sheer delight it provides in one or another way.

Something can be done with the art museum as an element of environment, a criterion, a model for the universe, and something can be done with the exhibition as an environment, *re ipse*. It may also be educational to consider and to discuss publicly the three major aspects of the role of art museums in the environment—the search and rescue role, the conservation and preservation role, and of course the interpretation role, in which one comes back to the broad question of the museum's role in relation to educational ecology.

A great many other questions can be raised for art museums in this ecological area: private art versus public art; or city planners versus architects; or the sacrifice of the individual to the overall plan, as in the beautiful city that leaves the poverty-stricken person without a personally expressive environment. Art museums must join with science and history museums in this educational endeavor. To do so is apropos, and it is timely. It is a new responsibility, and this is a new polemic.

It is clear that in line with what is proposed here man must be considered ecologically as more than a biological being. He is a historical, social, philosophical, and spiritual being too, responding to his environment in each of these contexts and at all levels, and capable as well of creating or destroying the aesthetosphere. It may be that the environment of the future will be entirely conceived as art; that is, man expressive and creative. Perhaps then the Existentialist point of view—that without art there is only chaos—will have more meaning.

Botanical Gardens and Environmental Education

William C. Steere
President
The New York Botanical Garden

Botanical gardens are concerned both with environment and with ecology in the basic sense of each word. A botanical garden is, among other things, a collection of plants; and plants furnish excellent experimental materials for teaching about the physical factors of the world in which we live.

The first and critical factor for plants is water. Unlike some small animals—such as the larvae of the clothes moth, which can derive adequate water for their processes from digestion of their food—no plants are able to survive in the total absence of water, even though some seeds may endure through many years of drought. Heat is a second critical factor for plants. In any area where

Courtesy, New York Botanical Garden, Bronx Park, New York.

the air or water temperature is always below freezing, only microscopic plants can grow. Although not critical in the same degree as water and heat, soil factors are also important.

Plants react perceptibly and often conspicuously to the physical factors that impinge upon them. The adaptation of plants to various combinations of habitat has led to evolution of many vegetational types—each one of which is characteristic of some special climate. It is easy to envision in the mind's eye several distinct types of vegetation that have adapted to particular climates.

In arid parts of the world, plants adapt to store water during the brief periods when it is abundant and conserve it during the long drought. Characteristic examples in the desert regions of the Old World, especially Africa, are euphorbias and membryanthemums, such as stone plants. The cacti occupy the same ecological niches in the New World.

Several major vegetation types exist in the United States: the northern coniferous forest; the eastern deciduous forest; the extensive midwestern prairies and western great

164

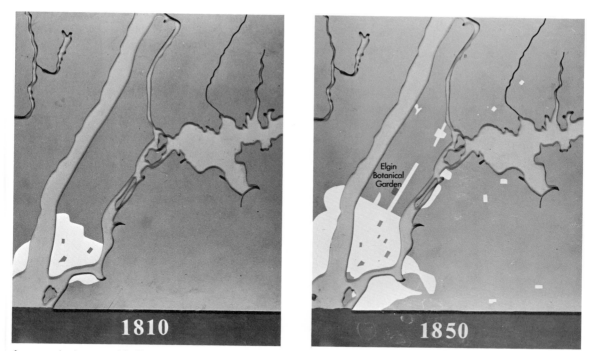

These four panels show graphically the disappearance of the natural vegetation and the increase of urbanization (white areas) in the five boroughs of New York City. They were prepared especially for an exhibit concerning the activities of The New York Botanical Garden at the New York World's Fair, 1964-1965, and were reproduced in the August, 1970 issue of "Garden Journal."

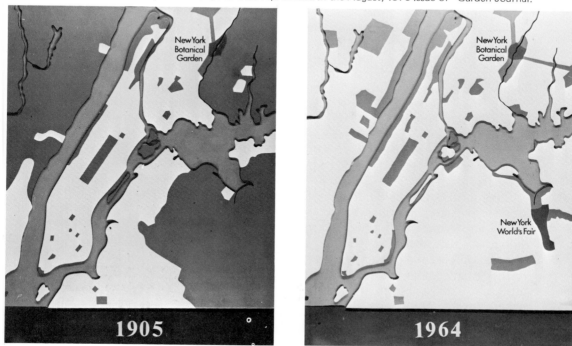

plains; the alpine vegetation of the Rocky Mountains, Cascades, and Sierra Nevada; the wet forests of the Pacific Northwest; the vast southwestern deserts and scrub forests; and the subtropical vegetation of our southeastern states.

North of the forest zone in the Northern Hemisphere lie great treeless plains, the Arctic tundra, in which the ground may be permanently frozen to depths of more than 1,000 feet. A specialized type of tundra exists on high mountains above timberline.

In the tropics are many kinds of forests. They range from evergreen rain forests in areas of continual rain to deciduous forests in areas where there is an extended dry season.

Botanical gardens present this diversity of habitats. The public can see characteristic types of vegetation growing in their natural habitats either out of doors or under glass.

Over the years, literally millions of school children have gained their first impression of a tropical rain forest or of a desert from visits to the New York Botanical Garden. Out of doors, they see the type of vegetation characteristic of their own climatic zone: groves of oak-hickory, beech-maple, and hemlock. This educational process has an impact on teachers, too.

Visitors also see the deterioration of environment that must be of concern to everyone. They can see how smog, and the pressure of too many people walking through the forest during many years, damage trees—especially the conifers. As in all other natural areas, the Botanical Gardens show the toll taken by long

droughts and occasional hurricanes.

Often botanical gardens are the only semiwild areas that are accessible to city children. They are the only places where children can experience a feeling of relationship to plants as important elements in their environment. For although they are given general science and general biology courses in the schools, children visiting the New York Botanical Garden are almost invariably impressed by the profusion of plants in forested areas and by the prodigality of plants in the conservatory. For the first time, they link up the fact that plants are the source of all energy to drive biological machines, including man, and the fact that plants are the source of all oxygen in the air, water, and earth.

Some museum exhibits at the New York Botanical Garden are consequently designed especially for school children. They now include displays of environmental significance and new exhibits being planned will place even more emphasis on environmental factors. For example, the Botanical Garden is establishing a new experimental program in ecology and environmental science designed specifically for school children. A full-time curator of environmental education has been employed. In-service courses will be offered to teachers, and the Board of Education will assign teachers to the Garden for training.

In addition to exhibits and programs concerned with general understanding of the environment, many of our specific technical activities coincide appropriately with the aims of a proposed new experimental arboretum to be dedicated to the betterment of mankind. For example:

Through careful observation we can gain a better understanding of the problems involved in the hardiness of trees. Our natural environment contains so many different influences, which operate on the organisms living within it, that to judge the effect of any one influence is difficult without scientific observation and instrumentation. A botanical garden can supply both in seeking answers to questions such as these:

What is the cause of death of trees in a climate to which they are only marginally adapted?

Is it too much heat in summer, or too low a temperature in winter?

Is the distribution of precipitation over the year important to its survival?

What about the amount of sunshine versus cloudy weather?

How important is the relative humidity of the atmosphere to the survival of certain species of trees?

Although tree genetics (or tree breeding) is a long-term activity, it can nevertheless bring hardier, more productive, or otherwise more desirable trees to the aid of mankind. Hybridization of corn and other cereals has resulted in tremendously increased yields of grains. (An outstanding example is the "miracle rice" introduced throughout the Orient by the Rice Institute in the Philippines, an endeavor supported by the Ford and Rockefeller foundations.) Grains, of course, are annual crops; every crop must come

from new seeds, from a new cross. Trees, on the other hand, are long-lived. A high-yielding cross would continue its beneficial effects over a period of many years.

Flowering trees and shrubs of the New York Botanical Garden, an oasis of fragrance, freshness, and beauty.

Many species of trees are close to the point of extinction. In order to protect trees from extinction, we urgently need to find out under what conditions their seeds can be stored for more or less indefinite periods.

The diseases and pests that attack trees are topics of environmental interest and importance. We have seen the devastation of American elms by the Dutch elm disease, and the virtual extinction of the American chestnut by chestnut blight. Just as the American Indians and Eskimos were decimated by measles and other normally nonfatal childhood diseases brought by European settlers, so standard European and Asiatic tree diseases destroy American trees that lack resistance to them. Extensive programs to select seedlings from crosses between species—one resistant and the other susceptible—will eventually result in hybrids that closely resemble the American species, but have a dominant factor for resistance. Unless this is accomplished, however, we will see the American elm wholly replaced by European and Asiatic species, and the American chestnut by Chinese species. We also need to keep a rigorous watch on other diseases of trees in order to control and prevent future epidemics, with their vast economic repercussions.

Some rule-of-thumb ideas on using trees to reduce noise already exist. However, no serious study has been made to test different kinds of trees on a large scale and at different densities, with a view to screening out noises. Information resulting from such research could be of inestimable value in the vicinity of airports, railroads, factories, and other producers of noise pollution.

The ability of forested areas to absorb toxic materials from the atmosphere, and to produce oxygen in sunlight, has long been known. The exact measurement of such functions has been very difficult, however, because of the size of trees. With modern equipment and materials, such problems can be solved.

These are but a few of the areas in which botanical gardens can bring their resources and knowledge to bear on the urgent matter of environmental education.

Urban Ecology and the Inner City Museum

Zora B. Martin
Assistant Director
Anacostia Neighborhood Museum

How does an inner city museum, barely three years old and run partially by children, teenagers, and adults who are traditionally non-museum oriented, deal with the problems of the urban dweller and his relationship to his environment? Are we to prepare an exhibit on air pollution and tell neighborhood domestics and day laborers to leave their cars at home or ride bicycles to their jobs in suburbia? If we consider an exhibition on population control, what do we say to those within our community who equate population limitation with genocide? Of what value would a display on organic gardening be to people piled high in the vertical ghettos of public housing? Or an exhibit on returnable bottles and phosphate-free containers to people who depend on food stamps to buy the most for the least?

These are questions that volunteers and staff members of the Anacostia Neighborhood Museum have been asking in the wake of the highly publicized ecology boom.

The Anacostia Neighborhood Museum of the Smithsonian Institution opened its doors in an abandoned movie theater in the fall of 1967. Located in a predominantly Black community, the Museum began as an experiment. Now it is no longer an experiment; it is a viable, forceful institution with strong community ties and a growing expertise in Black history and culture and urban problems.

Even to the most casual observer it is obvious that the Anacostia Neighborhood Museum is not a museum in the traditional sense of the word. Following the acquisition of a Mobile Division and two additional facilities to house both an Arts and Crafts Center and a Research Center and Library, we have become at once a museum, a multimedia center, a skills training facility, a meeting place for community groups, and a cultural arts center.

Anacostia Neighborhood Museum, Washington, D. C.

Our museum has been described as a living museum because of the involvement of people who live in its neighborhood. People take seriously the idea that a neighborhood museum means that ownership is vested with neighborhood people. Witness the fact that in the years since we opened there has been no vandalism here! And there are other examples. The Neighborhood Advisory Committee recently sent a proposal for an exhibit back to John Kinard, the director, with instructions that it be amended, expanded, and returned to them for final approval before the staff moved forward with its implementation. Our Youth Advisory Council, dissatisfied with current exhibits, worked with technicians in developing their own exhibit—"This Thing Called Jazz." A lot adjacent to the Museum that once was covered with garbage and trash has been transformed into a People's Park by neighborhood youth, and adults; it contains eight-foot photographs and murals of the neighborhood and those who live within it. The list is endless.

The area itself, predominantly Black, is also predominantly poor. Although spotted with high-rise luxury apartments and homes of the affluent, Anacostia consists largely of a juvenile population, inadequate schools and recreation facilities, and all of the poverty, misery, drugs, and crime seen in areas similar to ours across the country.

The Museum has succeeded in bringing together people of diverse racial, ethnic, and socioeconomic backgrounds. During one recent exhibit, on opening, an African ambassador rubbed shoulders with professional men and women of the community, long-time residents, former junkies, sneaker-clad teenagers, children, and winos. When the Museum hosted a reception for visiting foreign students, the neighborhood turned out in large numbers. Although no entertainment had been planned, before the evening ended we had seen a card trick demonstration and had participated in an old-fashioned foot-patting gospel songfest.

With this background in mind, it is clear that many of us who live in inner city areas tend to cast a wary eye in the direction of the current ecology inundation. Or perhaps it is simply that we look at our urban environment from a different perspective. We tend to think in terms of the lack of transportation rather than the presence of automobiles, buses, and air pollutants; rats and roaches rather than endangered species; drug abuse rather than questionable chemicals in our food; and the inability to purchase detergents with food stamps rather than the kinds of containers in which they are packaged.

In November, 1969 the children, teenagers, and adults of this Museum researched, designed, and installed a major traveling exhibition on rats.

Anacostia Neighborhood Museum, Washington, D. C.

Called "The Rat: Man's Invited Affliction," the evolution of the exhibit crystallized over a period of many months. Certainly everyone in our neighborhood was aware of the rat problem, but no one had put into words the idea of dealing with the question through an exhibit. Grad-

ually, though, the neighborhood peoples' hatred of rats began to show itself. For example, the Museum's white mice and gerbils frequently disappeared, and their remains always turned up in the cage of the snake housed in our small zoo. A pair of laboratory rats increased very rapidly by a litter of eighteen. In spite of the fact that they were favorites of the children, who even took baby rats home from time to time to board, to many of the older youth and adults they were an anathema. There were other incidents having to do with the Norway rat: one concerns a little boy who brought to school for "show and tell" a small rat he had found and kept at home in a box; another, the experiences of older teenagers who, having waited in a field after heavy rains for the rats to come out of their burrows, caught them, jammed firecrackers into their mouths, and tried to blow their brains out. This is the environment for us, and this is how many of us relate to it.

Many have asked whether the rat exhibit really did any good. Is 67 per cent of the total area of Anacostia still infested with rats? The answer to the latter is probably yes. Certainly, there has been no massive war on rats either by citizens of the area or by public health officials, and this may be yet another sign of the times in which we live.

In our small area there are many who believe that the problems of the inner city remain the problems of the inner city until and unless they spill over into the perimeters of the outer city. Witness the tragic and decimating problem of drug abuse among inner city youth that has

170

existed for well over twenty years, and try to remember the point at which an alarm spread through the country. The rats have been a part of the everyday life of ghetto dwellers for too long a time. Strangely enough, they become a problem only when there is danger of an epidemic or when city sanitation workers remain on an extended strike.

Nonetheless, because of our exhibit there is a new awareness in our neighborhood of the ecology of the rat. Many children did not know that Norway rats lived underground until they viewed our simulated environment that contained live specimens. They believed that rats lived only in abandoned automobiles, old mattresses, and in the homes of the children themselves. Many adults did not know what to do about getting rid of rats beyond keeping their garbage cans tightly closed and cleaning their kitchens before they went to bed. Many of those who are poor did not know of the availability of free rat poison or of the services offered by public health. Others in higher financial brackets had not realized that they were feeding and helping rats to multiply by leaving dogs' feeding dishes out overnight, by not picking up fruit that had fallen from their trees, and by raising tomatoes and corn in their spacious backyards. We believe that many of the preschoolers who came to visit us now know the difference between gerbils and rats, and have learned that the latter are not pets to be played with. Certainly, those of our neighbors who might be bitten by rats are now aware that one does not simply wash a rat bite with soap and water or

alcohol; that one must get to the nearest doctor or hospital for an immediate tetanus shot. They are aware, too, that tenants cannot be evicted by an angered landlord if they report the presence of rats to the health department. Finally, many more know that simply not being bitten by a rat does not preclude contracting a rat-borne disease.

The direction in which this Museum must move relative to urban ecology is clear. The evolvement of exhibits must continue to be a cooperative venture between professional staff and viewers. Professional staff can no longer seek the sanctity of cloistered cubicles to plan for, rather than with, people. It is imperative that they be sensitive and responsive to the need to understand, analyze, and creatively change that which has seemed changeless in the minds, spirits—and environments—of those they serve.

The Role of Zoos and Aquaria in Environmental Education

William G. Conway
General Director
The New York Zoological Society

The zoo and aquarium are essential to the education of modern man. Moreover, their role in environmental education, perhaps man's most urgently needed educational task, is increasingly important for a variety of reasons: zoos are directly and continuously involved with wildlife; most of them are in cities; they are heavily attended by school children; more and more they are becoming centers for scientific research.

The importance of wildlife preservation, however, has not been recognized, as may be illustrated by a comparison with the preservation of great works of art. There are said to be more than 600 paintings by Rubens in existence, and more than 750 paintings that have been represented as the works of Rembrandt. Think of the total monetary value man has attached to the works of such artists, a value as dependent upon rarity as on quality. Yet today there are only 497 Pere David deer,

Pere David Deer—New York Zoological Society.

281 European bison, and 160 Mongolian wild horses left on earth. Each of these species is extinct in the wild and may be seen only in captive collections or in semicaptive groups reintroduced from zoos into parks. There are thought to be less than 600 snow leopards and less than 200 Siberian tigers remaining in the wild. Yet remarkably little value is attached to *any* of these creatures in the marketplace of human affairs.

This situation throws into strong relief the basic problem of environmental education. It is time for a reordering of values; and as a biologist, in fact, I believe it is past time and probably too late.

The places where wild animals live are being destroyed, and zoos find their collections being affected to a greater extent than any other kind of museum. It is hardly surprising that they have been thrust into the middle of the new consciousness of impending environmental crisis. The loss of each living wild species is absolute.

The zoo's function as a repository for extinct and vanishing animals has become a subject for desperation if not despair. The need to maintain wild animals on a long-term basis means that zoos must discontinue attempts to expand their representation of species. Instead, responsible zoos are decreasing the number of kinds of animals they exhibit so that they may show larger, more secure breeding groups of those of special concern. We are faced with a need to find ways to breed and maintain, at one and the same time, specialized denizens of swamp and savannah and of deserts and rain forests. The mortal nature of our collections, as well as the need for providing a suitable selection of mates, a proper diet, a satisfactory environment, an adequate social group, and a proper space have all combined to require a depth of scientific technology never before contemplated in the repository function of *any* kind of museum. And if vanishing species are to be maintained for the future, it is immaterial whether it be only as a zoo relict to be studied in the same spirit of "wanting to know" as paleontological fragments are viewed in other kinds of museums. The problem today is how to do it—and how to pay for it.

The great majority of Americans now live in cities, and they will never, never again see any significant wildlife except in zoos. This is the key to the zoo's new role. How many city-dwellers too familiar with rats and roaches, starlings and pigeons, have ever seen a box turtle or a deer, an eagle or an alligator? Yet the opinions and the votes of this overwhelming urban population, wrapped within the morass of its own ever-increasing problems, must determine to a large extent the future of all wild lands and wild creatures. Inevitably, they will also de-

Flocks of American or West Indian flamingo are on exhibit in the New York Zoological Park. This beautiful bird has been exterminated over most of its original geographic range. It now occurs in the wild mostly in protected sanctuaries.

Many of the most popular zoo animals are likely to be gone in 30 years. The handwriting is clearly on the wall for most large mammals, birds, and reptiles. The avalanche of proliferating humanity will surely engulf many of them even if the effects of pollution and chemical biocides are alleviated or if a worldwide ecocatastrophe does not first reduce the matter to one of strictly academic interest.

termine the viability of the world ecosystem as well as the durability of their own civilization. We are urban men, and the nature of man's aspirations and his progress is shaped by his environment.

It is part of the zoo's role to contribute to the quality of man's urban environment. Zoo and aquarium attendance, in North America, will easily top the 100-million mark this year, and visits will be made by

173

people on all social and economic levels. This figure speaks well for the zoo's potential to convey the message of environmental education to significant numbers of people. Besides, most museum directors envy the zoo the appeal of its living exhibits and the emotional bond that has always characterized the relationship of human beings to other animals. The existence of a good zoo assures the city at least one oasis of living diversity among its architectural bones.

ly, this attitude is changing, and the association of the zoo with recreation is not to be sneered at, for it offers an unmatched foundation for efforts in environmental education.

After observing that truants frequently spend their free time at the Bronx Zoo, the New York Zoological Society recently initiated two special programs in cooperation with local school districts. The first concentrates upon teen-age boys, potential dropouts. It offers a combined program of school and paid

A painting by Carl Rungius depicts the teeming herds of bison that roamed the prairies of North America until the mid-nineteenth century. By the turn of the century the bison, which had numbered 60 million a few decades earlier, had been nearly exterminated by over-hunting. The species was saved from extinction largely by the captive breeding program of the New York Zoological Society in cooperation with other conservationists.

Moreover, zoos and aquaria have always enjoyed a special place in the recreation of the cities. It is part of the zoo's role to offer a respite from the city's concrete and brick, buses and bustle. The recreational aspect of the zoo is one of its most useful assets in its educational tasks. Yet zoo men are bedeviled in their search for financial support, by the curious fact that collections of dead animals have long been considered of great scientific and educational value whereas collections of live animals have been looked down upon as amusement for children. Fortunate-

zoo-keeper training. Graduates of the program have won jobs not only in zoos but also in laboratory animal-care centers. This program has also stimulated greater interest in scholarship and motivated several boys to pursue college careers in biology. The other program is curriculum-oriented and includes more than 1,000 fifth-grade children. Using the zoo's animal collection as a stimulus, and visits to the zoo itself as a regular part of the weekly school program, it has not only provided environmental education but also included such novel ideas as using the popular interest in elephants to teach mathematics and the interest in birds to explain geography.

Although many museums must strive to develop animated exhibits or struggle to find ways to involve their visitors with their displays, zoo collections provide their own activity. In fact, it is often a problem to keep visitors from becoming too involved with the collections exhibited.

The quality of zoo exhibits is fast improving. Until recently no zoo had a department of exhibition such as those found in many museums. Today such departments are becoming common, and the development of habitat exhibits and supplementary interpretive displays is proceeding rapidly.

Zoos and aquaria are also on the threshold of new technological achievement: already, by reversing their circadian activity patterns nocturnal animals are being exhibited, active and alert; birds are being displayed without barriers in living forests; and still other creatures, under the effects of controlled day length and climate, are reproducing for the first time.

It is now possible to point out basic ecological principles in a meaningful way, and in terms of living creatures, before the student's eyes: to aid an understanding of food chains and ecological pyramids, for example, through living exhibits of predators and prey; to better comprehend life cycles and the interdependence of animal life. And, of course, most large zoos conduct courses for teachers, present lectures, make films, and otherwise offer the usual range of museum activities.

One of the most promising contributions of zoos and aquaria to environmental education lies in the field of research. Biologists monitoring the captive environments of wild creatures under controlled conditions have a remarkable opportunity for intimate and consistent research. Within the past ten years graduate students working in fields as disparate as marine biochemistry and animal ethology have made significant scientific contributions and added ever-greater depth to the story of zoo education.

A pair of rare and endangered takin from the Himalayas in the Bronx Zoo. New York Zoological Society Photo.

Despite this bright picture of the zoo's role in environmental education, it is hardly possible to be optimistic. Most zoos are in a state of incipient institutional eutrophication. A richness of opportunity and newly realized responsibility are tending to smother the limits of life-supporting finances. And even the best of zoos require expensive improvement if their promise is to be realized.

More importantly, zoos and aquaria are inextricably entwined in the struggle for conservation. A concern with wildlife and with environmental science is likely to be the interest and consent of the urban majority of mankind.

Of all the institutions best equipped to lay the environmental message on the line, zoos and aquaria

Populations of the vast herds of hoofed mammals in Africa are kept under natural control by predators, such as the lion. In the African plains exhibit at the New York Zoological Park a herd of nyala are protected from their natural enemy by a deep moat.

viewed as a luxury in an increasingly overpopulated and strifetorn country—at least until it is too late.

Nevertheless in the years ahead the most important function of these institutions will be to give urban man some familiarity with the world of nature; to awaken his interest in the unfamiliar organisms with which he shares the planet earth; to offer him the opportunity to see and learn about the beauty and wonder of wildlife. For man's environment, and thus for man, much will depend upon the success of this confrontation, for if any of our wildlife and wilderness are to be preserved anywhere for future generations, it will be done only with

are outstanding. The visitor stands face to face with reality. Not many words are necessary, and those that are used need not be minced. Perhaps every zoo visitor should be confronted with the statement, or a variation of it, made in 1900 by William Beebe, the first curator of birds at the Bronx Zoo:

The beauty and genius of a work of art may be reconceived, though its first material expression be destroyed, a vanished harmony may yet inspire the composer; but when the last individual of a race of living things breathes no more, another heaven and earth must pass before such a one can be again.

Museums and the Ecological Imperative

Malcolm B. Wells
Architect/Conservationist

I am an architect and conservationist and for the past ten years I have observed the steady deterioration of our environment. I have come to realize that ecology means far more than saving the redwoods, using lead-free gasoline and having one less child. It may well be the big issue of all time. For it may have to do with the end of all life on this planet within our lifetime.

Museum professionals, among many others, have heard all this before, stated a hundred different ways, with different degrees of urgency. And some museums have launched splendid programs on the subject. But I submit that museums have barely scratched the surface of this issue.

Now I haven't the knowledge to tell anyone how to run a museum. But I do know that museums, like many other institutions, have to do with people and buildings. And I know what people and buildings do to the land. I know from reflecting on my first ten years as a practicing architect when I designed buildings and other land-paving improvements which now cover almost 50 acres of the American earth. In terms of run-off, in terms of erosion, in terms of wasted fuels, wildlife destroyed and living land snuffed out of use, the devastation I brought about is uncountable, and will continue year after year, until all my early monuments have been demolished and their parking lots torn up.

As institutions involving people and buildings, museums can work for, rather than against, our environment. But in terms of example and education, there is even more they can do if only their credibility, their sincerity, is not impaired.

The museum enjoys the privilege of being our only remaining institution whose word has not yet been seriously questioned. Current turmoil has undermined the credibility of schools and universities. That credibility of voice, the sincerity of purpose which museums retain, must be preserved. Yet I feel that most museums seem in all innocence, to have drifted into some hypocritical ways.

Consider the average museum in America today. You drive by and it looks so solid, so respectable, so involved. How could anyone even question its sincerity? It has no profit motive, no axe to grind. Why, it looks like the engraving on a twenty-dollar bill. Let's pull around to the parking lot in the rear . . . .

Whammo! Umpteen ecologic failures at a single glance; a scene so familiar anywhere in America today that you can't quite remember, for a

177

minute, whether it's the back of the museum or the back of the supermarket. Such a parade of failures might raise doubts about any museum's sincerity of purpose in what it may try to say about our environment.

On the other hand, such failures offer an opportunity for museums to make a contribution. What about the back door area we just saw? I do not propose tidying up your back door and trying to hide ecologic failures behind vine-covered louvres. Sincerity demands of each of us that we admit our mistakes and then try to do better. It took me ten years to see the ecological errors of my architectural ways, but now I am trying to build buildings that improve rather than destroy the land, and I refuse to build in wild areas of any kind.

That back door area can become your museum's most moving exhibit. You can interpret for your visitors what they see as they turn that last corner and enter your parking lot. Using whatever display tech-

niques you choose, you can say "Here are the mistakes we've made. Here's what we plan to do about them. Here's how it will work." You can suggest that conventional pav-

ing, uncycled wastes and lifeless land are always failures, even if they occur at the museum.

The museum's own physical impact on the land, in other words, is material for one of the most powerful and timely stories you could hope to tell. And you needn't wait until planning your new underground museum; there's much you can do today (see adjacent guide).

Each day, hundreds of visitors can go away forever aware that your building, like so many others, has, with its lawns, walks, plazas and parking lots, crushed land that should have been bursting with life. They can learn that not only living plants and living soil and living animals have been repelled, but that pondsful of fresh rainwater have been repelled too, in every rain, with terrible consequences to the American earth. And they can learn from your failures the true dimensions of this tragedy. But they will not hate you for this failure. On the contrary, they will respect and admire your awareness and your sincerity in tackling this problem in your own backyard.

Museum action programs then might well consist of graphic accounts of *their own* ecologic failures, and what they plan to do about them. There are in existence today, for instance, sewerless toilets that use the same water over and over, producing no sewage. There are heat-recovery techniques, incredible insulations, and solar energy traps that can slash fuel wastes. There are rainwater conservation practices that cost surprisingly little. And there are trash and garbage pulping and composting machines that can enrich museum lands with the waste materials museums now throw away.

Museums must not simply wring their hands over the environmental crisis; from now on they must take stands. They must say "Look; here are some things that can be done right now. *We're doing them.* Here's how they work." This must be a major consideration in the design of new museums, too, for we are about to embark on a 30-year building boom that will dwarf anything in history, and we can no longer afford to build as our grandfathers did, wiping out acres of land outdoors in order to sing its praises indoors.

One glance at all the proposals being put forth today proves that no one can predict what the cities of the future will be like. We are about to be inundated with solutions. So it is increasingly important for museums of all kinds to fill their roles by interpreting such proposals against the background of each museum's own specialty. A science museum can, for example, without too much editorializing, present the relative ecologic impact of megacities versus minicities, and hope that an enlightened electorate will vote for the better of the two. As the American Museum of Natural History exhibit "Can Man Survive?" states in its introduction, the basics of life do not change. The interdependencies of all living and nonliving things on this planet can change only slightly within several human lifetimes. With this constancy as a standard, everything done, or proposed to be done, by man can be evaluated. If the pre-Columbian wilderness in America was a near-ideal land-response, then the city of today can be compared with it quite objectively. Here is a typical comparison between what was and what is, with what could be.

To many people of other lands, the view of roadside America, the condition of our cities, and the character of the suburbia that surrounds them express an almost unbelievable disregard for the life-giving land. Having learned some of the lessons the hard way, the European, for example, is often shocked to find that we still have so few controls upon our own destructiveness. We seem to take freedom to mean license, and then we pay the penalty. But as any designer knows, rules make the game more interesting. They improve the results, too. No architect will produce a great building for a client who has no purpose for his building and no budgetary limitation. The point is that in our new-found concern for the environment rules are bound to come and this is another place where museums can offer enlightenment. When the rules are made they must be sound and fair. They must be based on proven ecologic facts and not on superficial whims as are so many zoning laws today.

Billboards and overhead wires, along with litter, used to disturb the aesthetes of America. But now, thanks to the efforts of ecologists, such annoyances are recognized as expressions of a far more serious condition.

The emerging role of the museum in America is to hold a mirror up to her uglinesses, to educate, and to offer healthy solutions. If you want to see tomorrow's civilization, look at today's kids. They will create it. And the way they create it will depend, to a large extent, on the quality of the alternatives presented to them by their museums and schools.

Museums have both the respect and the eye of almost every American. And they have many of the necessary resources. Now they must assume the responsibility of helping to change the values and priorities of the entire nation. It will be largely through their example and the example of the schools that the cities of our future will be shaped. Nothing less than total commitment to the ecologic imperative will do.

A MUSEUM OF THE FUTURE WILL EXERCISE ENVIRONMENTAL SELF CONTROL.

Buildings and Grounds

Prevent runoff; a paved acre sheds almost 30,000 gallons for each inch of rain. Use sunken pebble gardens, reverse wells, deep mulch, dense planting and ponds. Use nitrogen-producing legumes like Crown Vetch instead of grass. Use no pesticides. Provide bird and small game habitat. Use composted building wastes on the land.

Waste Management

Outlaw one-way bottles, paper and plastic spoons, cups, plates and napkins throughout building. Crack down on needless copying. Use no incineration. Neutralize lab chemicals. A $3,000 pulper will convert all trash and garbage into odorless pulp, an excellent rain-holder on soil. Investigate composting pulp, even adding treated sewage to the mix, as is done in some European countries.

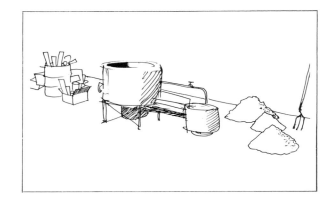

Utilities

Check burner combustion regularly. Get estimates on smoke-capturing devices. Add insulation, double glazing and weatherstripping wherever possible. Use heat-recovery devices on all air exhausts. Conserve water and electric power; local consulting engineers can name ten ways. Investigate solar power.

Building Additions

Use no redwood; little wood of any kind. Insulate building many times standard amounts. Create green areas. Build underground. Pave with porous materials. Stress simplicity, economy. Write specifications from an environmental-awareness point of view, both for construction practices and for final result.

New Buildings

This is your chance to make a huge contribution to our dying land and to our awareness of it. Build on these principles: improve the ecology of the site by building or do not build at all. Resolve to use less than recommended minimum amounts of fuel, water and power; find ways to do it. Re-use all wastes. Put parking and building underground.
Tell The Public What You're Doing, And Why.

181

Tomorrow's museum will restore its bit of the planet rather than destroy it. The new museum will practice what it preaches, expressing its ecological convictions by originating rain-catching ponds and rooftop plantings, wooded areas and topsoil-building fields of composted trash-garbage-sewage. Underground parking and solar energy traps will be further expressions of this new American land conscience.

A MUSEUM OF THE FUTURE, BUILT TO BE IN HARMONY WITH THE LAND

Earth and trees on roofs prevent fast run-off, insulate building, reduce maintenance, provide wildlife habitat, moderate weather, absorb noise.

Natural area

Solar energy traps

Mechanized trash and garbage composting enriches soil in area reserved for future additions

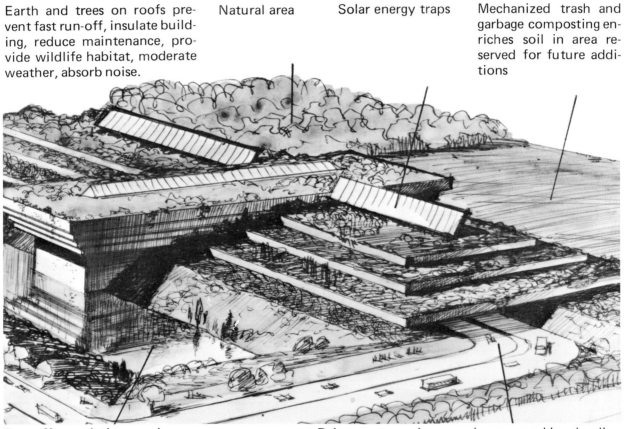

Run-off percolation pond

Driveway to underground garage and bus loading

chapter 7 / programs of action

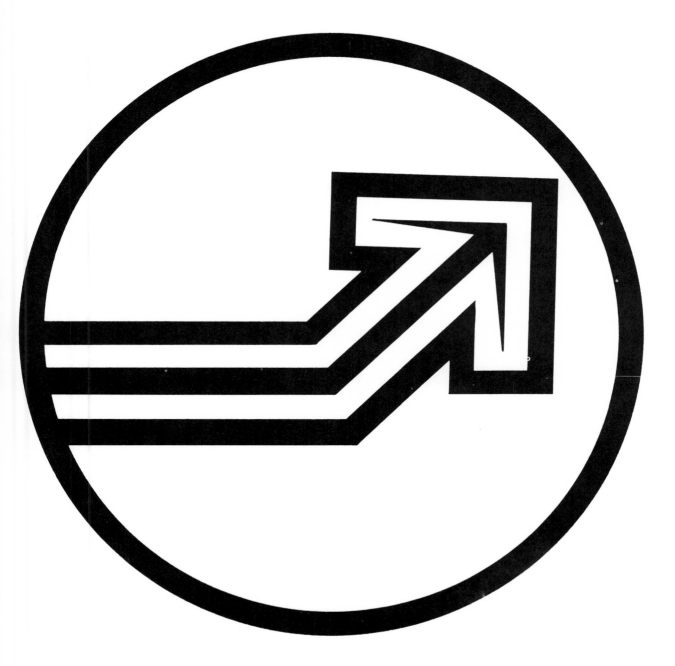

Programs of Action

"The journey of a thousand miles begins with one step."

Lao-Tze

Public Awareness: The Necessary Basis for Public Action

James A. Lee,
Director of Human Ecology
Environmental Health Service, U.S.
Department of Health, Education,
and Welfare

Man seemingly stands at high noon in his relationships to the environment. The twin explosions of population and technology give every promise of pushing us closer to the brink of an environmental crisis from which there may be no recovery. Unless ecologically sound overall direction of environment-shaping technology becomes reality, man's prospects would seem dim indeed. Why do we seem unable to stem this tide of environmental degradation that threatens the continued survival of man and environment alike? One answer is that the concepts of environmental abundance, technological efficiency, and utilitarianism—concepts ingrained in American cultural history—are responsible, in part, for the exploitative, destructive attitude toward the environment displayed by the American people. The egocentric view of man's place and role vis-a-vis his environment is still strongly held by Americans, who revere the image of the colonial patriot going forth to subdue a hostile

environment with gun, plow, and ax in hand.

Only of late has there been any sign that the United States may be entering an era of "environmental maturity." The attitudes long prevalent in this country concerning the role of the public and private sectors in administering the environment reflect the cavalier attitudes of its people toward its environment and its resources. A societal ethic contributory to such wanton abuse has hardly been conducive to the development of an "ecological conscience." It can be seen quickly that in a society composed of many competing users of the environment little or no popular consensus has emerged to shape an environmental policy based upon ecologic stewardship. Government's role was viewed as one of refereeing the conflicting economic interests in the environment, with adjudication favoring the side with the most political clout. For decades the national scene witnessed the one-sided conflict between the "conservationists" and the "economic interests." The conservationists, intent upon preserving the fast-dwindling remnants of the natural environment, clashed with the economic interests, equally intent upon exploiting the environment in support of a growing GNP. While the conservationists were militantly vociferous and mildly successful in awakening the American conscience to the ravages of the environment, government action tended to favor the economic interests. Such noneconomic factors as natural beauty and aesthetics, for example, received scant attention.

Not until the appearance of health-threatening problems like air and water pollution, pesticides, solid wastes, radioactive contamination, and mental disorders on an epidemic scale, to mention only a few, has the inadequacy of governmental machinery for dealing with them become apparent. America's environmental dilemma, although still perhaps neither well understood nor appreciated by the citizenry, is the stuff out of which headlines are made that increasingly give cause for public concern. Under the increasing pressure of these untoward events, many of them unfortunately irreversible in their consequences, there comes a suggestion for change in the conduct of our environment-affecting affairs. Somehow the foreboding aspects of smog in Los Angeles and New York, the Santa Barbara and Gulf Coast oil leaks, the demise of Lake Erie, the plague of urban sprawl with its increasing social dis-

An aerial view of urban sprawl.

cord, give form and substance to a growing national "feeling" about continued environmental deterioration. Out of the threats posed by these happenings and events may emerge an enlarged and enlightened concept of man's relationship to and

185

responsibility for his environment that finds expression in greater public stewardship.

Public policy that begets responsible public action rests upon public awareness. Only as our society moves toward an understanding of its environment, and especially its limitations for cleansing itself of the torrent of pollutants spewed into it,

Scene near East Haven junk yards and Quinnipiac River. Photo: Miller/Swift, East Haddam, Conn.

can the resulting public opinion bring about responsible public action. Environmental maturity on the part of our society is a prerequisite to political action. Recoginzing that environment-shaping purposes and goals in our pluralistic society are largely incoherent and inconsistent with what is known about the health and well-being of both man and his environment, the task of environmental administration at all levels of government becomes twofold. First, it seeks to insure that decisions affecting the environment, which it is charged to implement, are those that

a society able to understand its own needs and conscious of the risks and benefits entailed *ought* to make. In this task the functions of research, education, and public information are important. They influence the processes of public policy-making in a way that tends to make "correct" environmental decisions possible. Second, environmental administration must implement these decisions through national, state, and local programs in a manner that provides for continuing redefinition of goals and purposes based upon experience and "public feedback." In essence, the challenge facing environmental administration today is to resolve the conflicts among competing interests so as to help shape a popular consensus on environmental purposes and goals consonant with what is known about the health and welfare needs of society, and the ecology of its environment.

A concerned, aroused, and knowledgeable public, a public informed and aware of the fact that the quality of life is directly related to the quality of the environment, is necessary to reverse the tide of environmental destruction. Museums, with all their related functions and activities designed to inform and educate, can perform a vital role in this regard. Whatever kind of museum you have, whatever your responsibilities within it, the creative, innovative talents that characterize your profession can be focused on this most pressing of problems—*man's survival*. Speaking as one who daily sees the sands of time running out for man, I ask that you place human ecology high on your list of priorities in the decade ahead.

The Consequences of Activism

George O. Pratt, Jr.
Director
Staten Island Institute of Arts
and Sciences

What happens to a small museum when it attempts to become involved with the problems of the present?

What occurs when it takes a stand? When it becomes an activist institution?

At the Staten Island Institute of Arts and Sciences, we cannot answer those questions as they apply to every issue. But we now have some experience with the consequences of actively joining the conflict over environmental degradation. In developing its program of outdoor environmental education, the Staten Island Museum has discarded some old methods and adopted some new ones. The guided nature walk, for instance, is emblematic of an era when natural history could reasonably be considered an intellectual discipline pursued for its own enjoyment. Although we continue the guided walks with some school groups, there has lately arisen a sense of urgency about such education; learning about natural history has become education for survival.

Staten Island is probably typical in being subjected to atmospheric contaminants from manufacturing facilities which are often located outside its political jurisdiction, to the toxic by-products—carbon monoxide and lead—of years of urban planners' emphasis on automotive transportation. It is an area where man-made poisons are selectively reducing various species of tree, shrub and bird life, where a generous-sized coastline is now useless for swimming or fishing.

The Staten Island waterfront. As seen from harbor cruise on Earth Day trip. Photo: Eric Aerts.

All parts of the Staten Island Institute have become engaged in the effort of outdoor environmental education, but the heart of the overall effort to arouse concern for our environment, particularly among adults, is the Staten Island Museum. Founded as a general museum in 1881, it has a long, rich history and possesses important local collections in the natural sciences of Staten Island, and equally important collections in history—primarily books, manuscripts, records of the artistic accomplishments of the Island, and paintings.

For decades we, as a Museum, have been quietly calling attention to conservation problems, both local and regional, such as protection and preservation of marshlands, especially estuarine marshlands. Our specialization developed, among both staff and members of the Museum, an appreciation of the urgency of conservation issues long before their public recognition. However, the attempt to communicate awareness of these problems was confined largely to printed publications, and Museum exhibits remained, and to a large extent still remain, oriented toward old and familiar natural science themes.

In 1965, the attitude of Museum staff and members toward the role of the Museum in outdoor environmental education began to change. In a sense, the Museum became radicalized. The process had its roots in the sense of anger and anguish at what was happening to the Staten Island environment, and to nearby suburban and urban areas. We began to realize that the older, established forms of institutional education and, protest—publications, seminars, symposia and lectures—appeared to be the proverbial gnat trying to slay the pollution dragon. We were certain losers. The opportunity to become directly involved in outdoor education *action* arose when a proposed high-rise apartment development threatened the existence of one of the Institute's three primary components, the 72-acre park known as High Rock. With a background of having successfully led in the establishment in 1955 of the

Institute's second major component, the W.T. Davis Wildlife Refuge, and with the support of the New York City Department of Parks, and other agencies and groups, the Museum took the lead in establishing the High Rock Park Conservation Center.

College involvement in Ecological Education Programs offered at High Rock Park Conservation Center by the Staten Island Museum. Photo: Eric Aerts.

This woodland and marsh habitat in the middle of the Island, is one of the first urban outdoor conservation and environmental education centers.

In 1966, partly in response to growing social pressures for a still more activist role on the part of the Staten Island Museum, the Board of Trustees voted to revise the By-laws and increase its membership from 21 to 40 members. This increase in Board size meant that not only the traditional disciplines—that is, art, science and history—would be represented at Board level, but that articulate, effective and dedicated preservationists and conservationists could be included from the Staten Island community. Members were drawn from among college and high school teachers, Wall Street lawyers, advertising executives—from many disciplines and professions. But all were motivated by an awareness of, and an apprehension about, the destruction of the environment.

This conscious strengthening of the Board in the direction of environmental interest culminated in a decision of historic importance to the Staten Island Museum and, possibly, to museums generally. Confronted with a proposed highway location that would run through the area's finest remaining scenic and natural woodland and pond areas, the Staten Island Museum took a strong public stand. It declared its opposition to the construction of the federally financed highway along the proposed route. Many other conservation organizations and individuals joined the effort and the result was a victory; a different route will be selected. Following that success, there have been other actions demonstrating the Museum's involvement in environmental issues:

The Curator of Science of the Museum wrote and published in the Institute's "Proceedings" an article in which she questioned the wisdom of permitting further dredging of Raritan Bay. Her article was read into the record of the public hearing held as a prerequisite to the granting of a dredging permit. The permit was denied.

The Museum founded the Staten Island Committee on Scientific Information, which has sought to enlist broadly based citizen and professional aid in the scientific testing and measurement of air and water pollution in and around Staten Island. This committee recently spearheaded a successful effort to reduce exhaust fumes from city-owned buses as they were warmed up early in the morning for daily operation. One hundred or more buses, their engines idling for hours, were sickening residents of the area near the maintenance garage; as a result of pressures brought by this committee, other citizens and the Air Resources Department of New York City, the practice was stopped.

On Earth Day the Museum and High Rock organized, with the sanction of New York City, a DDT burial. Additionally, a New York Har-

A DDT burial on Earth Day. Photo: Eric Aerts.

bor cruise was organized for important college, political and other leaders for viewing the polluted waters immediately surrounding Staten Island. Two leaflets: "Pesticides—Do's and Don'ts" and "Environmental Action for the Individual" were published under Museum auspices.

The active involvement of the Museum has had positive catalytic effects. Not only has membership in the Museum greatly increased, but the newer members are representative of all of the elements of the population—businessmen, artists, writers, teachers, professionals—and, most important, the youth of the community. In turn, the Staten Island Museum is seeing itself in a deeper and wider role and is beginning to realize how it can use its existing resources and collections to enrich its education program in new ways. Specifically—and funds permitting—the Museum proposes to engage in the following programs:

Participation in the collection and testing of water samples, for various contaminants. This would be part of an extended program for adults leading toward an understanding of the complexities of water pollution. The testing would be done using local college laboratories.

Interdisciplinary use of artistic and historic material in Museum collections as an environmental preface to current urban problems on Staten Island. (This requires larger facilities than are presently available.)

Environmental record-keeping through the collection of photographs to complement the present collection of over 10,000 photos from 1859 to the present.

Increased emphasis on and the collection of data relative to Staten Island as well as receiving and collecting publications from national and international museums.

Establishment of a permanent water quality testing laboratory at the W.T. Davis Wildlife Refuge to monitor and measure the effects of various landfill operations; also to measure types and degrees of marine pollution off estuarine and beach areas.

Exhibits in the science area of the Museum to describe and explain environmental problems. Currently, an exhibit on eutrophication is being opened. Another exhibit under consideration would use a live aquarium containing fresh water fish and other aquatic life characteristic of the Northeast and Middle Atlantic Seaboard area. The equipment necessary to maintain the sanitizing environment in which the fish survive and prosper will be shown in the exhibit. The pumps, the filters, the food supply all will be key features of the exhibit and shown appropriately. The point will be to show in an attractive, informative manner a simplified, man-made sanitative environment. Near the aquarium, will be an exhibit showing how these same processes are at work in our global environment and showing the very tiny percentage of that global area which is the Biosphere, where all or nearly all life exists. Emphasis here will be upon the natural sanitative processes and upon pollution defined as that additional amount of material which when added to the environment cannot be removed by natural processes.

Establishment of antipollution store front centers. This project was recently suggested to the Museum by a 17-year-old Staten Island High School senior. At the time, funding for personnel was the principal obstacle. But with involvement of Urban Corps students from Richmond College, division of City University system, approximately 10 students were available to work at least 30 hours a week on anti-pollution projects. The students expect to create *their own* program, with technical assistance (and a small amount of money for rent and utilities) from the Museum.

With 70 percent of our population living on one percent of the land, and with mounting evidence that environmental pollution has caused and is causing damage to an extent greater than previously realized, environmental outdoor education must increase if we are to survive. The activities, programs and ideas of the Staten Island Museum demonstrate that environmental outdoor education is part of a sophisticated fight against public apathy, government bureaucracy, corporate greed, trustee timidity, college and university aloofness, and some cherished but essentially outworn idols, e.g., gross national product.

Museums of natural science, art and history will find it rewarding to participate in this effort. They will create for themselves a sense of involvement and immediacy. As an institution takes up an active role in this most important battle, it can be certain that it will attract enormously talented people who will lend their time, talents and skills. In turn, this public involvement will generate funds which will likely become increasingly available to institutions which show an awareness of the environment and its relationship to people.

Expanding the Museum Outward

The ways to expand the museum into the community are boundless. Depending upon the special skills and talents of your staff and volunteers, you can . . .

. . . Move the museum's exhibits outside its own walls and into the community. For example, look around for opportunities to place suitable exhibits in high traffic areas, or within reach of special-interest groups. Bank and department store windows, libraries, the lobby of a major hotel, and employees' cafeterias are promising locations.

. . . Organize school children and community groups who are already fully involved, alerted and motivated by the museum exhibit programs into "environmental vigilance" groups.

. . . Encourage appropriate groups—especially students—to undertake community surveys and other team projects.

. . . Sponsor public discussions to take stock of area ecology problems.

. . . Arrange an organizational meeting of local action groups—under the aegis of the museum—to coordinate a common effort on local environmental questions.

. . . Seek the cooperation of local industries in setting up programs. Offer to provide exhibit material or consultation to business firms that wish to set up employee-oriented programs.

. . . Cooperate with the local public or university library in the development and distribution of environmental reading lists that are adapted to varying age levels and intellectual interests.

... Offer appropriate recommendations about urban renewal projects, river-bed improvement, parks and recreation areas, private business and industry projects, etc. Art museums can enlist the interest of local cultural groups and advertising clubs in improving outdoor advertising.

... Document the growth of the community as a guide to understanding how environment has influenced progress and as a possible blueprint for future action. Historical societies might incorporate such documentation into a pictorial exhibit—or publish it as a pamphlet.

How to Involve the Community in Museum Programs

Open, two-way lines of communication and active cooperation with organized community groups will advance the objectives of your museum's environmental program. Close relationship of museums with both the established and the new conservation, population and environmental groups can be beneficial to the whole community.

Local chapters of groups engaged in ecological activities may offer valuable assistance. (See Appendix for a comprehensive list of such organizations.)

Of equal importance is the establishment of rapport with service clubs, neighborhood associations, parents' groups and professional organizations. Their support and participation should be solicited in the forwarding of museum programs. Individual groups may give valuable assistance in specific projects: their members may participate in surveys, field trips, and other activities. It is axiomatic that people are most concerned with causes to which they have contributed their efforts.

The Power of the Group

An organized, informed group can carry out substantial programs.

The effectiveness of group action in programs requiring public support or financing depends in large measure on the accuracy of the analysis that is made of the problem, the number of supporting facts gathered, and the clarity and drama with which the matter is presented. Hearsay is never a good basis for action. Only verified data, obtained from the best authority, are useful.

There is no limit to what an imaginative, determined group can do about problems of the environment. Citizen action forced the halt of plans to construct a large jetport threatening the Florida Everglades and also stopped further construction of the Cross Florida Canal, which would have destroyed thousands of acres of rich wildlife habitats; it forced the halt of further filling of San Francisco Bay; citizens demanded—and got—tighter restrictions on air-pollution standards in Chicago; they forced the city of Cleveland to launch a campaign to clean up the Cayuhoga River; they stopped the use of DDT in several states; they insisted on—and won—better protective measures against oil pollution in Maine; they prevented the installation of a new water system that threatened the few surviving condors in California; they won a reprieve on the construction of a bridge that "would have turned the historic city of Charleston, South Carolina into an automobile commuter route...." And new actions are being initiated daily in nearly all parts of the country. Science, history and art museums can provide reliable data pertaining to various kinds of environmental problems on which responsible and effective group action can be based.

The Role of Volunteers

Except in our major cities, the museum network of this country has been made possible almost entirely by the work of capable, knowledgeable volunteers, and even in large cities, the role of volunteers has always been a crucial one. Many important components of our educational system would not be in existence without those volunteers who helped set them up, got them going and kept them in operation.

The same kind of individual commitment is required today. Fortunately, large numbers of people are eager to participate in programs related to ecology. Many college and high school students are deeply concerned about the environmental crisis, and these enthusiastic young people can be recruited as active volunteers. Increasing numbers of well-trained people reaching retirement age seek volunteer work related to their own fields, and will devote free time to helping with programs they consider worthwhile.

Many individuals among these potential volunteers have skills and creative talent, executive ability and energy that can be directed toward the design or implementation of effective action programs. Among those whose skills would be valuable in establishing a program to explain and interpret environmental problems are lawyers, teachers, writers and artists, advertising and public relations people, physicians and engineers, to name just a few categories. Once it is fully recognized that museums have become concerned with the solution of ecological problems, the development of a corps of volunteers from new sectors of the public may be anticipated—with results that can be beneficial to both the museum and the community.

Ideally, a large museum should have a department devoted solely to directing the efforts of volunteers. It should also have a regular program for recruitment and registration of skilled volunteer personnel. In any organization, large or small, however, volunteers should not be segregated from the administration and staff. Rather, the organization should emphasize its eagerness to make use of the valuable talents and services available in the community by blending the work of the volunteers into the mainstream of the museum's work. Volunteers should be fully integrated into the museum organization, made welcome, and given as much latitude as possible for effective action.

The Role of Local Experts

Where possible, local authorities should be invited to participate in discussion meetings, in order to provide greater awareness as to *what* is being done and what possible solutions offer the greatest potential for achievement. Invite these individuals to serve as advisers on projects involving their areas of competence. Ask local or otherwise accessible experts, university professors, business leaders, and elected officials to speak to your group and offer their opinions on specific problems that have demanded their attention. Local governmental agencies, as well as university extension services, are other good sources of advice and participation. Trade associations and corporations often supply materials and speakers; and public relations officers in industry are daily becoming more eager to undertake campaigns and cooperative efforts that will help dispel the image of their companies as "gross national polluters." Some of the materials they prepare—data sheets, art work, photography—can be used effectively in educational programs, and representatives can be invited to join in symposia and debates.

Working with Students

Museums have a special opportunity to help students of different ages develop environmental awareness by means of programs developed either in the museums, or jointly with local schools. It is important that these programs inspire the involvement of young people in worthwhile, productive activity. Some programs teach the scientific method of inquiry and analysis based on facts; others offer new historical perspectives and provide new ways of perceiving the biotechno-aesthetosphere. They train the students in organization, and demonstrate to them the value of group participation, and—to use a phrase virtually a bromide today—they provide relevance for the energies and goals of the young.

School classes usually approach the museum with a carefully-constructed program related to their classroom curriculum. Therefore, it is advisable in ecological programming, as in the programming of other activities, to devise exhibits that enrich classroom studies and offer opportunity for meaningful follow-up activity. Supervisors or classroom teachers at every grade level can offer valuable help in the planning, development, and use of exhibits.

Developing an Apprenticeship Program

One example of an ecologically-oriented program is that of the New Britain Children's Museum, in Connecticut. Operating with a limited staff and budget, the museum, which was founded and manned mostly by Junior League volunteers for the first six of its 13 years, has maintained continual interaction with the community.

The museum has a multi-purpose program for junior staff. They begin as volunteers, 10 years of age and up, and are promoted to paid jobs as junior staff, working after school and Saturdays. All junior staff members are required to research and understand the subjects exhibited. Some of the older boys and girls prove very capable as docents and teachers; some are good at exhibit conservation and preservation techniques. While they demonstrate and conduct workshops, they reinforce their understanding of the relationship of man and the environment.

The all-encompassing theme of the museum for the opening of this decade was "Survival Seventy." It intends to continue offering programs and circulating loan boxes on topics ranging from "A Forest Food Chain" to "Our City Then and Now," and from "Adopt Your Own Tree" to "Ethnic Cultures in our City."

Exhibits in history and social studies takes cognizance of the various groups that make up the city's population. Along with exhibits on English Colonies and the American Indian, the museum has mounted programs on the Caribbean and Puerto Rico.

Variations on the theme "Survival Seventy" can be adopted by other museums and adapted to their basic orientation—science, art or history.

Cooperating with Other Museums

In addition to making effective use of their separate strengths, museums within a given locality can achieve excellent results by cooperating in inter-museum programs that take advantage of their cumulative skills and talents.

For example, granting that the staffs of scientifically-oriented museums may have the basic scientific training and the skills most relevant to the technical problems of the environment, their specific capabilities may be amplified and extended significantly by exposure to the perspective and cultural orientation of history and art museum personnel. In return, science museums can offer seminars for the history—and art—museum people that will provide education in some of the basic principles of ecology.

With such reciprocity, it is possible to establish an effective, coordinated, community-wide effort in which each museum contributes what it can do best. With such enhancements as wide publicity, the whole may even, in its impact, exceed the sum of its parts; and the museums may gain new popular recognition as an effective consortium for education and action.

Setting up General Programs

Establish a Research and Information Center for groups and individuals who need factual and research support, or advice. Help high schools to organize debates and discussions on environmental problems, to initiate courses, create environmental displays for fairs, or carry out science projects on ecological subjects. Whenever appropriate and possible, all aspects of the museum's formal education program should relate the topic of the moment to the environment.

Develop workshops, symposia, lecture series and courses on problems such as the growth of population, waste management, (see detailed action program below) urban sprawl and endangered species. See that these are well publicized.

Organize a Speakers' Bureau comprised of specialists on a variety of localized subjects.

Present an Ecology Film Festival, an Earth Poetry Program, an Environmental Concert, an Ecology Walking Tour, an Environmental Street Fair, a Cartoon and Poster Competition, or a Candid Camera Contest on a subject of special concern to your audience.

Calling upon all the resources at hand—government officials, business and professional leaders, as many experts as possible, your volunteers and students—plan ecological celebrations at appropriate season intervals, such as the first day of spring, harvest time, Thanksgiving and Ground-hog Day. You don't have to wait for the annual Earth Day; you can have mini-days in between. Seek the support and participation of local residents and businesses. Secure permission to close specific streets for "environmental observation"; for 24 hours stop traffic in designated areas and direct surveys of the resulting changes in air and noise pollution. Stage a parade. Plan

games, exhibits, maps, soap-box debates, interviews, light shows on building walls—employ every means possible to help each participating citizen achieve a new sensitivity to his environment.

Organize community teams to take inventory of factors contributing to environmental problems in your area:

. Conduct field trips to the inner city to determine how environmental conditions can be improved
. Conduct field trips to the outskirts of the city
. Visit industrial sections
. Supervise cleanup tours
. Survey the condition of waterways

The cooperation of camera clubs and art groups should be enlisted to secure pictures for use as:

. Exhibit material for museum displays and for circulating exhibits
. Illustrations for newspaper or magazine articles
. Evidence concerning enforcement of regulations

Set up an environmental action "hot-line" by which people can report pollution offenses.

A Specific Community Action Program

Waste Disposal for a Livable
    Environment:
Goal: To enlist community support to
  1. Design and develop a multi-media museum exhibition emphasizing the dimensions of the problem in the community or the region, and its impact on health, economy,

and environmental quality.

   a. Adapt the cartoon-style illustrations from
"Needed: Clean Water"[1]
"Needed: Clean Air"
to achieve a 3-D effect. Use illuminated transparencies, taped sounds, and messages, etc. to explain

     The problem (past, present, future)

     What can be done about it (immediately; for the long pull)

     Who must do it (including personal commitment)

     One section might be headed: "Local governments are the first line of defense."

   b. Organize a photo report[2] on pollution and environmental degradation—add sounds, and odors. Include slide shows that are (1) continuous, (2) on demand (push button), or (3) activated by electric eye signal.

   c. Include a box score[3] or thermometer that can be adjusted to show changes—improvements or worsening conditions, newly detected violations, oil spills, dumping and littering—documented by photographs taken by "environmental vigilantes."

   d. Include a temperature Inversion Warning Indicator and a map delimiting the danger zone.

2. Organize film festivals (*The Gifts, The River Must Live, Who Killed Lake Erie?*), seminars, library displays and book reports, and hearings on legislative proposals. Relate these activities as directly as possible to ideas and information presented in the exhibit. (See appendix for list for additional films.)

3. Organize *show-me tours* to sewage disposal plants, sanitary landfill operations, stream channel dredging and spoil bank operations, industrial installations, airports, monitoring stations, and then evaluate these businesses and projects.

4. Encourage appropriate groups—especially students—to undertake some of the following

Proposed Group Projects

I. Surveys of the Local Air Pollution Situation

Many methods may be used to estimate air pollution. Your museum might assign different techniques to a number of classes, clubs or groups, and incorporate all the findings into a special exhibit for use at science fairs, school open-houses, environmental conferences, etc. Show the detection equipment used in each case, its operation by students, and graphs presenting findings in relation to such standards as legal limits, the differing tolerances of sensitive plants (tobacco, foliose lichens, white cascade petunias, lilacs, etc.).

Borrow simple air-pollution monitoring equipment, such as the sticky tape sampler and dust bucket, from the appropriate state agency, and conduct spot checks with the purpose of locating significant sampling sites. Follow instructions carefully to obtain valid results.

On the basis of wind direction data, determine sources of particulates and analyze types represented in the sampling. This can only be a qualitative test, since the amount of air involved will not be known.

Devise methods of collecting particulates and oxidants at a variety of elevations, making use of airborne collecting devices carried by balloons or model airplanes.

Arrange for a demonstration of more elaborate and professional, but portable, equipment for collecting and analyzing suspended particulates and oxidants.

Fill out and submit standard complaint forms for reporting pollution to official agencies.

Collect specimens of dichromatic oak beauty moths and compare the proportion of dark and light specimens with old collections in major museums.

Collect a pound of new snow, and continue collecting snow samples at 24-hour intervals. Melt, filter, weigh, examine and compare them.

Watch for buses whose motors are kept idling for more than three minutes (legal limit in some states). Look for evidence of damage to foliage of sensitive conifers or other vegetation at bus stops, on steep grades, at highway rest stops, etc.

Examine annual growth patterns of trunks of recently-cut coniferous trees in areas of excessive air pollution, or take core samples with an increment borer. Compare with growth of similar species in areas not exposed to pollution.

II. Surveys of the Local Water Pollution Situation

Organized activities by clubs and groups, culminating in a combined exhibit, will inspire interest in the solution of water-pollution problems in your area.

Determine the nature of rain-water disposal systems in relation to the handling of sewage and the efficiency of sewage treatment by area communities.

Check local streams for possible industrial pollution or influx of untreated sewage.

Determine the acreage of nearby farmland currently unprotected against erosion.

Watch for evidence of erosion in parks, construction projects and road building operations, and report failure or absence of safeguards designed to control erosion.

Collect water samples above and below suspected pollution sources and make microscopic and chemical observations.

With the approval or assistance of biologists from wildlife agencies, seine above and below pollution sources to determine populations of fish—and other types of aquatic life —characteristic of different stretches of the stream and different degrees of pollution.

III. Surveys of Solid Waste Management Problems

Enlist the cooperation of clubs and community groups, or members of museum classes, to study and report on conditions of littering and solid-waste disposal in your community. A number of separate activities might be undertaken by various teams:

Collect samples of litter in parks, along city streets and along rural roadsides. Choose area units of comparable size.

Compare volume of litter and va-

riety of material collected in each of the areas
. Try to determine the sources (picnickers, motorists, neighbors)
. Rate the extent of health hazard and other unsafe factors
. Estimate the length of time required for disintegration of the material collected

Make a supermarket survey of packaging materials used by competitive brands of products, to determine which of them create more of a disposal problem than others.

Distribute anti-litter posters, literature and disposal equipment, and organize cleanup campaigns.

When all the projects are completed, reports in various forms may be used to constitute a special exhibit. Give the exhibit wide publicity, being sure to give ample credit to the individuals and groups who participated.

Keeping the "Action" Current

Since there are not instant solutions to our environmental problems, museum programs need to sustain interest and action over a period of time. To this end, of course, exhibits must be upgraded; new films scheduled and old ones screened again; poster contests and new photo shows set up at suitable times.

A Changing Exhibit on "Citizen Action"

Each month, at the same location in the museum and using the same technique each time, demonstrate one action that a private citizen can take to improve the environment. If you have mannequins, or can obtain them, display them in a setting to illustrate the action: proper methods of leaf disposal, use of low-lead gasoline, anti-pollution measures for family campers, or similar efforts.

As suggested in "Expanding the Museum Outward," you might enlist the cooperation of a local department store and plan a satellite exhibit in a display window. Banks or other agencies might also welcome the opportunity to participate in such a "citizen action" program.

Keep interest at a high level with bulletins on the progress of vigilance groups patrolling local conditions, and periodic reports from other parts of the country on research, innovative approaches, identification of leaders and successful action programs.

"Exhibit of the Month"

The contents of a small exhibit case near the entrance of a museum can be changed periodically, perhaps each month. The exhibits may be displays relating to current happenings in the environment. Often stories in the news media of ecological crises will provide the idea for an exhibit, and the very timeliness of the museum presentation will lead to further effective publicity. In addition, teachers can be encouraged to relate a visit to the exhibit to studies of current events.

The American Museum of Natural History in New York City has had success with a number of such exhibits. One dealt with the threat to the Brown Pelican from DDT. The exhibit explained that the DDT finds its way through the food chain into the systems of the pelicans, where its effect on calcium metabolism creates eggs so soft of shell that the weight of the mothers breaks them in nesting. Pelicans on the west coast of the United States are facing extinction because of this situation.

Another exhibit at the Museum showed the harm being done by the Crown of Thorns starfish to large coral reefs in several parts of the Pacific. In this case the great increase in starfish is caused by ecological changes of unknown cause; the effect on the coral may be disastrous.

Both exhibits were small and simple, but the effective use of photographs, specimens and copy attracted widespread attention. All the materials came from Museum collections except the damaged pelican eggs, which were loaned by a California ornithologist. A mounted pelican, the damaged eggs, the chemical formula for DDT and a few paragraphs of copy—all in a 3' x 4' case—told the story.

Circulating Exhibits

Utilize circulating exhibits by individual museums (e.g., Cranbrook's *No Place to Play; Urban Transit: Problem and Promise*); and by government agencies and private citizens' groups.

Organize task forces to visit, observe and evaluate displays at major expositions and other museums, for exchange of ideas. Rather than leading to mechanical duplication of displays seen, such tours can promote productive brain-storming and result in effective interpretation and adaptation to local situations.

For example, the New York State Council on the Arts currently has 20 exhibitions in constant circulation throughout the state. One of these, "Erie Canal, 1817-1967," is a documentary commemorating the one-hundred fiftieth anniversary of the beginning of construction of the Erie Canal. It is based on an exhibition first presented by the Council in 1967. A converted canal boat, the "Erie Maid," was outfitted as an exhibition boat. It traveled to 30 Canal communities during a period of ten weeks in the sesquicentennial year, 1967, and attracted 140,000 visitors. In conjunction with the visit of the "Erie Maid," each community planned its own local celebration. Although history was the subject of the exhibition, the objective of the program was to arouse awareness of the Canal as an environmental factor in many communities where it had been neglected and turned into a sewer.

And don't forget the communications media! Television, radio and newspapers are eager for news reports on community-involved environmental quality projects, and will cooperate in carrying your message if they are kept informed of plans and schedules.

A news release should be a brief, well-written announcement of a program, exhibit, publication or special event. The key, newsworthy statement should be at the top. The body copy should give all the facts necessary for an editor to determine either to print the release or an edited version of it, or to send a reporter to cover the activity it describes. The five basic questions of journalism—"who? what? where? when? how?" —should be answered in the release. Radio stations will often use well-prepared public service announcements verbatim. The date of release, name of the person to contact in the museum and office telephone number should be clearly marked. Be sure to give a home telephone number if you think the timing of the announcement warrants it.

Timing is everything. The release must be mailed or delivered early enough (but not too early) for the media to use or make arrangements for coverage of the event. Remember that television producers need several days' notice to assign a crew.

Keeping up-to-date, making the community aware, leading public action—these are roles that museums can play effectively and productively in today's world.

Charts Showing Programs for Immediate Action by Citizens

The charts that follow enumerate some of the important environmental problems that must be acted upon. Similar charts related to different aspects of the environment can be developed and followed up with positive action.

THE CONSERVATION CRISIS
THE RESULT OF A DISEASE CALLED *MAN-CENTEREDNESS.*
What you can do, right now, about the quality of the environment.

SYMPTOMS	TODAY, in these United States	YESTERDAY, for thousands of years ....
too many PEOPLE	200 million of us, or *400 times* as many as there were when nature was in balance. We wreck the land, but continue to talk of growth as the only kind of progress.	Half a million Indians lived here for eons, their numbers so in harmony with the numbers of other creatures that the land was unharmed.
	SOMEDAY, if we live to see it	**SLIGHT RELIEF,** right now, while we press for real solutions ....
	An enlightened people will reduce their numbers to some compromise between today's hordes and yesterday's quiet few.	Practice voluntary population control before some natural disaster—or war—controls it for us. Don't believe the misleading reports about the U.S. birth rate. *The number of births here grows each year.* Learn about the starvation in India, China, Latin America, Africa, and relate it to our lives here.

SYMPTOMS	TODAY, in these United States	YESTERDAY, for thousands of years ....
too much TRASH	100 pounds of trash per year per person, most of which we still burn and then dump into the sky.	In Indian days the land itself was able to process the few wastes left behind. No paper, no plastics, no metals.
	SOMEDAY, if we live to see it	**SLIGHT RELIEF,** right now while we press for real solutions ....
	All trash will be re-used at home or by the growing waste-recovery industry. Following nature's example, we will learn to manage all materials without waste.	Buy no more "one way" containers or bottles; refuse to accept fancy or excessive wrappers; push for publication of newspapers and magazines printed on salvaged waste materials. (Store managers and their suppliers are very sensitive to public pressures. Try it—it works; my grocer never offers me a bag anymore when I buy only a few items.)

SYMPTOMS	TODAY, in these United States	YESTERDAY, for thousands of years . . . .
too much **GARBAGE**	100 pounds per person per year, all wasted. Enough to feed legions of the world's starving. It's tragic.	The food wasted in Indian times was fast consumed by the living earth—the living earth we're so quickly destroying.
	SLIGHT RELIEF, **right now, while we press** **for real solutions . . . .**	**SOMEDAY,** **if we live** **to see it . . . .**
	As with trash, we will learn to use all parts of the food, extracting its energy and nutrients to feed man and animals, or the land itself.	Almost all of us overeat by 30%. Eat less, live longer. Use all vegetable garbage for compost or throw it into the shrubbery (it beats peat moss). Not meat, though; meat brings rats and flies. Ready-to-serve products appear to eliminate waste. Don't be misled; there are mountains of garbage at the factory.

SYMPTOMS	TODAY, in these United States	YESTERDAY, for thousands of years . . . .
too much **SEWAGE**	200 gallons of sewage per person every day! And it all ends up in the rivers, often completely untreated. Almost nothing can live in such vile waters.	The land consumed the little sewage produced, just as it still does in the wilderness. All rivers were pure and clear a few years ago, full of fish and waterfowl.
	SOMEDAY, **if we live** **to see it . . . .**	**SLIGHT RELIEF,** **right now, while we press** **for real solutions . . . .**
	Kitchens, laundries, and bathrooms will have devices to extract wastes for re-use, and recycle the same water, over and over. Sewers will at last become obsolete, thank God.	Don't grind garbage down the drain; if you must leave food wastes, *use* them if at all possible. Don't over-use dishwashers or detergents. We use too much too often; it's so easy to do. Don't wash so often. Bathe and launder half as much; our friends will stick by us. Don't flush toilets so often; a tissue or cigaret butt flushed away with 8 gallons of precious water is criminal in these times. Try to cut all water-use in half; it's far more noble than you think. Patriotic, too.

203

SYMPTOMS	TODAY, in these United States	YESTERDAY, for thousands of years . . . .
WATER WASTE	Almost total waste; 1500 gallons per person, every day! And we wonder why there are water shortages!	Our forefathers on this continent cooked and washed with only *1 gallon per person per day*—less than 1% of the amount we use.
	SOMEDAY, if we live to see it	SLIGHT RELIEF, right now, while we press for real solutions . . . .
	Desalting the sea is not likely to be the long-range answer; it will only accommodate our excesses. We must learn to approach more natural water use levels, surely less than 10 gallons per person per day.	With a proper respect for the true value of water we will begin to use less of it automatically. We'll follow the "don'ts" (above) and buy only those appliances that use little water. Lawn-sprinkling should be ended *at once*; natural gardens and woodlands get by beautifully on rainwater alone, and when they're mulched with compost or garbage they thrive.

SYMPTOMS	TODAY, in these United States	YESTERDAY, for thousands of years . . . .
WASTED RAINFALL (overpaving)	Roads, parking lots, houses, buildings, lawns and even most farms are made to repel the rain, to flush it into the nearest sewer, from which it erodes and floods its way to the sea, polluted.	With huge forests and grasslands to catch and hold it, most rainfall was used by the land, and the sweet excess ran slowly to the sea.
	SOMEDAY, if we live to see it	SLIGHT RELIEF, right now, while we press for real solutions . . . .
	When we learn to build and live following nature's proven methods, parks, forests, and garden terraces will distinguish the new cities and towns of America.	Don't use waterproof paving materials (blacktop, concrete) if you can possibly avoid it. Use crushed stone or, if you must pave, let the run-off drain to sunken pebble gardens. Don't just pour the precious liquid down a storm drain. And, please, don't call rainy weather "bad weather" any more! Rain is a blessing, a free gift for which we should give thanks. Besides, our skins are waterproof; a little rain won't hurt them.

SYMPTOMS	TODAY, in these United States	YESTERDAY, for thousands of years ....
POLLUTED AIR	Foul, brown air, and rising rates of lung disease. Uncounted millions of cars causing most of the pollution, but we're too weak to walk.	Breathtakingly beautiful skies and brilliant starry nights.
	SOMEDAY, if we live to see it	SLIGHT RELIEF, right now, while we press for real solutions ....
	When we learn to manage aerial wastes along with all the others we'll have those beautiful skies again. At the present rate this will *never* happen, but if all waste-dumping were penalized NOW we could have fresh air again within ten years. Imagine!	Walk whenever possible; cars are the big air-foulers, and their smoke-control devices still aren't worth anything; they last only a few months. Use public transportation. Walking is healthful and it teaches lasting lessons about what foul-smelling inventions our precious automobiles are. Never say "haze" or "smog;" both are rare and the words are misleading. The stuff you see in the air is *smoke*—man-made wastes dumped into the sky.

SYMPTOMS	TODAY, in these United States	YESTERDAY, for thousands of years ....
POISONS	Unlimited sale and use of insecticides and herbicides. Poisons soaking into the land, killing wildlife, and getting ready to kill us.	No poisons; a world in which most "pests" were held in check by natural balances.
	SOMEDAY, if we live to see it	SLIGHT RELIEF, right now, while we press for real solutions ....
	Pest control through a restored "balance of nature."	Use pesticides—if you decide you must —with extreme respect for the consequences. Never use DDT or the newer and even more dangerous poisons. Protest highway salting in winter; it alone can kill streams. We must find less harmful answers.

SYMPTOMS	TODAY, in these United States	YESTERDAY, for thousands of years . . . .
Atomic RADIATION	An unseen but ever-present force, it is attacking us 24 hours a day.	Before X-rays and the atomic age, only mild, natural radiations were present.
	SOMEDAY, if we live to see it	**SLIGHT RELIEF,** right now, while we press for real solutions . . . .
	If we live is the key phrase. *If* we live, it will be in a world in which we thoroughly shield all radiation, permanently.	Avoid all unnecessary X-rays. But as far as nuclear radiation is concerned, relax and enjoy it; there's nothing you can do. Anyway, why worry; the dreaded effects may not show up for two or three generations, and who cares about life that far away in the future?

SYMPTOMS	TODAY, in these United States	YESTERDAY, for thousands of years . . . .
FOOD ADULTER- ANTS	Almost every food we buy and eat today has its load of unwanted chemicals, with some foods so loaded as to be almost unrecognizable. Reading the lists of ingredients is often enough to induce sickness. Puridoxine hydrochloride, artificial flavors, BTH added, etc. Ugh!	Left alone, nature produced only pure, wholesome foods.
	SOMEDAY, if we live to see it	**SLIGHT RELIEF,** right now, while we press for real solutions . . . .
	Strict laws and a new respect for the wonders of real, untouched foods may bring them back again.	Read the labels! Look at the junk you're about to eat. It's amazing how few of us ever read the fine print, and how few refuse to buy the stuff. Boycotts are the only force the food processors feel. And remember, all fruits and vegetables are loaded with insect spray; wash them thoroughly. Doctors now admit that weakness leading to disease comes from eating those poisons.

SYMPTOMS	TODAY, in these United States	YESTERDAY, for thousands of years . . . .
NOISE	Constant noise, car noise, electronic noise, aircraft noise, and human noise, all growing in intensity by the day. Soon: Sonic BOOM!	Tender silence; the condition for which all ears were made.
	SOMEDAY, if we live to see it	**SLIGHT RELIEF,** right now, while we press for real solutions . . . .
	We can't change the human body fast enough to accommodate it so we've got to reduce and isolate the noise.	Turn it down a bit. In this increasingly crowded world we must be more considerate or we'll be at each other's throats.

SYMPTOMS	TODAY, in these United States	YESTERDAY, for thousands of years . . . .
lack of PRIVACY	No escape. We have less privacy each day as we let society, government, and modern life intrude more and more.	Utter privacy in the wilderness whenever noise in the tent or cave got too loud.
	SOMEDAY, if we live to see it	**SLIGHT RELIEF,** right now, while we press for real solutions . . . .
	Utter privacy again, or an Orwellian nightmare came true.	Resist the use of snooping devices and other invasions of privacy. Try to abolish the anti-fence laws that make many residential areas wide open to every view. Every other country did this long ago.

SYMPTOMS	TODAY, in these United States	YESTERDAY, for thousands of years . . . .
destruction of NIGHT	Unless a lot of us care there is not much we can do. Kiss the stars goodbye, I guess, and get ready to tell our grandchildren why we wrecked so many wonders.	Soft, restful darkness in the shadows, under really heavenly heavens. Perfect settings for the deep rest all creatures require.
	SOMEDAY, if we live to see it	**SLIGHT RELIEF,** right now, while we press for real solutions . . . .
	Strict laws, needed even now, will limit artificial lighting to the surfaces that need light and prevent all light-spillage into the sky or onto others' properties.	Night totally destroyed; a generation unfamiliar with the wonder of darkness, moon, and bright stars. Possibly one of the biggest problems of all. It's too soon to tell.

The only real cure for man-centeredness, and its result, the conservation crisis, is a whole new way of life based on respect for the miracle we call creation, a respect for all the creatures with whom we share this planet, and a respect for the resources we now so tragically waste. Malcolm B. Wells, 1969

Thomas Cole. "The Pic-Nic", (1846). Oil, 47" x 71-3/4" Collection, The Brooklyn Museum, A. Augustus Healy Fund.

Earth Day has been observed by museums of all types in a variety of ways. The Brooklyn Museum in New York City noted the day with a highly effective and appropriate exhibit showing this painting by Thomas Cole with the Earth Day symbol alongside the painting. The display evoked a very favorable response from the public.

appendices

Appendix A

In August, 1970 President Nixon transmitted to the Congress the *First Annual Report of the Council on Environmental Quality*.* The message of transmittal is of particular interest to all who are concerned with increasing the public understanding of environmental problems. Excerpts from the President's Message are reprinted below:

To the Congress of the United States:

This first report to the Congress on the state of the Nation's environment is an historic milestone. It represents the first time in the history of nations that a people has paused, consciously and systematically, to take comprehensive stock of the quality of its surroundings.

It comes not a moment too soon. The recent upsurge of public concern over environmental questions reflects a belated recognition that man has been too cavalier in his relations with nature. Unless we arrest the depredations that have been inflicted so carelessly on our natural systems—which exist in an intricate set of balances—we face the prospect of ecological disaster.

The hopeful side is that such a prospect *can* be avoided. Although recognition of the danger has come late, it has come forcefully. There still are large gaps in our environmental knowledge, but a great deal of what needs to be done can be identified. Much of this has already been begun, and much more can be started quickly if we act now.

Getting at the Roots

"Environment" is not an abstract concern, or simply a matter of esthetics, or of personal taste—although it can and should involve these as well. Man is shaped to a great extent by his surroundings. Our physical nature, our mental health, our culture and institutions, our opportunities for challenge and fulfillment, our very survival—all of these are directly related to and affected by the environment in which we live. They depend upon the continued healthy functioning of the natural systems of the Earth.

Environmental deterioration is not a new phenomenon. But both the rate of deterioration and its critical impact have risen sharply in the years since the Second World War. Rapid population increases here and abroad, urbanization, the technology explosion and the patterns of economic growth have all contributed to our environmental crisis. While growth has brought extraordinary benefits, it has not been accompanied by sufficiently foresighted efforts to guide its development.

At the same time, in many localities determined action has brought positive improvements in the quality of air or water—demonstrating that, if we have the will and make the effort, we can meet environmental goals. We also have made important beginnings in developing the institutions and processes upon which any fundamental, long-range environmental improvement must be based.

The basic causes of our environmental troubles are complex and deeply imbedded. They include: our past tendency to emphasize quantitative growth at the expense of qualitative growth; the failure of our economy to provide full accounting for the social costs of environmental pollution; the failure to take environmental factors into account as a normal and necessary part of our planning and decision-making; the inadequacy of our institutions for dealing with problems that cut across traditional political boundaries; our dependence on conveniences, without regard for their impact on the environment; and more fundamentally, our failure to perceive the environment as a totality and to understand and to recognize the fundamental interdependence of all its parts, including man himself.

It should be obvious that we cannot correct such deep-rooted causes overnight. Nor can we simply legislate them away. We need new knowledge, new perceptions, new attitudes—and these must extend to all levels of government and throughout the private sector as well: to industry; to the professions; to each individual citizen in his job and in his home. We must seek nothing less than a basic reform in the way our society looks at problems and makes decisions.

Our educational system has a key role to play in bringing about this reform. We must train professional environmental managers to deal with pollution, land planning, and all the other technical requirements of a high quality environment. It is also vital that our entire society develop a new understanding and a new awareness of man's relation to his environment— what might be called "environmental literacy." This will require the development and teaching of environmental concepts at every point in the educational process.

While education may provide ultimate answers to long-range environmental problems, however, we cannot afford to defer reforms which are needed now. We have already begun to provide the institutional framework for effective environmental improvement.

Toward A Land Use Policy

Lately, our attention as a people has repeatedly and insistently been seized by urgent concerns and immediate crises: by the sudden blanketing of cities or even whole regions with dense clouds of smog, for example, or the discovery of mercury pollution in rivers. But as we take the longer view, we find another challenge looming large: the mounting pressures of population. Both the size and the distribution of our population have critical relevance to the quality of our environment and thus to the quality of our lives.

Population growth poses an urgent problem of global dimensions. If the United States is to have an effective voice in world population policies, it must demonstrate willingness to face its own population problems at home.

The particular impact of any given level of population growth depends in large measure on patterns of land use. Three quarters of our people now live in urban areas, and if present trends continue most of them in the future will live in a few mammoth urban concentrations. These concentrations put enormous pressure on transportation, sanitation and other public services. They sometimes create demands that exceed the resource capacity of the region, as in the case of water supply. They can aggravate pollution, overcrowd recreation facilities, limit open space, and make the restorative world of nature ever more remote from everyday life. Yet we would be blind not to recognize that for the most part the movement of people to the cities has been the result neither of perversity nor of happenstance, but rather of natural human aspirations for the better jobs, schools, medical services, cultural opportunities and excitement that have traditionally been associated with urban life.

If the aspirations which have drawn Americans to the city in the first instance and subsequently from the city core to the suburbs are often proving illusory, the solution does not lie in seeking escape from urban life. Our challenge is to find ways to promote the amenities of life in the midst of urban development: in short, to make urban life fulfilling rather than frustrating. Along with the essentials of jobs and housing, we must also provide open spaces and outdoor recreation opportunities, maintain acceptable levels of air and water quality, reduce noise and litter, and develop cityscapes that delight the eye and uplift the spirit.

By the same token, it is essential that we also make rural life itself more attractive, thus encouraging orderly growth in rural areas. The creation of greater economic, social, cultural, and recreational opportunities in rural parts of the country will lead to the strengthening of small cities and towns, contributing to the establishment of new growth centers in the nation's heartland region.

Throughout the nation there is a critical need for more effective land use planning, and for better controls over use of the land and the living systems that depend on it. Throughout our history, our greatest resource has been our land—forests and plains, mountains and marshlands, rivers and lakes. Our land has sustained us. It has given us a love of freedom, a sense of security, and courage to test the unknown.

We have treated our land as if it were a limitless resource. Traditionally, Americans have felt that what they do with their own land is their own business. This attitude has been a natural outgrowth of the pioneer spirit. Today, we are coming to realize that our land is finite, while our population is growing. The uses to which our generation puts the land can either expand or severely limit the choices our children will have. The time has come when we must accept the idea that none of us has a right to abuse the land, and that on the contrary society as a whole has a legitimate interest in proper land use. There is a national interest in effective land use planning all across the nation.

I believe that the problems of urbanization which I have described, of resource management, and of land and water use generally can only be met by comprehensive approaches which take into account the widest range of social, economic, and ecological concerns. I believe we must work toward development of a National Land Use Policy to be carried out by an effective partnership of Federal, State and local governments together, and, where appropriate, with new regional institutional arrangements.

Recycling of Wastes

The prospect of increasing population density adds urgency to the need for greater emphasis on recycling of "waste" products. More people means greater consumption—and thus more rapid depletion—of scarce natural resources; greater consumption means more "waste" to dispose of—whether in the form of solid wastes, or of the pollutants that foul our air and water.

Yet much of this waste is unnecessary. Essentially, waste is a human invention: Natural systems are generally "closed" systems. Energy is transformed into vegetation, vegetation into animal life, and the latter returns to the air and soil to be recycled once again. Man, on the other hand, has developed "open" systems—ending all too often in an open sewer or an open dump.

We can no longer afford the indiscriminate waste of our natural resources; neither should we accept as inevitable the mounting costs of waste removal. We must move increasingly toward closed systems that recycle what now are considered wastes back into useful and productive purposes. This poses a major challenge—and a major opportunity—for private industry. The Council on Environmental Quality is working to foster development of such systems. Establishment of the proposed Environmental Protection Agency would greatly increase our ability to address this need systematically and creatively.

Everyone's Task

As our government has moved ahead to improve our environmental management, it has been greatly heartening to me to see the extent and effectiveness of citizen concern and activity, and especially the commitment of young people to the task. The job of building a better environment is not one for government alone. It must engage the enthusiasm and commitment of our entire society. Citizen organizations have been in the forefront of action to support strengthened environmental programs. The Citizens Advisory Committee on Environmental Quality, under the chairmanship of Laurance S. Rockefeller, has provided an important link between the Federal Government's effort and this broad-ranging citizen activity.

Similarly, the active participation of the business community is essential. The government's regulation and enforcement activities will continue to be strengthened. Performance standards must be upgraded as rapidly as feasible. But regulation cannot do the whole job. Forward-looking initiatives by business itself are also vital—in research, in the development of new products and processes, in continuing and increased investment in pollution abatement equipment.

On the international front, the level of environmental concern and action has been rapidly rising. Many of our most pressing environmental problems know no political boundaries. Environmental monitoring and pollution of the seas are examples of major needs that require international cooperation, and that also provide an opportunity for the world's nations to work together for their common benefit.

In dealing with the environment we must learn not how to master nature but how to master ourselves, our institutions, and our technology. We must achieve a new awareness of our dependence on our surroundings and on the natural systems which support all life, but awareness must be coupled with a full realization of our enormous capability to alter these surroundings. Nowhere is this capability greater than in the United States, and this country must lead the way in showing that our human and technological resources can be devoted to a better life and an improved environment for ourselves and our inheritors on this planet.

Our environmental problems are very serious, indeed urgent, but they do not justify either panic or hysteria. The problems are highly complex, and their resolution will require rational, systematic approaches, hard work and patience. There must be a *national* commitment and a *rational* commitment.

The newly aroused concern with our natural environment embraces old and young alike, in all walks of life. For the young, it has a special urgency. They know that it involves not only our own lives now but the future of mankind. For their parents, it has a special poignancy—because ours is the first generation to feel the pangs of concern for the environmental legacy we leave to our children.

At the heart of this concern for the environment lies our concern for the human condition: for the welfare of man himself, now and in the future. As we look ahead to the end of this new decade of heightened environmental awareness, therefore, we should set ourselves a higher goal than merely remedying the damage wrought in decades past. We should strive for an environment that not only sustains life but enriches life, harmonizing the works of man and nature for the greater good of all.

* Available from the Superintendent of Documents, U.S. Government Printing Office, Washington, D.C. 20402, for $1.75

Appendix B

AMERICAN ASSOCIATION OF MUSEUMS

2233 Wisconsin Avenue, N.W.   Washington, D. C. 20007   (202) 338-5300

February 11, 1970

Mr. Jack Hardesty
Project Officer
Consumer Protection and Environmental Health Service
801 North Randolph Street, BC Tower #2
Arlington, Virginia 22203

Dear Mr. Hardesty:

On behalf of the American Association of Museums, I am pleased to be able to transmit to you, in draft, the report called for by Contract CPS 69-004, dated June 30, 1969, between the Consumer Protection and Environmental Health Service and the American Association of Museums. In accordance with this contract, the report covers the development of museum education techniques for human ecology, following the topics enumerated on page 3 of the contract.

The committee appointed by the American Association of Museums to perform the study and to prepare the report required by this contract represents an extraordinarily broad spectrum of background, discipline, interest and experience in America's museums. On behalf of both the committee and the Association, I express the hope that this report will be found satisfactory. Actually, the committee became so interested in the timely subject of the report that it worked well beyond the call of duty and has prepared a report far more comprehensive than would ordinarily be anticipated from the amount of time that was available. In fact, the committee has opened up so many fascinating and potentially effective avenues of procedure, yet without adequate time or funds to pursue them further, that I take the liberty of expressing to you the hope that the Consumer Protection and Environmental Health Service may well wish to make further funds available to the American Association of Museums in order to continue the work of the committee in greater depth and broader scope.

The American Association of Museums is grateful to your organization for its support of this important project, as well as for your recognition of the great educational potential of museums in a direction that has been relatively neglected.

Sincerely yours,

William C. Steere
President

WCS/gd

215

Appendix C

Organizations Engaged in Environmental Programs

The number of organizations conducting environmental programs is growing daily. The list that follows is a selected compilation of agencies, public and private, that prepare and distribute resource materials related to problems of the environment which they are very willing to share with educational institutions.

Government Agencies

When writing to government agencies, it is suggested that inquiries be addressed to the Division of Information.

Council on Environmental Quality
722 Jackson Place, N.W.
Washington, D.C. 20006

Environmental Protection Agency
1626 K Street, N.W.
Washington, D.C. 20006

U.S. Department of Agriculture
14th Street and Independence Avenue, S.W.
Washington, D.C. 20250

U.S. Department of Commerce
14th Street between Constitution Avenue and E Street, N.W.
Washington, D.C. 20230

U.S. Department of Health, Education, and Welfare
330 Independence Avenue, S.W.
Washington, D.C. 20201

U.S. Department of Housing and Urban Development
451 Seventh Street, S.W.
Washington, D.C. 20410

U.S. Department of the Interior
C Street Between 18th and 19th Streets, N.W.
Washington, D.C. 20240

U.S. Department of State
2201 C Street, N.W.
Washington, D.C. 20520

Private Organizations

Air Pollution Control Association
440 Fifth Avenue
Pittsburgh, Pennsylvania 15213

American Association for the Advancement of Science
1515 Massachusetts AVenue, N.W.
Washington, D.C. 20005

American Association for Conservation Information
1416 Ninth Street
Sacramento, California 95814

American Association of Museums
2233 Wisconsin Avenue, N.W.
Washington, D.C. 20007

American Conservation Association
30 Rockefeller Plaza
New York, New York 10020

American Forest Institute
1835 K Street, N.W.
Washington, D.C. 20006

American Forestry Association
1919 17th Street, N.W.
Washington, D.C. 20006

American Geographical Society
Broadway at 156th Street
New York, New York 10032

American Institute of Architects
1785 Massachusetts Avenue, N.W.
Washington, D.C. 20036

American Littoral Society
Sandy Hook
Highlands, New Jersey 07732

American Nature Study Society
Milewood Road
Verbank, New York 12585

American Society of Landscape Architects
2000 K Street, N.W.
Washington, D.C. 20006

Association for Voluntary Sterilization
14 West 40th Street
New York, New York 10018

Boy Scouts of America
National Headquarters
North Brunswick, New Jersey 18902

Camp Fire Girls, Inc.
65 Worth Street
New York, New York

Citizens' Advisory Committee on Recreation and Natural Beauty
1700 Pennsylvania Avenue, N.W.
Washington, D.C. 20006

Citizens Committee on Natural Resources
1346 Connecticut Avenue, N.W.
Washington, D.C. 20036

Citizens for Clean Air
502 Park Avenue
New York, New York 10022

Citizens for a Quieter City
345 Park Avenue
New York, New York 10022

Committee for Environmental Information
438 N. Skinker Boulevard
St. Louis, Missouri 63130

Congress on Optimum Population and Environment
65 East Huron Street
Chicago, Illinois

Conservation Foundation, The
1717 Massachusetts Avenue, N.W.
Washington, D.C. 20036

Defenders of Wildlife
731 Dupont Circle Building
Washington, D.C. 20036

Educational Foundation for Nuclear Science
935 East 60th Street
Chicago, Illinois 60637

Environmental Action, Inc.
2000 P Street, N.W.
Washington, D.C. 20036

Environmental Defense Fund
P.O. Drawer 740
Stony Brook, New York 11790

Ford Foundation
320 East 43rd Street
New York, New York 10017

Friends of the Earth
451 Pacific Avenue
San Francisco, California 94133
and 30 East 42nd Street
New York, New York 10017

Garden Club of America, The
598 Madison Avenue
New York, New York 10022

General Federation of Women's Clubs
1734 N Street, N.W.
Washington, D.C. 20036

Girl Scouts of the U.S.A.
National Headquarters
830 Third Avenue
New York, New York

Hugh Moore Fund
60 East 42nd Street
New York, New York

International Planned Parenthood (Western Hemisphere Region)
51 East 42nd Street
New York, New York 10017

International Union for the Conservation of Nature and Natural Resources
1110 Morges, Switzerland

Izaak Walton League of America,
1326 Waukegan Road
Glenview, Illinois 60025

John Muir Institute for Environmental Studies
451 Pacific Avenue
San Francisco, California 94133
and Box 11
Cedar Crest, New Mexico 87008

Junior Leagues of America, Inc.
Waldorf Astoria Hotel
New York, New York 10022

Keep America Beautiful, Inc.
99 Park Avenue
New York, New York 10016

The League of Women Voters of the United States
1730 M Street, N.W.
Washington, D.C. 20036

Massachusetts Audubon Society
South Great Road
Lincoln, Massachusetts 01773

Men's Garden Clubs of America
Morrisville, New York 13408

National Association of Soil and Water Conservation Districts
1025 Vermont Avenue, N.W.
Washington, D.C. 20005

National Audubon Society
1130 Fifth Avenue
New York, New York 10028

National Council of State Garden Clubs, Inc.
4401 Magnolia Avenue
St. Louis, Missouri 63110

National Parks Association
1701 18th Street, N.W.
Washington, D.C. 20009

National Recreation and Park Association
1700 Pennsylvania Avenue, N.W.
Washington, D.C. 20036

National Wildlife Federation
1412 16th Street, N.W.
Washington, D.C. 20036

Natural Resources Council of ner-America
719 17th Street, N.W.
Washington, D.C. 20005

Natural Resources Defense Council, Inc.
36 West 44th Street
New York, New York 10036

Natural Science for Youth Foundation
763 Silvermine Road
New Canaan, Connecticut 06840

Nature Conservancy, The
1522 K Street, N.W.
Washington, D.C. 20005

North American Wildlife Foundation
709 Wire Building
Washington, D.C. 20005

Open Space Institute
145 East 52nd Street
New York, New York 10022

Planned Parenthood-World Population
515 Madison Avenue
New York, New York 10022

The Population Council
245 Park Avenue
New York, New York 10017

Population Crisis Committee
1730 K Street, N.W.
Washington, D.C. 20006

Population Reference Bureau
1755 Massachusetts Avenue
Washington, D.C. 20036

Resources for the Future, Inc.
1755 Massachusetts Avenue, N.W.
Washington, D.C. 20036

Rockefeller Foundation
111 West 50th Street
New York, New York 10020

Scenic Hudson Preservation Conference
500 Fifth Avenue, Suite 1625
New York, New York 10036

Scientists' Institute for Public Information
30 East 68th Street
New York, New York 10021

Sierra Club
1050 Mills Tower
San Francisco, California 94104

Soil Conservation Society of America
7515 N.E. Ankeny Road
Ankeny, Iowa 50021

Sport Fishing Institute
Suite 503, 719 13th Street, N.W.
Washington, D.C. 20005

The Urban Coalition
2100 M Street, N.W.
Washington, D.C. 20037

The Urban Land Institute
1200 18th Street, N.W.
Washington, D.C. 20036

The Wilderness Society
729 15th Street, N.W.
Washington, D.C. 20005

Wildlife Management Institute
709 Wire Building
Washington, D.C. 20005

World Wildlife Fund
Suite 728, 910 17th Street, N.W.
Washington, D.C. 20009

Young Women's Christian Association
National Board
600 Lexington Avenue
New York, New York 10022

Zero Population Growth
367 State Street
Los Altos, California 94022

Appendix D
Publications

GENERAL REFERENCE—BOOKS

Man and The Environment

Bernarde, Melvin A. 1970. *Our Precarious Habitat.* New York. Norton.

Boulding, Kenneth E. 1964. *The Meaning of the 20th Century.* New York. Harper Colophon.

Boyle, Robert H. 1969. *The Hudson River: A Natural and Unnatural History.* New York. Dutton.

Carvajal, Joan and Martha E. Munzer. 1968. *Conservation Education: A Selected Bibliography.* Billings, Montana. Conservation Education Association.

Commoner, Barry. 1966. *Science and Survival.* New York. Collier.

Dansereau, Pierre. (Editor) 1970. *Challenge for Survival: Land, Air and Water for Man in Megalopolis.* Columbia University Press.

Darling, F. Fraser and Noel Eichorn. 1967. *Man and Nature in the National Parks.* Washington, D.C. The Conservation Foundation.

Darling, F. Fraser and John P. Milton. 1966. *Future Environments of North America.* New York. Natural History Press.

Dasmann, Raymond F. 1967. *A Different Kind of Country.* New York. Macmillan.

Dasmann, Raymond F. 1968. *Environmental Conservation.* New York. Wiley.

Dasmann, Raymond F. 1968. *An Environment Fit for People.* New York. Public Affairs Pamphlet No. 421.

Dubos, Rene. 1965. *Man Adapting.* New Haven. Yale University Press.

Dubos, Rene. 1969. *So Human an Animal.* New York. Scribner's.

Ewald, William. (Editor) 1968. *Environment and Change: The Next Fifty Years.* Bloomington. Indiana University Press.

Ferkiss, Victor C. 1969. *Technological Man: The Myth and the Reality.* New York. Braziller.

Fisher, James, Noel Simon and Jack Vinvent. 1969. *Wildlife in Danger.* New York. Viking.

Fortune. 1970. *The Environment, A National Mission of the Seventies.* New York. Harper and Row (Perennial Library).

Grossman, Mary Louise, Shelly Grossman and John N. Hamlet. 1969. *Our Vanishing Wilderness.* New York. Madison Square Press.

Helfrich, Harold, Jr. 1970. *The Environmental Crisis: Man's Struggle to Live With Himself.* New Haven. Yale University Press.

Krutch, Joseph Wood. 1966. *The Great Chain of Life.* New York. Pyramid.

Leopold, Aldo. (Editor) 1966. *A Sand Country Almanac.* New York. Oxford University Press.

Linton, Roy M. 1970. *Terracide. America's Destruction of Her Living Environment.* Boston. Little, Brown.

Little, Charles E. 1968. *Challenge of the Land.* New York. Open Space Action Institute.

Love, Glen A. and Rhoda M. 1970. *Ecological Crisis Readings for Survival.* New York. Harcourt, Brace, and Jovanovich.

McClung, Robert M. 1969. *Lost Wild America.* New York. Morrow.

McHale, John. 1969. *The Future of the Future.* New York. Braziller.

McHale, John. 1969. *The Ecological Context.* New York. Braziller.

McHarg, Ian S. 1969. *Design with Nature.* New York. Natural History Press.

Mitchell, John. (Editor) 1970. *Ecotactics, The Sierra Club Handbook.* Pocket Books.

Moore, John A. 1970. *Science for Society. A Bibliography.* Washington, D.C. American Association Advancement of Science.

Murphy, Robert. 1968. *Wild Sanctuaries: Our National Wildlife Refuges—A Heritage Restored.* New York. Dutton.

Nash, Robert. 1967. *Wilderness and the American Mind.* New Haven. Yale University Press.

National Academy of Sciences—National Research Council. 1969. *Resources and Man: A Study and Recommendations.* Committee on Resources and Man, Division of Earth Sciences, National Academy of Science—National Research Council. Freeman.

Odum, Eugene P. 1963. *Edology.* New York. Holt, Rinehart and Winston.

Osborn, Fairfield. 1948. *Our Plundered Planet.* Boston. Little, Brown.

Ottinger, Betty Ann. 1970. *What Every Woman Should Know—and Do—About Pollution.* E.P. Press.

Payne, Roger S. 1970. *The Whale Book and Record.* Del Mar, California. C/R/M.

Porter, Eliot. 1967. *In Wilderness Is The Preservation of the World.* New York. Sierra Club—Ballantine.

Post, R.G. and R.L. Seale. (Editors) 1966. *Water Production Using Nuclear Energy.* Tucson. University of Arizona Press.

Prince Philip, Duke of Edinburgh and Fisher, James. 1970. *Wildlife in Crisis.* New York. Cowles.

Rienow, Robert and Leona T. 1967. *Moment in the Sun.* New York. Ballantine.

Roosevelt, Nicholas. 1970. *Conservation: Now or Never.* New York. Dodd, Mead.

Saxe, Joseph L. 1971. *A Strategy for Citizen Action.* New York. Knopf.

Sears, Paul B. 1966. *The Living Landscape.* New York. Basic Books.

Shepard, Paul. 1967. *Man in the Landscape: A Historical View of the Esthetics of Nature.* New York. Knopf.

Shepard, Paul and Daniel McKinley. (Editors) 1969. *The Subversive Science: Escape Toward and Ecology of Man.* Boston. Houghton Mifflin.

Smithsonian Institution. 1967. *The Fitness of Man's Environment.* Smithsonian Institution Press.

Snyder, G. 1969. *Earth House Held.* San Francisco. New Directions.

Train, Russell, E. 1966. *A New Revolution.* Washington, D.C. Conservation Foundation.

Train, Russell E., Robert Cahn and Gordon J. MacDonald. 1970. *Environmental Quality.* Washington, D.C. Superintendent of Documents. U.S. Government and Printing Office.

Tunnard, Christopher and Boris Puskarer. 1963. *Man-Made America: Chaos or Control?* New Haven. Yale University Press.

Udall, Stewart L. 1963. *The Quiet Crisis.* New York. Aron.

Udall, Stewart L. 1969. *1976: Agenda for Tomorrow.* New York. Harcourt, Brace and World.

Whiteside, Thomas. 1970. *Defoliation.* New York. Ballantine-Friends of the Earth.

Whyte, William H. 1967. *The Last Landscape.* New York. Doubleday.

Population

Borgstrom, George. 1965. *The Hungry Planet.* New York. Collier-Macmillan.

Borgstrom, George. 1969. *Too Many: A Study of Earth's Biological Limitations.* New York. Macmillan.

Brown, Harrison. 1954. *The Challenge of Man's Future.* New York. Viking Compass.

Day, L.H. and A.T. Day. 1965. *Too Many Americans.* New York. Dell.

Ehrlich, Paul R. and Anne H. Ehrlich. 1970. *Population, Resources, Environment: Issues in Human Ecology.* San Francisco. Freeman.

Freedman, R. (Editor) 1964. *Population: The Vital Revolution.* New York. Doubleday.

Gordon, John E. 1969. *Social Implications of Nutrition and Disease.* Archives of Environmental Health, Vol. 18, pp. 216-34.

Hall, Edward T. 1966. *The Hidden Dimensions.* New York. Doubleday.

Hardin, Garrett. 1969. *Population, Evolution, and Birth Control: A Collage of Controversial Ideas.* San Francisco. Freeman.

Massachusetts Institute of Technology. 1969. *Symposium on Malnutrition, Learning, and Behavior.* MIT Press.

Paddock, William and Paul. 1964. *Hungry Nations.* Boston. Little, Brown.

Paddock, William and Paul. 1967. *Famine, 1975.* Boston. Little, Brown.

Petersen, William. 1964. *The Politics of Population.* New York. Doubleday, Anchor Book.

Population Council. 1969. *Basic Library in Population.* New York.

Population Council. 1970. *Family Planning and Population.* New York.

Population Reference Bureau, Inc. 1970. *Population Reference Bureau Data Sheet.* Washington, D.C. Population Reference Bureau.

Prindle, Richard A., M.D. 1969. *The Population Crisis: The Major Problem on Environmental Control.*

Archives of Environmental Health. Vol. 19, pp. 564-8.

Publications About Planned Parenthood. 1969. New York. Planned Parenthood-World Population.

A Selected Bibliography: Family Planning, Population, Related Subjects. New York. Planned Parenthood-World Population.

Taylor, G.R. 1968. *The Biological Time Bomb.* New York. World.

Young, Louise B. (Editor) 1968. *Population in Perspective.* New York. Oxford University Press.

Population—Cities

Abrams, Charles. 1966. *The City is the Frontier.* New York. Harper and Row.

Cantry, Donald. 1969. *The New City: National Committee on Urban Growth Policy.* New York. Frederick Praeger.

Gruen, Victor. 1965. *The Heart of Our Cities.* New York. Simon & Shuster.

Jacobs, Jane. 1964. *The Death and Life of Great American Cities.* New York. Random House.

Mumford, Lewis. 1961. *The City in History.* New York. Harcourt, Brace and World.

Scientific American. 1965. *Cities.* New York. Knopf.

Whyte, William H. 1968. *The Last Landscape.* New York. Doubleday.

Pollution

Alexander, P. 1965. *Atomic Radiations and Life.* Baltimore. Penguin.

American Chemical Society. 1969. *Cleaning our Environment: The Chemical Basis for Action.* Report by the Subcommittee on Environmental Equipment. Washington, D.C. American Chemical Society.

Bardach, John. 1967. *Harvest of the Sea.* New York. Harper and Row.

Blake, Peter. 1964. *God's Own Junkyard: The Planned Deterioration of America's Landscape.* New York. Holt, Rinehart and Winston.

Carson, Rachel. 1962. *The Silent Spring.* New York. Houghton Mifflin

Cowan, Edward. 1968. *Oil and Water: The Torrey Canyon Disaster.* Philadelphia. Lippincott.

Dorset, Jean. 1970. *Before Nature Dies.* Boston. Houghton Mifflin.

Esposito, John C. and Larry J. Silverman. 1970. *Vanishing Air: The Ralph Nader Study Group Report on Air Pollution.* New York. Grossman.

Goldman, Marshall I. (Editor) 1967. *Controlling Pollution: The Economics of a Cleaner America.* Englewood, New Jersey. Prentice-Hall.

Kneese, Alan V. 1962. 1968. *Water Pollution: Economic Aspects and Research Needs.* Washington. Resources for the Future.

Mannix, Daniel P. 1969. *Troubled Waters.* New York. Dutton.

Marx, Wesley. 1967. *The Frail Ocean.* New York. Coward McCann.

National Academy of Sciences-National Research Council. 1966. *Waste Management and Control.*

PERIODICALS

Museums of all types publish excellent bulletins and journals as part of their educational programs. Increasingly, these journals present discussions of environmental topics of immediate interest.

For example, in 1969 the Museum of Natural Science of Cleveland held a very significant environmental symposium, perhaps the first sponsored by a museum, and printed the proceedings in their bulletin, *Explorer*. The New England Aquarium has published highly informative articles on water resources in *Aquasphere*. Readers of the *Bulletin* of the Field Museum of Natural History in Chicago learned, in a recent article by the museum's curator of mineralogy, of the causes of airborne lead pollution, its effects, and the possibilities for eliminating this environmental contaminant. Another issue reprinted a very controversial address delivered by ecologist Paul Ehrlich at the First National Congress on Population and Environment, evoking a vigorous readership response.

Agricultural extension services and conservation departments of a number of states publish newsletters and bulletins that contain valuable information for the residents of a given region. These, too, should be consulted regularly for background information about local issues as well as for the ideas they may stimulate for development of new projects.

Following is a selected listing of periodicals and journals that often present articles related to environmental concerns. These are available in libraries, by subscription, or as benefits of membership in the sponsoring organization. Prices are for annual subscription or membership dues, unless otherwise stated.

American Forests. Monthly. $6.00. Articles on resources, parks, and recreation. American Forestry Association. 919 17th Street, N.W., Washington, D.C. 22226.

Architectural Forum. 10 times annually. $10.00. Includes discussion about the improvement of urban environments. Urban America. 115 West 57th Street, New York, N.Y. 10019.

American Institute of Architects Journal. Monthly. $5.00. Broad coverage of environmental topics, well illustrated. American Institute of Architects. 1735 New York Avenue, N.W., Washington, D.C. 20006.

Audubon. Bimonthly. $8.50. Extensive, beautifully illustrated coverage of conservation and ecology. National Audubon Society. 1130 Fifth Avenue, New York, N.Y. 10028.

BioScience. Twice monthly. Institutional subscription price $18.00. Journal for members of the American Institute of Biological Sciences. Includes discussions of environmental problems by leading scientific authorities. American Institute of Biological Sciences. 3900 Wisconsin Avenue, N.W., Washington, D.C. 20016.

Bulletin of the Atomic Scientists. Educational Foundation for Nuclear Science. 935 East 60th Street, Chicago, Illinois 60637.

Catalyst For Environmental Quality. Monthly. $5.00. All aspects of environmental concerns. 274 Madison Avenue, New York, N.Y. 10016.

C. F. Letter. Monthly. Free. Includes news of environmental action. Conservation Foundation, 1717 Massachusetts Avenue, N.W., Washington, D.C. 20036.

City. Bimonthly. $5.00. Review of urban America. Free to members and contributors. Urban America. 1717 Massachusetts Avenue, N.W., Washington, D.C. 20036.

Daedalus. Quarterly. $7.50. Usually, an issue covers one topic. Excellent treatment is given to such topics as problems of the cities, the changing environment, science and technology in our society. American Academy of Arts and Sciences.

Environment. 10 times annually. $8.50. Covers all aspects of the environment. Committee for Environmental Information. 438 North Skinker Boulevard, St. Louis, Missouri 63130.

Environmental Action Newsletter. Biweekly. Environemtnal Action, Inc. 2000 P Street, N.W., Washington, D.C. 20036.

Environmental Education. Quarterly. $7.50. Primarily research articles, project reports, and critical essays designed to advance the scientific study of conservation communications and improve field practice in environmental education. Dembar Educational Research Services, Inc. Box 1605, Madison, Wisconsin 53701.

Journal of Forestry. Monthly. $12.00. Forest resources. Society of American Foresters. 1010 16th

Street, N.W., Washington, D.C. 20036.

The Living Wilderness. Quarterly. Covers wilderness, wildlife, scenic beauty. Membership publication of The Wilderness Society. 729 15th Street, N.W., Washington, D.C. 20005.

National Wildlife. Six times annually. $6.50 with associate membership. National Wildlife Federation. 1412 16th Street, N.W., Washington, D.C. 20036.

Natural History. 10 times annually. $7.50. All aspects of natural history, including anthropology, geology, and astronomy. Excellent illustrations. The American Museum of Natural History. Central Park West at 79th Street, New York, N.Y. 10024.

Not Man Apart. Monthly. Articles on conservation and environmental protection. Annual dues are $15.00, of which $3.00 is for subscription to this publication. Friends of the Earth. 8016 Zuni Road, S.E., Albuquerque, New Mexico, 87108.

Pacific Discovery. Bimonthly. $4.00. California Academy of Sciences. Golden Gate Park, San Francisco, California 94118.

Parks and Recreation. Monthly. $7.50. National Recreation and Parks Association. Washington, D.C.

Ranger Rick's Nature Magazine. 10 times annually. $6.00. Illustrated nature magazine for children and people who work with children. Many features are related to problems of the environment. Educational bulk rates available. National Wildlife Federation. 1412 16th

Street, N.W., Washington, D.C. 20036.

Science. Weekly. $12.00. Includes articles and notes on environmental topics. American Association for the Advancement of Science. Free to members. 1515 Massachusetts Avenue, N.W., Washington, D.C. 20005.

Scientific American. Monthly. $10.00. Articles, and especially single topic issues, cover major environmental topics comprehensively. 415 Madison Avenue, New York, N.Y. 10017.

Sierra Club Bulletin. Monthly except January. $5.00 for non-members. Annual dues $12.00, of which $3.00 is for subscription to Bulletin. Sierra Club. 1050 Mills Tower, San Francisco, California 94104.

Smithsonian. Monthly. $10.00. Representative of the Smithsonian's fields of research and education. Smithsonian Associates. 900 Jefferson Drive, Washington, D.C. 20560.

HANDBOOKS, INSTRUCTIONAL JOURNALS, AND CATALOGUES

Brennan, Matthew J. (Editor), **People and Their Environment, Teachers' Curriculum Guide to Conservation Education.** Chicago: J.G. Ferguson Publishing Company, 1968-69.

Citizens Advisory Committee on Recreation and Natural Beauty, **Citizen Manual for Community Action.** Washington, D.C.: U.S. Government Printing Office, 1968.

——————, **Community Action for Environmental Quality.** Washington, D.C.: U.S. Government Printing Office, 1970.

——————, **Community Action for Natural Beauty.** Washington, D.C.: U.S. Government Printing Office, 1966.

De Bell, Garrett, **The Environmental Handbook.** New York: Ballantine-Friends of the Earth, 1970.

Harden, Cleo E., **How to Preserve Animals and Other Specimens in Clear Plastic.** Naturegraph Company. 8339 West Dry Creek Road, Healdsburg, California.

Mitchell, John G., with Constance Stallings, **Ecotactics: The Sierra Club Handbook for Environmental Activists.** New York: Sierra Club-Pocket Books, 1970.

National Audubon Society, **Audubon Aids in Natural Science.** A catalogue of educational materials, including charts, films, and slides, is available upon request. New York: National Audubon Society, 1971.

National Wildlife Federation, **Our National EQ: The First National Wildlife Federation Index of Environmental Quality.** Washington, D.C.: National Wildlife Federation, 1969, 1970.

Neal, Arminta, **Help! for Small Museums.** Pruett Press. Box 1560, Boulder, Colorado.

Percy, H.M., **New Materials in Sculpture.** Alec Tirandi, Ltd., 1966. 72 Charlotte Street, London.

President's Council on Recreation and Natural Beauty, **From Sea to Shining Sea: A Report on the American Environment—Our National Heritage.** Washington, D.C.: U.S. Government Printing Office, 1968.

Appendix E

Films on Environmental Education

Motion pictures are a valuable asset in museum programs on ecology. They can be used singly, as part of an over-all exhibit, or combined in series to form "film festivals."

There are a great many excellent films available on ecological problems. Some have been made by government agencies, others by private organizations, many by producers of materials for schools, and some by the television networks.

An extensive, alphabetized listing of sources for motion pictures and filmstrips will be found on the pages that follow. Films are classified according to chapter headings: "Man and the Environment"; "Pollution"; "Population."

Queries sent to these sources will bring you catalogs which will classify films in regard to subject matter and fully describe film contents, as well as indicating prices for rental or purchase and preview privileges. For additional information you would be well advised to contact local public libraries, colleges and universities, and audiovisual centers.

When the film distributors have classified films according to age levels, this information is included, and coded as follows: P/Preliminary, I/Intermediate, J/Junior High School, S/Senior High School, C/College, A/Adult.

The information describing each film is presented as it appears in the original catalog or list of the individual distributor or producer.

Producers and Distributors

American Documentary Films, 336 West 84th Street, New York, New York

American Film Productions, 1540 Broadway, New York, New York 10036

American Institute of Biological Science, 2000 P Street, N.W., Washington, D.C. 20006

American Museum of Natural History, Central Park West and 79th Street, New York, New York 10024

Association Films, 600 Madison Avenue, New York, New York 10022

Association of Instructional Material, 347 Madison Avenue, New York, New York 10017

Bailey-Film Associates, 11559 Santa Monica Boulevard, Los Angeles, California 90025

Bell Telephone and Telegraph, 195 Broadway, New York, New York 10007

B. F. A. Educational Media, Division of Columbia Broadcasting System, Inc., 2211 Michigan Avenue, Santa Monica, California 90404

Boy Scouts of America, New Brunswick, New Jersey 08903

Bureau of Community Environmental Management, Public Health Service, U.S. Department of Health, Education, and Welfare, 433 West Van Buren, Chicago, Illinois 60607

Bureau of Land Management, Department of the Interior, Washington, D.C. 20240

Carousel Films, Inc., 1501 Broadway, New York, New York 10036

CBS/Holt Group, 383 Madison Avenue, New York, New York 10017

CCM Films, 600 Grand Avenue, Ridgefield, New Jersey 07657

Cenco Educational Films, 1700 Irving Park Road, Chicago, Illinois 60613

Churchill Films, 6671 Sunset Boulevard, Los Angeles, California 90025

Classroom Film Distributors, 5620 Hollywood Boulevard, Hollywood, California 90038

Colonial Williamsburg, Richmond, Virginia 23219

Columbia University Press, 2960 Broadway, New York, New York 10027

Contemporary Films/McGraw-Hill, Inc., 330 West 42nd Street, New York, New York 10036

Coronet Films, 65 East South Water Street, Chicago, Illinois 60601

Department of Conservation and Economic Development, State of Virginia, 911 Broad Street, Richmond, Virginia 23219

Du Art Film Laboratories, 245 West 55th Street, New York, New York 10019

Educational Development Center Film Library, 39 Chapel Street, Newton, Massachusetts 02160

Educational Recordings Library, State University of New York, Thurlow Terrace, Albany, New York

Encylopaedia Britannica Education Corporation, 425 North Michigan Avenue, Chicago, Illinois 60611

Encyclopaedia Britannica Films, Inc., 1150 Wilmette Avenue, Wilmette, Illinois 60091

Environmental Control Administration, U.S. Department of Health, Education, and Welfare, Environmental Health Service, Rockville, Maryland 20852

Federal Water Quality Administration, U.S. Department of Interior, 33 East Congress Parkway, Chicago, Illinois

Film Service Library, 3805 West Magnolia Boulevard, Burbank, California 91505

FilmFax Productions, Inc., Station Plaza, Bedford Hills, New York 10507

Films, Inc., 1144 Wilmette Avenue, Wilmette, Illinois 60091

Filmstrip House, 432 Park Avenue South, New York, New York 10016

Freeman, W. H. & Co., 660 Market Street, San Francisco, California 94104

Graphic Curriculum, 41 East 42nd Street, New York, New York 10017

Holt, Rinehart & Winston, Inc., 383 Madison Avenue, New York, New York 10017

Indiana University, Audio-Visual Center, NET Film Service, Bloomington, Indiana 47401

Informative Classroom Picture Publishers, 31 Ottawa Avenue, N.W., Grand Rapids, Michigan 49502

International Business Machines, Armonk, New York 10504

International Film Bureau, 332 South Michigan Avenue, Chicago, Illinois 60604

Jam Handy, 2821 East Grand Boulevard, Detroit, Michigan 48211

Keep America Beautiful Productions, 99 Park Avenue, New York, New York 10016

Learning Corporation of America, 711 Fifth Avenue, New York, New York 10022

Life Magazine, Filmstrip Division, 9 Rockefeller Plaza, New York, New York 10020

Lutheran Film Associates, 315 Park Avenue South, New York, New York 10010

McCall's Educational Service, 230 Park Avenue, New York, New York 10017

Modern Learning Aids, 315 Springfield Avenue, Summit, New Jersey 07901

McGraw-Hill Text Films, 330 West 42nd Street, New York, New York 10018

Michigan State University, Instructional Media Center, East Lansing, Michigan 48824

Modern Picture Library, P.O. Box 11222, Fort Worth, Texas 76110

Modern Talking Pictures Service, 3 East 54th Street, New York, New York 10022

Modern Talking Pictures Service, 1212 Avenue of The Americas, New York, New York 10036

229

Moody Institute of Science, 12000 East Washington Boulevard, Whittier, California 94120

National Aeronautics and Space Administration, 1520 H Street, N.W., Washington, D.C. 20025

National Audiovisual Center (General Services Administration), Washington, D.C.

National Audubon Society, 1130 Fifth Avenue, New York, New York 10028

NBC Educational Enterprises, 30 Rockefeller Plaza, New York, New York 10020

National Council of State Garden Clubs, 4401 Magnolia Avenue, St. Louis, Missouri 63110

National Education Association, 1201 16th Street, N.W., Washington, D.C. 20046

National Educational Television, Inc., 12 Columbus Circle, New York, New York 10023

National Film Board of Canada, 680 Fifth Avenue, New York, New York 10019

National Medical Audiovisual Center (Annex), Station K, Atlanta, Georgia 30324

National Wildlife Federation, Washington, D.C. 20036

New York State Environmental Conservation Department, Albany, New York 12201

Niles, Fred A. Production, 6555 North Waukesha, Chicago, Illinois 60646

Northern Illinois University, Instructional Media Distribution Department, Altgeld Hall, Room 114, DeKalb, Illinois 60115

Ohio Department of Natural Resources, 1106 Ohio Department Building, Columbus, Ohio 43215

Planned Parenthood-World Population, 267 West 25th Street, New York, New York 10011

Population Dynamics, Ninth Avenue, N.W., Seattle, Washington

Procter and Gamble Education Department, 301 East 6th Street, Cincinnati, Ohio 45202

Shell Film Library, Shell Oil Company, 50 West 50th Street, New York, New York 10020

Sierra Club, 1010 Mills Tower, San Francisco, California 94104

Sigma Educational Films, P.O. Box 1235, Studio City, California 91604

Silver-Burdett, Morristown, New Jersey 07960

Silvermine Films, 49 West 45th Street, New York, New York 10036

Society for Visual Education, 1345 Diversey Parkway, Chicago, Illinois 60614

Soil Conservation Service, Motion Picture Library, Box 11222, Fort Worth, Texas 76110

South Carolina Audio-Visual Library, 1416 Senate Street, Columbia, South Carolina 20201

Sperry-Rand Corp., Graphic Service Department, Sperry-Rand Building, New York, New York 10019

Sterling Educational Films, Inc., 241 East 34th Street, New York, New York 10016

Tennessee Valley Authority, Box 1050, Knoxville, Tennessee 37901

United States Atomic Energy Commission, Division of Public Information, Washington, D.C. 20025

United States Department of Agriculture, Forest Service, South Building, 12th Street and Independence Avenue, S.W., Washington, D.C. 20250

United States Department of Agriculture, Motion Picture Service, Washington, D.C. 20250

United States Department of Health, Education, and Welfare, 330 Independence Avenue, Washington, D.C. 20201 (see also BCEM and ECA)

United World Films, Inc., 221 Park AVenue South, New York, New York 10003

University of Southern California, Film Distribution Section, University Place, Los Angeles, California 90007

Walt Disney Productions, Educational Film Division, 350 South Buena Vista Avenue, Burbank, California 91503

Walter Reade-Sterling Films, Educational Films, Inc., 241 East 34th Street, New York, New York 10016

Wave Hill Center for Environmental Studies, 675 West 252nd Street, Bronx, New York

Westchester Audio Visual Center, 8 Spencer Place, Scarsdale, New York 10583

Wilderness Society, 729 15th Street, N.W., Washington, D.C. 20005

World Book Encyclopedia, Merchandise Mart Plaza, Chicago, Illinois 60654

Xerox Films, High Ridge Park, Stamford, Connecticut 06904

Young American Films, McGraw-Hill, 327 West 41st Street, New York, New York 10036

Man and The Environment

ALONE IN THE MIDST OF THE LAND   NBC Educational Enterprises
0060C1/16mm. color/27 min./Purchase $330/Rental $15
Winner: Emmy; Atlanta Film Festival; International Film & TV Festival Awards

This is a dramatized account of man's destruction of his own environment. In it, the last man on earth is reduced to living in a protective suit after the rest of the population has been destroyed by man-made pollution.

Although it purports to be a drama about the future, it is actually a report on the present balance of nature. It *will be* a picture of man's future, if he continues to destroy his environment.
I / J / S / C / A   1970

THE AMERICAN WILDERNESS   NBC Educational Enterprises
0107C1/16mm. color/Reel I 27 min.; Reel II 26 min. Purchase $500/Rental $25

Man needs space to reflect, and be in contact with an unspoiled nature. Our technological society exerts great pressure on wild areas in terms of development and raw materials, and also in terms of recreational use. This film, photographed in the remaining wilderness areas of the western United States, shows that they must be preserved in spite of these pressures. Once destroyed they cannot be legislated back into existence.
I / J / S / C / A   1971

AUDUBON   Indiana University
16mm./58 min., color: order No. NSC-1200—lease $140 per yr., rental $18.00
A documentary which traces the travels of John J. Audubon (1785-1851) throughout Europe and North America.

THE CHANGING FOREST   McGraw-Hill Films
15 min. Color. Code 601051—purchase $195, rental $8.50. Junior-Senior High School—College level.
An essay on the ecology of a deciduous forest area of the type found along the southern fringes of the Laurentian Shield, showing the forest as an integrated community of living things, both plant and animal. Produced by the National Film Board of Canada.

COMMUNITY ACTION FOR BEAUTY 1967. 30 min./color—free   NCSGC

DISCOVERY   Tennessee Valley Authority
Youth involvement. Filmed at TVA's Conservation Education Center. Land Between the Lakes. 1967. 21 minutes. Color. Free Loan.

Film prices and availability are subject to change.

THE GREAT BARRIER REEF   NBC Educational Enterprises
0080C1/16mm. color/Reel I 27 min.; Reel II 27 min. Purchase $500/Rental $25

A unique ecosystem off the coast of Australia is in danger. The Crown of Thorns, a variety of starfish which eats live coral, is multiplying. Its numbers are threatening to destroy the Great Barrier Reef.

The Reef is a living shelter for many unusual sea creatures. Its function, beauty, and variety of life make it a habitat unlike any other; therefore, its destruction must be prevented.

Man must struggle with the dilemma of whether to risk the dangers of introducing new elements into the Reef, or to leave the Reef alone and wait.
I / J / S / A   1970

ICE PEOPLE   NBC Educational Enterprises
0098C1/16mm. color/23 min./Purchase $275/Rental $13

Over 10,000 years ago man moved into the Arctic and adapted to its hostile environment. This anthropological study shows that the modern Eskimo must adapt again. These ingenious people lived with strong family ties, but no feeling of nation. They prized freedom and individuality. Land and game were shared; aggression was abhorred.

These admirable qualities are now making life difficult for the Eskimo because they are the antithesis of attitudes that bring success in the Western culture. The Arctic people are finding that their old traditions and skills have been subverted. If they are to survive they must create a new life style which bridges the two cultures. (See Man and The Environment exhibits and projects.)
J / S / C / A   1970

ISLANDS OF GREEN   National Audubon Society
16mm. motion picture, Islands of Green, in sound and color, 24½ minutes. The film is available on loan (at a $5 handling charge) or for sale, at $105, plus $5 handling.
Cooperatively produced by the U.S.D.A. Motion Picture Service, the U.S. Forest Service, and the National Audubon Society, Nature Centers Division. Tells the story of the preservation and wise use of large "islands of green" which are our national forests, and the necessity of saving small islands of green in and around our cities. Describes what nature centers are, their objectives, and their place and value in safeguarding a segment of our natural environment. Strong emphasis is placed on natural beauty and the concept of using land for learning and enlightenment. Narration is by John Charles Daly.

MULTIPLY . . . AND SUBDUE THE EARTH   Indiana University
NET/16mm./67 min./b & w/order No. CS-1979 (sale $270/rental $13.50 color/order No. CSC-1979/sale $450/rental $18.50   (Produced 1969)

lems caused, in part, by unplanned use of our natural environment. Suburban developments are being built with little regard for the natural life surrounding them. Eighty-two per cent of midtown Manhattan's population have been found to exhibit various degrees of mental illness which is thought to be partially caused by overcrowding. The central message of this film, as stated by Ian McHarg, is that man must use ecological planning and seek not a conquest of nature but unity with nature.

NET/16mm./67 min./b & w/order No. CS-1979 (sale $270/rental $13.50 color/order No. CSC-1979/sale $450/rental $18.50   (Produced 1969)

THE MYTHS AND THE PARALLELS   Silvermine Films
Presents a forceful conservation message, with score of modern original music as background.

SEA SORCERY color/15 min.; purchase $220/rental $21   McGraw-Hill
The camera dives at depths varying from ten to fifty feet below the surface in this beautiful film of undersea life. Accompanied by a score composed to complement its tone and movement. Has been used very effectively by the New York Aquarium in combination with one reel of "Who Killed Lake Erie," to show the contrast between the beauty of the natural world and the ugliness of polluted waters.

SURVIVAL ON THE PRAIRIE   NBC Educational Enterprises
0055C1/16mm. color/Reel I 19 min.; Reel II 35 min. Purchase $500/Rental $25

The prairie is a vast area of land covered with grass, animals, and a few people. Years ago, it was a paradise for the prairie dog, the gopher, the buffalo, and the elk. All these creatures of the grass lived on it, or on each other, and the balance of nature protected them and the land.

Then came man with his plow and his work animals . . . the land was turned over. The rich grass and humus were destroyed, drought followed, and the air filled with dust. Man, almost too late, realized the land had to be protected.
I / J / S / A   1970

THE TIME OF MAN 50 min.—free   American Museum of Natural History
A beautiful, thoughtful, stimulating exposition of the basic meaning of the word, "environment." Starting with evolution of the earth and primitive life and progressing to the present, it shows our ability not only to alter and interfere with the environment, but also to maintain it so that life itself may be maintained. Narrated by Richard Basehart.

TIME TO BEGIN
Dept. of Conservation and Economic Development. Richmond, Va. 23219.

WATER RESOURCE RELATED FILMS. Produced by Stuart Finley. Free loan at film libraries. Sale. Stuart Finley, Inc. 3428 Mansfield Road, Falls Church, Va. 22041.

THE WORLD AROUND US (25 min., color: McGraw-Hill Films: code 672406; purchase $300, rental $16.00)

An introduction to ecology. Produced by NBC News for the "Smithsonian" series. Demonstrates what an ecosystem is and why it is important; shows interdependence of all life. Brings up issues of pollution and conservation and indicates what man can do to better his surroundings.

Water Resource Related films produced by Stuart Finley. Free loan at film libraries. Sale. Stuart Finley, Inc. 3428 Mansfield Road, Falls Church, Va. 22041.

Population

ADLAI STEVENSON TALKS ABOUT POPULATION AND OUR SHRINK-ING WORLD—Planned Parenthood-World Population

Adlai Stevenson, then Ambassador to the United Nations, addresses the annual meeting of PPWP in 1963.

ANACOSTIA: MUSEUM IN THE GHETTO (16mm./17 min., black and white: Indiana University, sale $100, rental $4.15)

Describes how this neighborhood museum is bringing beauty, creativity, and joy to the children there. Candid scenes depict the museum's policy of involving children in its activities. Scenes of the museums surroundings emphasize a plea for more institutions to enter the ghettos. (see article by Zora B. Martin, entitled "Urban Ecology and the Inner City Museum.")

CITIES HAVE NO LIMITS   NBC Educational Enterprises
0003C1/16mm. color/Reel I 25 min.; Reel II 28 min. Purchase $500/Rental $25
Winner: Cine Golden Eagle

An examination of today's urban crisis: the widening division between the central city and its surrounding areas. Poverty amid affluence, social unrest, employment and unemployment, money problems, riots and crime—"symptoms" of a spreading disease afflicting U.S. cities. With Daniel P. Moynihan and Charles V. Hamilton, political scientist and co-author of "Black Power."
J / S / C / A   1968

THE COSTLY CROWD   Planned Parenthood-World Population

Overpopulation in terms of community problems. Geared specifically to businessmen or persons of upper-level affluence.

FAIR CHANCE—Planned Parenthood-World Population
Color: purchase $75/rental $5; b & w: purchase $45/rental $4
Two fathers waiting in the maternity ward of a hospital. One has planned his family and is prospering. The other's family is suffering through non-planning.

LEWIS MUMFORD ON THE CITY. Based on his book *The City in History*

Series of 6 half-hour films. Produced by National Film Board of Canada. Black and White. Rental. Sterling Educational Films. Contemporary Films, others.

THE LOST FRONTIER.
1967. 28 minutes. Color. Free loan. Shows fate of earlier frontiers, and the effects of urban sprawl. Demonstrates need for wise decisions in management of remaining open lands.
Bureau of Land Management. U.S. Department of
Interior, Washington, D.C. 20240.

MYTHS AND PARALLELS—Association Films

Dated 1965. Excellent and timely, very good for adults (high school, college, etc.).

POPULATION ECOLOGY—Encyclopaedia Britannica Films, Inc.

Demonstrates how natural forces control growth of population among certain species, and interrelationships of species. It makes the point that man has learned to adapt and control his environment.

THE POPULATION PROBLEM, film series, available from Indiana University. The individual films are:
  The European Experience
  Answer to the Orient
  Brazil: The Gathering Millions
  India: Writings on the Sand
  U.S.A.: Seeds of Change—analyzes the population trend in the U.S. from Colonial days to the present, and probes the many problems affected by this trend.
  Gift of Choice—describes research on the reproductive process.

THE SLOW GUILLOTINE   NBC Educational Enterprises
0075C1/16mm. color/Reel I 23 min.; Reel II 30 min. Purchase $500/Rental $25
Winner: Emmy; Dupont-Columbia Broadcast Journalism Awards

If no corrective action is taken, most of our urban centers will be unliveable before the year 2000, ecologists warn. It is not only the quality of life that is in danger, but the actual existence of life in the face of medical and agricultural problems caused by foul air.

This film focuses directly on Los Angeles but makes it painfully clear that air pollution is a grave danger to the whole country.

J / S / C / A

1969

THE SQUEEZE
Planned Parenthood-World Population

This is an offbeat piece of cinema art, designed for sophisticated audiences. It illustrates overcrowding in the United States.

URBANISSIMO (6 min., color: McGraw-Hill Films, purchase $90, rental $10)

An entertaining animation showing the blight perpetrated by chaotic urban development with the city personified as an uncontrollable monster. First presented at Expo 67 in Canada.

Pollution

DDT—KNOWING IT SURVIVES US (16mm./30 min., color: Xerox Films; Purchase $325, Rental information available from Xerox.)

In this film, scientists from several fields explain why DDT is a dangerous pollutant, and they describe the effects it is having on wildlife, the environment in general, and on man. DDT pollution is a worldwide problem, not restricted to any one area by either social or political boundaries, and use of the chlorinated hydrocarbons as pesticides anywhere in the world affects men and animals at surprisingly great distances.

DOWN THE ROAD
McGraw-Hill

Treats young people's concern about pollution and other environmental problems. 1967. 20 minutes. Color.

THE NOISE BOOM
NBC Educational Enterprises

0048C1/16mm. color/26 min./Purchase $330/Rental $15

Noise is a health hazard. Two out of three cases of deafness are due to noise. It can lead to a high blood pressure and increase the cholesterol level in the blood. This is a report on noise—a particularly dangerous form of environmental pollution and on what interested citizens can do to lessen it.

J / S / C / A

1969

NOISE: THE NEW POLLUTANT
Indiana University.

Reports on research into harmful effects of noise on human beings. Produced for National Educational Television with a grant from Acoustical Materials Association. 1967. 30 minutes. Black and White. Rental or sale.

POLLUTION IS A MATTER OF CHOICE   NBC Educational Enterprises
0073C1/16mm. color/Reel I 26 min.; Reel II 27 min. Purchase $500/Rental
$25
Winner: Dupont-Columbia Broadcast Journalism; International Environmental Film Festival Awards

This is an examination of the environmental dilemma of modern man who has it in his power to preserve or ruin his environment. This predicament of wanting what technology creates, yet being destroyed by its wastes, is shown in the microcosm of the Everglades and of Machiasport, Maine.

People want the jobs and prosperity that industry creates, but not the destruction of their surroundings. Resources grow scarce, yet no one wants to give up the affluence that technology produces. What are the priorities?
J / S / C / A   1970

THE PROBLEM WITH WATER IS PEOPLE (30 min., color: McGraw-Hill Films. Purchase $350, Rental $18)

Examines the use and abuse of our water supply. Viewers are taken along the course of the Colorado River and into cities and towns across the nation. Narrated by Chet Huntley. Produced by NBC News.

THE RAVAGED EARTH   NBC Educational Enterprises
0041C1/16mm. color/27 min./Purchase $330/Rental $15

Eroded and barren, the land of the strip mines is a desolate moonscape. What was once rolling countryside is now wasteland because of man's avarice and lack of concern for his environment.

The path of the mining companies across much Appalachian land is marked by acidic soil, sulphuric rivers, and unhappy people. This defacement has not been stopped because it is the economic base for the region. Stewart Udall points out that although strip mining is presently profitable, when land is permanently destroyed, it is both foolish and shortsighted.
J / S / C / A   1969

UP TO OUR NECKS   NBC Educational Enterprises
0047C1/16mm. color/26 min./Purchase $330/Rental $15

Our society has a colossal problem of waste disposal. New York City produces eight million tons of garbage per year. At that rate, by 1975 all of the city's land-fill will be exhausted. Chemical and atomic wastes do not break down naturally. How do we get rid of all this waste? This film explores some of the alternatives now available.
J / S / C / A   1969

WHAT ARE WE DOING TO OUR WORLD (Part I—27 min., Part II—25 min., color: McGraw-Hill Films. Purchase $350, Rental $18)

A two-part film from the CBS 21st Century Series that examines the way technology is altering our environment. Part I focuses on Lake Erie and also discusses the "greenhouse" effect and nuclear power. Part II shows an ecosystem under study in New Hampshire, the Everglades and the Panama Canal. Narrated by Walter Cronkite and produced by CBS News.

WHO KILLED LAKE ERIE? NBC Educational Enterprises
0025C1/16mm. color/Reel I 29 min.; Reel II 22 min. Purchase $500/Rental $25
Winner: Cine Golden Eagle; Peabody; International Environmental Film Festival; Headliner Achievement Awards

Muck, foam, oil slicks, and debris cover much of the surface of Lake Erie. Pollutants are poured into the lake by the millions of gallons every day. They are changing the chemical composition of the water and altering the delicate balance of plant and animal life.

Pollution, costly to industry, dangerous to life, and deadly to the human spirit is something that man can control. Yet by pleading that the cost will be enormous, we are ignoring the fact that man is making this planet uninhabitable.
J / S / C / A

1969

Key to abbreviations listed in the descriptive text is given below. Addresses will be found in the list of producers and distributors of films.

BCLM — Bureau of Community Land Management
CBS — CBS Holt Group
ECA — Environmental Control Administration
EDC — Education Development Center
ISU — Iowa State University
IU — Indiana University
KSP — King Screen Productions
LCA — Learning Corporation of America
MSU — Michigan State University
MTPS — Modern Talking Picture Service
NBC — NBC Educational Enterprises
NCSGC — National Council of State Garden Clubs
NIU — Northern Illinois University
NMAC — National Medical Audiovisual Center
PHS — U.S. Public Health Service
PL — Public Library

Recently, two totally unrelated organizations, the Junior Leagues of America, Inc. and Wave Hill Center for Environmental Studies, conducted successful film festivals that would make excellent examples for other organizations to follow.

At a national conference held in Chicago to discuss Strategies for Environmental Control, the Junior Leagues scheduled the following films:

ALONE IN THE MIDST OF THE LAND See Films—Man and The Environment for description.

BOOMSVILLE (11 min., color: LCA-free) This animated film recreates with wit and clarity, without a single word, man's interaction with his surroundings, tracing step by step the process by which man took a virgin land and made of it a frantic, congested "Boomsville."

THE CRY OF THE MARSH (12 min., color: PL-free; UI-$4.75) A poignant wordless essay on the despoliation of nature and the destruction of wild life by man's irresponsible use of concrete and bulldozer.

DON'T LEAVE IT ALL TO THE EXPERTS (16 min., color: TBI-free; NMAC-free) This film explains the effects of the Clean Air Act, and the essential part to be played by concerned citizens in bringing about healthful air.

FOREST MURMURS (9 min., color: PL-free; N/N-$10) A beautifully photographed plea against littering our forests and parks; appropriate music with no narration.

THE GIFTS (28 min., color: MTPS-free) A new film about the misuse of our Nation's legacy of pure air and virgin land, especially emphasizing that of clean water; and the necessity to use our special genius in a call to action to restore environmental sanity. Narrated by Lorne Greene.

THE GREEN CITY (22 min., color: MSU-$7.50; SF-$15) A film about green and open spaces in urban areas and how proper planning can preserve these valuable attributes.

ILL WINDS ON A SUNNY DAY (29½ min., color: TBI-free; NMAC-free; PHS-free) This documentary points out how air pollution has evolved over the past few decades from a relatively simple and obvious smoke problem, primarily of local concern, to a more complex and dangerous problem affecting the entire Nation. The film stresses the need for increased understanding of the problem and cooperative action by industry, citizens, community and government officials at all levels.

LITTLE MAN, BIG CITY (10 min., color: PL-free; SIU-$5.35) An animated light-hearted approach to solving the problems of urban living—traffic, pollution, crowding, renewal, etc., concluding with a plea for community action. Made by Pannonia Studios, Budapest, Hungary.

MEN AT BAY (25½ min., color: KSP-$29.50) The film looks at San Francisco and a policy of misplaced values which seems certain to turn the city into another Los Angeles. While excellently filmed shots of pollution (including problems of land fill, garbage disposal, air and water pollution, and autos) fill the screen, off-screen voices of San Franciscans, not experts or politicians, give pro and con arguments from the banal to the frantic.

MULTIPLY AND SUBDUE THE EARTH See Films—Man and The Environment.

NO TIME FOR UGLINESS (24 min., color: PL-free; ISU-$3.15) Examines the deterioration of both urban and suburban environments and suggests opportunities for improvements in river development, housing, business and recreational facilities. Cites examples throughout the country of successful planning ventures.

PANDORA'S EASY OPEN POP-TOP BOX (15 min., color: BCEM-free; NMAC-free; ECA-free) This film contrasts the sound and the fury of the city with the serene unspoiled countryside, involving all aspects of environment, including social.

THE POISONED AIR (50 min., color and black & white: PL-free; NMAC-free; PHS-free; UMn-$9.85; UC-$15; AIM-$17.50) CBS documentary spanning our country and the world with scenes of air pollution disasters. Shows how cities of St. Louis, Pittsburgh, Los Angeles, and New York have fought for their citizens' lives and health in combatting the deadly menace of air pollution.

POLLUTION (3 min., color: PL-free; TBI-free; PHS-free; IU-$3; USC-$5; UEVA-$12.50) A devastating, black-humored song spoof on pollution, in which visitors to the United States are warned not to drink the water or breathe the air. Lyrics written and sung by Tom Lehrer.

THE RISE AND FALL OF THE GREAT LAKES (17 min., color: PL-free; UI-$8.80; Py-$15) An engaging history of the origins and life of the Great Lakes, now in peril from pollution, told through animation, with folk song accompaniment, and the hilarious adventures of a hapless canoeist on its waters. It shows how the Great Lakes have been altered by Nature and by Man. A marvelous example of how a teaching film can also be entertaining. By the National Film Board of Canada.

THE RIVER MUST LIVE (21 min., color: PL-free; SFL-free; FWQA-free) Excellent film which illustrates how society has abused one of the most valuable and universal resources—clean water. Informative microphotography reveals the delicate balance of life in a river and how it becomes upset when a waterway is used as a cess-pool. This film shows not only what the problems are but also some successful solutions.

THE RUN-AROUND (11 min., color: TBI-free; NMAC-free) With satirical animation, the film traces the adventures of Mr. Hack, our average man who is determined to track down the sources of air pollution. His search leads him from one pollution source to another, each admitting partial fault, each claiming vast attempts at clearing the air, and each passing the buck on to the next party. At the conclusion of the trip, Mr. Hack proves that he too is part of the vast Run-Around in placing his own personal interests before the need to participate in the fight against air pollution.

THE SECRETS OF SECRECY (47 min., color: NBC-$21.75, or sometimes free) Silent, microscopic killers sprayed from planes or poured into water supplies could wipe out whole populations. This is the prospect of chemical, biological warfare in which plague, arthrax, nerve gas, and rabbit fever are weapons in the arsenal. The Emmy Award winning production prepared without the approval or cooperation of the Dept. of Defense, probes a story long withheld from the public.

THE THIRD POLLUTION (23 min., color: PL-free; ECA-free; SIU-$6.80; UMn-$6.65; PSU-$8.30; NIU-$7.40; PHS-free) Excellent film which describes the environmental, economic and technical problems of solid waste disposal, and demonstrates new techniques in solid waste management. Despite its subject matter, garbage, it is an important film with a positive outlook.

THE TIME OF MAN See Films—Man and The Environment.

LIFE OF THE ESKIMO

Wave Hill Center for Environmental Studies held an Environmental Film Festival during a three-day period in the winter of 1970. Their offerings:

> An intimate look at the ecology of nomadic Eskimos in the Pelly Bay region of the Canadian Arctic. Survival is still the primary concern in this contemporary culture, dependent on the skill and resourcefulness of every member of the tribe.

> Filmed by the National Film Board of Canada, and jointly supported by the Education Development Center, National Science Foundation, and Ford Foundation.

> Edited into a one-hour print for CBS by EDC from a series of 9 films.

URBANISSIMO color/6 min.
An entertaining animation showing the city personified as an uncontrollable monster spreading chaos and waste wherever it goes. Available from McGraw-Hill Films

AMERICA ON THE EDGE OF ABUNDANCE b & w/30 min.
A cinematic collage of the extravagance in American production, from the lights of Times Square to the ticky-tacky of Levitt-town. Available from Audio-Visual Center, Indiana University.

WORLD POPULATION 1000 BC—1965 AD color/4 min.

An alarming representation of how world population has begun to increase with uncontrolled rapidity. Available from Southern Illinois University.

NOISE BOOM See Films—Pollution

MULTIPLY AND SUBDUE THE EARTH See Films—Man and The Environment.

THE RUN-AROUND color, 11 min.

An animated satire about the "run-around" one encounters when trying to track down the sources of air pollution. Produced by National TB and Respiratory Disease. Available from National Medical Audio-Visual Center.

TOM LEHRER SINGS POLLUTION color, 3 min.

Scenes of pollution set to Tom Lehrer's typically biting and humorous lyrics pin-pointing diseases in the environment. Available from National Medical Audio-Visual Center

AUTOMANIA 2000 color/10 min. McGraw-Hill

Delightfully animated prophesy of world-wide traffic jam.

RUGGIE AND THE MOMMA JUNKIE b & w/10 min. NYU Film Library

Whimsical romp through an automobile junkyard. Produced by students at the New York University Institute of Film and Television.

HUNGER IN AMERICA b & w/57 min. American Documentary Films

A stark and compelling look at the causes and effects of poverty and malnutrition in the land of plenty. Filmed by the CBS documentary crew in 1968, but unfortunately not yet out-dated since no substantial changes have been affected. Although the film was violently criticized by Orville Freeman, Secretary of Agriculture at the time it was first screened, it prompted a Senate investigation of government food programs. Nonetheless, malnutrition is still rampant.

THE ABANDONED color/10 min. NBC Educational Enterprises

An artfully filmed piece on the metallic eye-sores created by the eight million automobiles abandoned each year. Set to a score of electronic music.

ALONE IN THE MIDST OF THE LAND See Films—Man and The Environment.

STRINGBEAN b & w/17 min. New York Public Library/Donnell Branch

A wistful tale about the persistance of nature in the city, and the courage of an elderly French woman who fights for it.

Appendix F

Analysis of Museum Activity in Human Ecology

In 1969 the American Association of Museums requested information from its 1060 member institutions on their past and present programs in the field of human ecology and their interest in conducting such programs in the future. Of the 582 institutions responding, 157 had no current programs or exhibits on pollution, population problems, endangered species, urban sprawl, or similar topics and expressed no interest in developing such programs (art, 76; history, 81). All science museums indicated that they either had programs or would be interested in having them.

The other 425 institutions—73 percent of those responding—expressed interest in initiating or expanding such programs, and virtually all of them expressed a need for help: financial support, technical assistance, additional space, or exhibit materials. One hundred and seventy (40 percent) indicated that they had no programs but wished to initiate some; all the others had programs and wished either to expand them or develop new ones.

Table I gives the percentages of institutions in each category desiring specific types of assistance, regardless of whether they have current environmental programs or exhibits.

Table II gives a breakdown of existing programs.

Additional needs mentioned by some of the institutions are for trained teachers, supplementary personnel, speakers, relevant literature, visitor interest, and, in one case, "Board of Trustees sympathy."

Member institutions listed a number of specific activities that they were conducting or planning. These include programs on ghetto problems, mass transit, city planning, architecture, traffic control, the city, rats, beautification, landscaping, conservation of wetlands, appreciation of natural resources, wilderness conservation, habitat destruction, ecology, littering, forest fires, Dutch Elm disease, protection of San Francisco Bay, natural history, game and fish, minority cultures, primitive cultures, cultural trends, anthropology, disease, yellow fever, nutrition, exercise, agricultural chemicals, garbage disposal, oceanography, aviation and space, historic preservation, historic perspectives, humanities, and the environment.

Table I

Percentages of Institutions Requiring Assistance for Environmental Programs

Type of Institution	Responding	Financial	Technical	Type of Assistance Exhibit Space	Material
Art[1]	76	74%	34%	13%	57%
History[1]	89	79	39	33	44
Science[1]	68	58	27	35	39
General[2]	102	78	33	45	42
Children's	19	74	21	32	32
Univ. & Coll.	56	69	16	29	33
Other[3]	11	50	30	20	30
Planetarium	1	—	—	—	—
Zoo	2	—	x	—	x
Botanical Garden	1	x	x	—	x

Table II

Percentages of Institutions Carrying Out Environmental Programs

Type of Institution	Responding	Any Type of Program*	Breakdown of Specific Programs Pollution	Population	Endangered Species	Urban Sprawl
Art[1]	76	37%	7%	7%	3%	17%
History[1]	89	34	15	0	10	6
Science[1]	68	79	35	44	44	13
General[2]	102	84	33	16	38	10
Children's	19	63	10	21	53	21
Univ. & Coll.	56	59	29	12	18	18
Other[3]	11	70	60	20	30	30
Planetarium	1	x	x	—	x	—
Zoo	2	x	x	—	x	—
Botanical Garden	1	x	—	—	—	—

* Includes exhibits or programs on pollution, population, endangered species, urban sprawl, and any other environmental problems.

Footnotes

1. See the Official Museum Directory 1971, American Association of Museums, for a breakdown of each category.
2. General—any museum that emphasizes at least two of the Art, History, and Science categories.
3. Other—includes any institution not covered by the above categories.

Appendix G

Biographies of Members of the Environmental Committee

NORMAN C. BILDERBACK. Director of exhibits, California Museum of Science and Industry, Los Angeles, 1945- . Born November 2, 1915, Phoenix, Ariz. Studied at Art Center School of Los Angeles, 1945. Apprenticeship as scientific illustrator and exhibit preparator, San Diego Museum of Natural History, 1936-39. Zoology textbook illustrator, University of California, 1939-40. Exhibit preparator at California Museum of Science and Industry, starting in 1941 and interrupted by wartime experience as an aircraft production illustrator. Past chairman of California Color Society.

RICHARD FARGO BROWN. Director, Kimbell Art Foundation, Fort Worth, Texas, 1966- . Born September 20, 1916, New York City. B.A., 1940, Bucknell; M.A., 1948, and Ph.D., 1952, Harvard University; Institute of Fine Arts, N.Y. University, 1940-42. Research scholar and lecturer, The Frick Collection, 1949-54. Visiting professor of fine arts, Harvard, 1954. Chief curator, Los Angeles County Museum of History, Science, and Art, 1954-60. Director, Los Angeles County Art Museum, 1960-66. Past president, College Art Association of America and Western Association of Museums. Member, American Association of Museums Council, 1960-68; California State Arts Commission, 1964-66; U.S. Treasury Dept. Advisory Commission on Art, 1968- , . Hon. D. Litt., Legion of Honor, Arts and Letters, Republic of France.

246

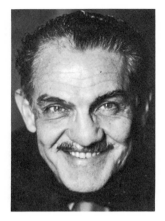 

FREDERICK J. DOCKSTADER. Director, Museum of the American Indian, Heye Foundation, New York City, 1960- . Born February 3, 1919, Los Angeles, Calif. A.B., 1939, A.M., 1946, Arizona State College; Ph.D., 1951, Western Reserve University. Teacher, Flagstaff, Ariz. schools, 1939-41; Cranbrook, Mich., schools, 1942-50. Staff ethnologist, Cranbrook Institute of Science, 1950-52. Curator of anthropology, Dartmouth College, 1952-55. Assistant director, Museum of the American Indian, 1955-60. Commissioner, Indian Arts and Crafts Board, U.S. Department of Interior, 1955-67; chairman, 1962-67. Fellow, Cranbrook Institute of Science; Rochester Museum of Arts and Sciences; American Association for the Advancement of Science; American Anthropological Association. Adjunct professor of art and archaeology, Columbia University, 1961-64. Member and past president, New York State Museum Association and New York City Museums Council. Author, *Indian Art in America*, and numerous other books and articles.

G. CARROLL LINDSAY. Director, Museum Services, New York State Museum and Science Service, Albany, New York, 1966- . Born September 28, 1928, Cochranville, Pa. B.A., 1950, Franklin and Marshall College; M.A., 1955, University of Delaware. Assistant to the director, Henry Francis Du Pont Winterthur Museum, Delaware, 1955-56. Assistant curator of ethnology, 1956-57; associate curator of cultural history, 1957-58; curator of Smithsonian Museum Service, 1958-59; director of Smithsonian Museum Service, 1964-66, Smithsonian Institution. Former vice president, Alexandria (Va.) Association. Former president and member of the board of directors, Greater Washington Educational TV Association. Member, board of directors, Albany Symphony. Member, Council of the American Association of Museums. Secretary, New York State Museums Association. Member, Museums Audio-Visual Applications Group; and Committee Furnishing Official Reception Rooms, U.S. State Department. Lecturer in early American decorative arts and architecture. Consultant and writer in the field. Author, "George Brown Goode," *Keepers of the Past*, 1964, and articles.

GEORCE EDMUND LINDSAY. Director, California Academy of Sciences, San Francisco, Calif., 1963- . Born August 17, 1916, Pomona, Calif. B.A., 1950, Ph.D., 1955, Stanford University. Director, San Diego Natural History Museum, 1955-63. Member, Executive Committee, American Association of Museums. President-elect, Pacific Division, American Association for the Advancement of Science. Fellow, California Academy of Sciences, Cactus and Succulent Society of America, San Diego Society of Natural History, American Association for the Advancement of Science.

KYRAN M. MC GRATH. Director, American Association of Museums, Washington, D.C., 1968- . Born August 24, 1934, Chicago, Ill. B.S.S., 1956, LL.B., 1959, Georgetown University. Attorney, Washington, D.C., 1959-61. Legislative counsel to United States Senator Paul H. Douglas, 1961-65. Chief, Washington Office, Illinois Department of Business and Economic Development, 1965-67. Special assistant to the chairman (Governor Otto Kerner), National Advisory Commission on Civil Disorders, Washington, D.C., 1967-68.

CHARLES EDWARD MOHR. Executive Director, Delaware Nature Education Center, Inc., Greenville (Wilmington), Delaware, 1966- Born June 3, 1907, Reading, Pa. A.B., 1930, A.M., 1931, Bucknell University. Science instructor, Public Museum and Reading High School, Reading, Pa., 1931-38. Director of Education, The Academy of Natural Sciences, Philadelphia, 1939-46. Director, Audubon Nature Center and Camp, Greenwich, Conn., 1947-59. Director, Swiss Pines Park, Valley Forge, Pa., for the Academy of Natural Sciences, 1959-62. Educational Director, Kalamazoo, Mich. Nature Center, 1962-66. Past president, American Nature Study Society; National Speleological Society; Pennsylvania Academy of Science, Delaware Recreation and Parks Society. Former conservation consultant, National Council of State Garden Clubs. Fellow, American Association for the Advancement of Science. Writer of numerous books and articles.

M. GRAHAM NETTING. Director, Carnegie Museum, Pittsburgh, Pa., 954- . Born October 3, 1904, Wilkinsburg, Pa. B.S., 1926, University of Pittsburgh; M.A., 1928, University of Michigan. Curator of Herpetology, 1932-54, assistant director, 1949-53, acting director, 1953-54, Carnegie Museum. Associate professor of geography, University of Pittsburgh, 1944-63. Officer and member of the board of directors, The Nature Conservancy. Trustee, National Parks Association. Vice president, Boone and Crockett Club. Adviser, Fort Ligonier Memorial Foundation; the Council of the Alleghenies, Frostburg, Md.; The Conservation Foundation, Washington, D.C.; the Atlantic Research Station, Salisbury, Rhodesia. Lecturer and writer in herpetology, animal geography, museology, conservation, and nature interpretation.

JAMES A. OLIVER. Director, The New York Aquarium, Brooklyn, N.Y., 1970- . Born January 1, 1914, Caruthersville, Mo. B.A., 1936, M.A., 1937, Ph.D., 1942, University of Michigan. Asst. curator of herpetology, 1943-47 (on leave, 1943-46, USNR). Associate curator 1947-48, The American Museum of Natural History. Assistant professor of biology, University of Florida, 1948-51. Curator of reptiles, new York Zoological Society, 1951-58. Assistant director, 1958, director, 1958-59, New York Zoological Park. Director, 1959-69, Coordinator of Scientific and Environmental Programs, 1969-70, The American Museum of Natural History. Treasurer and trustee, *Biological Abstracts*. Vice president, New York State Association of Museums. Member, board of directors, Caribbean Conservation Corporation. Vice-chairman, American Committee for International Wildlife Protection. Member, Survival Service Commission of the Internation Union for the Conservation of Nature; U.S. Committee of the International Council of Museums. Consultative representative to the United Nations for IUCN. Re-

searcher in herpetology. Author, *The Natural History of North American Amphibians and Reptiles, Snakes in Fact and Fiction*, articles.

CHARLES P. PARKHURST, JR. Assistant Director, The National Gallery, Washington, D.C., 1971- . Born January 23, 1913, Columbus, Ohio. B.A., 1935, Williams College; M.A., 1937, Oberlin College; M.F.A., 1941, Princeton University. Assistant curator and registrar, National Gallery of Art, Washington, D.C., 1941-43. Military service, U.S. Navy, 1943-46. Assistant to director, Albright-Knox Art Gallery, Buffalo, N.Y., 1946-47. Assistant professor of art and archaeology, Princeton University, and assistant curator, Princeton Art Museum, 1947-49. Professor, head of Department of Fine Arts, and director of the Art Museum, Oberlin College, 1949-62. Director, Baltimore Museum of Art, 1962-70. Member of the executive committee and past president of the American Association of Museums. Past president, College Art Association. Chevalier, Legion of Honor, Republic of France. Chairman, Governor's Council on Arts, Maryland, 1966- .

GEORGE O. PRATT, JR. Director, Staten Island Institute of Arts and Sciences (comprising High Rock Park Conservation Center, William T. Davis Wild Life Refuge, Staten Island Museum), St. George, Staten Island, New York, 1962- . Born May 1927, Kansas City, Mo. B.A., 1951, Harvard University; graduate studies, American University. Registrar, Curator, Commercial Museum (now Trade and Convention Center Museum), Philadelphia. President, Staten Island Arboretum Member, Board of Directors, Staten Island Citizens' Planning Committee; Member, Advisory Board, Staten Island Greenbelt Natural Areas League.

CHARLES E. ROTH. Environmental Education Consultant/Director of Education, Hatheway School of Conservation Education, Massachusetts Audubon Society, Lincoln, Mass., 1961- . Born January 14, 1934, Danbury, Conn. B.A., 1956, University of Connecticut; M.S., 1960, Cornell University. Teacher of Junior High School Science, Ardsley (N.Y.) Public School, 1956-1958. Operator of Natural Science Center (weekends), American Museum of Natural History, New York City, 1956-1957. Naturalist-Teacher (weekends), National Audubon Center of Greenwich, Conn., 1958-59. Former teacher and currently Consultant, Wave Hill Environmental Center (formerly Riverdale Outdoor Laboratories), New York City. Teacher, administrator and consultant in conservation education and nature centers and programs. Author of encyclopedia and magazine articles.

WILLIAM CAMPBELL STEERE.
President, The New York Botanical
Garden, 1970-   . Born November 4,
1907, Muskegon, Mich. B.S., 1929,
M.A., 1931, Ph.D., 1932, University
of Michigan. Instructor, 1931-36,
assistant professor, 1936-42, associate professor, 1942-46, professor,
1946-50, and chairman, 1947-50,
Department of Botany, University
of Michigan; professor of biology,
1950-58, dean of the Graduate Division, 1955-58, Stanford University;
professor of botany, Columbia University, 1958-   . Past president,
American Association of Museums.
Member of board and former president, *Biological Abstracts*. Senior
Biologist, Alaska Terrain and Per-
mafrost Section, U.S. Geological
Survey, 1949-54. Program director
for systematic biology, National Science Foundation, 1954-55. Director, The New York Botanical Garden, 1958-70. Fellow and former
vice-president, section chairman,
and committeeman-at-large, AAS.
Fellow, Arctic Institute of North
America; California Academy of Sciences; American Geographical Society; American Institute of Biological

Sciences. Board member, New York
Botanical Garden, Bayard Cutting
Arboretum. Liberty Hyde Bailey
Medal, American Horticulture Soci-
ety, 1965; U.S. Antarctica Service
Medal, 1968. D. es-Sci., University
of Montreal, 1959; D.Sci., Univer-
sity of Michigan, 1962.

MALCOLM B. WELLS. Architect;
consultant on landscape, conservation architecture, and environmental
education; writer. Born March 11,
1926, Camden, N.J. Studied at Georgia Institute of Technology. Architect of industrial plants presently
under construction in Wales and Bel-
gium, and of a proposed outdoor
education center to be built underground in New Jersey's Pine Barrens.

WILLIAM H. WOODIN. Director, Arizona-Sonora Desert Museum, Tucson, Arizona, 1954- . Born December 16, 1925, New York City. B.A., 1950, University of Arizona; M.A., 1956, University of California. Fellow, American Association for the Advancement of Science. Past president and fellow, Arizona Academy of Science. Trustee, Museum of Northern Arizona. Director, Southwest Parks and Monuments Association. Director, American Association of Zoological Parks and Aquariums. Former member of the Council and former State Representative, American Association of Museums. Member, Advisory Council of the Desert Protective Council.

Photographs of all committee members by Morris Warman.

Appendix H

Chapter 1

1. Fewer acres were planted in the U.S. in forest in 1968 than in 1960 (1,468,624 vs. 2,137,460). Today about one-third of the total land area of the U.S. is forested.
2. E.P. Dutton & Company, New York, 1966.

Chapter 2

1. Little, Brown and Company, Boston, 1967.
2. AAAS Annual Meeting, Boston, 1969.
3. International Conference, Prague, 1969.
4. AAAS Annual Meeting, Boston, 1969.
5. Newsweek Magazine, New York, January 25, 1971.
6. Ibid.
7. Ibid.
8. Journal of Medical Education, Vol. 44, No. 11, Part II, Washington, D.C., November, 1970.
9. Ibid.
10. Ibid.
11. BSCS=Biological Sciences Curriculum Study (see Appendix).

Chapter 3

1. The terms "smog" or "photochemical smog" are now widely used to describe a condition resulting from the reaction of ultraviolet light on the hydrocarbons emitted in automobile exhausts. Ozone is one of the deadly "photochemical pollutants" produced in this reaction.
2. Data are from a report prepared by the National Academy of Sciences—National Research Council.
3. Symposium on Science, Engineering and the Quality of Life, St. Louis, Mo., March 5, 1970.
4. John R. Clark, Scientific American, Vol. 220, No. 3, pp. 18-27, March 1969.
5. Daniel Merriman, Scientific American, Vol. 22, No. 5, pp. 42-52, May, 1970.
6. George Braziller, New York, 1969.

Glossary

aesthetosphere—the organization of the environment in terms of visual and sensory perception and apprehension.

algae—simple green plants without stems, leaves or roots, almost all of them living in fresh water or in the ocean where they are commonly called seaweed. Some of them have further masking colors such as red, brown, or blue.

amino acids—organic acids that are the chief components of proteins.

anadromous—ascending rivers from the sea for the purpose of breeding.

atmosphere—the mass of air surrounding the earth; the gaseous envelope surrounding the earth.

bacteria—microscopic organisms that live in soil, water, organic matter.

biophysics—branch of science that applies the principles of physics to biology.

biosphere—the part of the earth's crust, waters, and atmosphere where organisms can subsist; the sum of all the biotic communities of the earth.

biotic communities—the groups in which plants and animals live and interrelate with one another, linked by food chains and food webs.

cadmium—a metallic element often used in making alloys and in protective plating.

carbon dioxide (CO_2)—a heavy colorless, odorless, incombustible nontoxic gas that is absorbed from the air by plants during photosynthesis; product of complete combustion of hydrocarbons.

carbon monoxide—a colorless, odorless, very toxic gas that is a major pollutant of the atmosphere wherever there are automobiles; the product of any process that involves the incomplete combustion of hydrocarbons.

carnivores—flesh-eating animals.

chain of life—the generation and transfer of energy among four basic components of the environment: nonliving matter, producers (plants), consumers (higher organisms), and decomposers.

chlorine—a heavy, greenish-yellow, incombustible, water-soluble, poisonous gas of pungent odor used in bleaching and in water purification.

circadian—pertaining to biological cycles.

conservation—the planned management of man's environment to prevent the overexploitation, or destruction, of natural resources.

contaminants—substances that soil, stain, or infect by contact or mixture.

contraception—prevention of fertilization, conception, or impregnation by any of various methods, devices, or medications.

decibel—a unit used to measure relative loudness of sounds or to express the intensity of a sound wave.

demography—the statistical study of human population.

detergent—a synthetic organic preparation that is similar to soap.

deuterium—the hydrogen isotope that occurs in water (H_2O); it is twice the mass of ordinary hydrogen.

dieldrin—a light tan, crystalline, water-insoluble, poisonous solid, used as an insecticide.

ecology—the study of ecosystems, or the networks of living creatures, from microorganisms to man, living in precarious balance with their physical and biological environment.

ecosystem—the carefully balanced network of dependence between living and nonliving processes in the environment; disruptions anywhere in the system can effect changes elsewhere with unforeseen results.

energy—the mainstream of everything that happens; the expression of power in action.

environment—the biophysical complex of systems that surround an organism or ecological community.

enzyme—any of various complex organic substances originating from living cells and capable of producing certain chemical changes in organic substances by catalytic action.

epoxy—sometimes called epoxy resin, used chiefly in adhesives, coatings.

erosion—the slow destruction of a substance, such as the washing away of fertile topsoil from the land; the process by which the surface of the earth is worn away by the action of water, glaciers, winds, waves, etc.

estuary—an arm or inlet of the sea at the lower end of a river; that part of the mouth or lower course of a river in which the river's currents meet the sea's tide.

euphorbiaceae—the spurge family, a widely distributed family of herbs, shrubs and trees with usually milky and often poisonous juice, which is usually strongly purgative. This family includes many useful plants such as those yielding castor and croton oils, hevia or brasil, rubber and cassava. In their form and ecology euphorbiaceae parallel, in the deserts of Africa, the cactus family of the Americas.

eutrophication—the ecological process of water bodies as they age and become enriched with nutrients; an abundant accumulation of nutrients that supports a dense growth of plant and animal life, the decay of which depletes the shallow waters of oxygen in summer.

family planning—the process of regulating the number of children a man and woman will have, by means of contraception.

fluorine—a pale yellowish, flammable, irritating toxic gas.

fossil fuels—fuels formed from fossil plants and extracted from the earth, such as coal.

fungi—a major group of lower plants characterized chiefly by a lack of chlorophyll and by their subsistence upon dead or living organic matter; molds, rusts, mildews, mushrooms, smuts, etc.

fungicide—an agent, such as a spray or dust, used to destroy fungi.

geothermal power—power derived from the heat of the earth's interior.

glucose—a sugar that is the usual form in which carbohydrates are assimilated by man and animals.

herbicide—a substance or preparation that is used to destroy or inhibit plant life.

hormone—a chemical substance, formed in one organ or part of the body and carried in the bloodstream, which has a specific effect on the functioning of an organ.

hydrocarbons—any of a family of organic compounds containing carbon and hydrogen, often occurring in petroleum, natural gas, and coal; liquid and gaseous substances made up of carbon atoms linked to each other and to hydrogen atoms.

hydroelectric power—electrical power generated by waterpower.

hydrosphere—the water on or surrounding the surface of the earth, including the water in the oceans and in the atmosphere.

incaparina—a mixture of grains and bean meal.

insecticide—a substance that is toxic to insects.

invertebrate—an animal that does not have an internal skeleton.

lithium—the lightest metal known, occurring combined in certain minerals used in nuclear reactions.

lithosphere—the crust or solid part of the earth, such as land and rock.

lurrain—the surface of the moon.

malnutrition—a state of impaired functional ability or deficient structural integrity or development brought about by a discrepancy between the supply to the body tissues of essential nutrients and calories and the specific biologic demand for them. (*Journal of the American Medical Association*, August 13, 1970)

mesembryanthemum—one of many closely-related genera of plants native to southern Africa, with fleshy leaves and often very brilliantly colored

metabolism—the sum of the chemical and physical changes in living cells by which energy is provided for vital processes.

museum—an organized and permanent nonprofit institution, essentially educational and aesthetic in purpose, with professional staff, which owns and utilizes tangible objects, cares for them, and exhibits them to the public on some regular basis.

non-biodegradable wastes—materials such as aluminum cans and glass bottles that will not decompose biologically; they are a form of permanent pollution unless recycled industrially.

noxious—harmful or destructive.

nuclear power—power generated by the nucleus of the atom, such as the atomic bomb.

nuclear fission—the splitting of the nucleus of an atom into nuclei of lighter atoms, especially applied to heavy atoms producing atomic energy.

nuclear fusion—a thermonuclear reaction in which nuclei of light atoms join to form nuclei of heavier atoms, as the combination of deuterium atoms to form helium atoms.

overpopulation—a condition in which the number of organisms in a given area is too great for the natural resources or space available.

oxide—a compound containing oxygen and one or more elements or groups.

ozone (O^3)—highly reactive form of oxygen typically present in electric discharges and photochemical smog.

particulate matter—small airborne particles of solid or liquid materials that contribute to the occurrence of haze and smog.

pathogen—a disease-producing organism.

pelagic—pertaining to the open seas or oceans; living or growing far from land, as certain animals or plants.

pesticide—a chemical substance that destroys specific pest organisms.

phosphate—a salt or ester of phosphoric acid.

photochemistry—branch of chemistry treating the effects of radiant energy in producing chemical changes.

photosynthesis—the process by which chlorophyll-containing ("green") plants convert light energy from the sun into chemical energy in the form of carbohydrates.

physiology—the science dealing with the organic processes of life.

phytoplankton—planktonic plant life.

plankton—microscopic, passively floating animal and plant life of water.

plasma—the fluid part of blood in which the corpuscles are suspended; or lymph, not including cells or corpuscles.

pollution—the soiling or defiling of the environment by unclean materials released in such large quantities that natural forces cannot assimilate or disperse them.

polyurethane—thermoplastic resins used in tough, chemical-resistant coatings and adhesives.

potable—suitable for drinking.

radiation—the process whereby radiant energy is discharged in the form of waves or particles.

radioactive isotopes—a radioactive atom, the nucleus of which is identical to a similar nonradioactive atom.

radioactive pollutant—an uncontained radioactive element released into the environment.

reforestation—the replanting of trees in a forest that has been burned or cut.

sanitary landfill—the filling in of valley, stream, swamp, estuary, or bay with garbage or other solid wastes.

sludge—solid residue from sewage treatment plants that is dumped by most large cities into nearby rivers, causing water pollution.

solar—pertaining to the sun.

sonic boom—a sound resembling an explosion, produced when an aircraft travels at supersonic speed; a potential source of noise pollution.

sound barrier—also known as sonic barrier; the sudden increase in aerodynamic "drag" as the speed of an aircraft approaches the speed of sound.

sterilization—the process of making a person incapable of reproduction, by removing the sex organs or inhibiting their functions; the destruction of microorganisms either by heat or a chemical compound.

strontium 90—a heavy radioisotope of the metallic element strontium that is present in the fallout from nuclear explosions; it is hazardous because it can be assimilated by man and animals.

sulfur oxides—oxidized gases that come from the burning of fossil fuels containing sulfur.

surface mining—also known as strip mining; the destruction of a natural terrain by scooping off the land's surface in order to get to underground minerals.

technosphere—the unnatural, man-made areas of man's habitat, such as urban centers with their paved lands, houses and office buildings with controlled environments, and industrial complexes.

terrain—hard surface of the earth; a tract or region of ground immediately under observation.

thermal pollution—pollution in water or air caused by heat, such as the industrial wastes that overheat rivers, causing the death of fish and other life.

tidal—pertaining to the ocean tides.

toxic—poisonous.

tritium—a radioactive isotope of hydrogen.

urbanization—the gradual expansion of cities, city life, and man-made environments and problems.

vasectomy—the surgical excision of a male's spermatic duct, resulting in sterility.

vertebrate—an animal that has a spinal column.

zooplankton—planktonic animal life.

Resource Management

The paper used in the manufacture of this book was made from the trunks of second-and third-growth birch and maple trees that grew in Maine. Each living tree, on the average, yielded enough pulp to manufacture about 250 books. Ink was manufactured primarily from carbon black, a by-product of the petroleum industry, and synthetic resins made of coal tar derivatives. On discarding this book please bear in mind that it must not be dumped into the sky via incineration or onto the land by way of conventional waste disposal. Ideal disposal consists of shredding or pulping followed by mechanical composting, with a mixture of other non-poisonous wastes, for use as a nutritious mulch on the life-giving land.